NURTURING YESTERDAY'S CHILD

A Portrayal of the Drake Collection of Paediatric History

Menschen Intreede op deeze Waereld
[The Child's Passage through Life]

Wood engraving
Publisher: Schalekamp and van der Grampel
Amsterdam
Probably early 18 C
39.0 × 30.6 cm

Moralistic vignettes on the early stages of a child's life demonstrate the need for both mother and baby to be thankful for their blessings. Learning to walk alone is emphasized and the child is rewarded by being allowed to wear a hat.

NURTURING YESTERDAY'S CHILD

A Portrayal of the Drake Collection of Paediatric History

Mary Spaulding and Penny Welch
Museum of the History of Medicine
Academy of Medicine, Toronto,
Ontario, Canada

1991 B.C. Decker, Inc.

Publisher

B.C. Decker
320 Walnut Street
Suite 400
Philadelphia, Pennsylvania 19106

Sales and Distribution

United States and Puerto Rico
Mosby–Year Book Inc.
11830 Westline Industrial Drive
Saint Louis, Missouri 63146

Canada
Mosby–Year Book Limited
5240 Finch Avenue East, Unit 1
Scarborough, Ontario M1S 5A2

Australia
McGraw-Hill Book Company
Australia Pty. Ltd.
4 Barcoo Street
Roseville East 2069
New South Wales, Australia

Brazil
Editora McGraw-Hill de Brasil, Ltda.
rua Tabapua, 1.105, Itaim-Bibl
Sao Paulo, S.P. Brasil

Colombia
Interamericana/McGraw-Hill
de Colombia, S.A.
Carrera 17, No. 33–71
(Apartado Postal, A.A., 6131)
Bogota, D.E., Colombia

Europe, U.K., Middle East and Africa
Wolfe Publishing Limited
Brook House
2–16 Torrington Place
London WO1E 7LT England

Hong Kong and China
McGraw-Hill Book Company
Suite 618, Ocean Centre
5 Canton Road
Tsimshatsui, Kowloon
Hong Kong

India
Tata McGraw-Hill Publishing Company, Ltd.
12/4 Asaf Ali Road, 3rd Floor
New Delhi, 110002, India

Indonesia
Mr. Wong Fin Fah
P.O. Box 122/JAT
Jakarta, 1300 Indonesia

Japan
Igaku-Shoin Ltd.
Tokyo International P.O. Box 5063
1–28–36 Hongo, Bunkyo-ku,
Tokyo 113, Japan

Korea
Mr. Don-Gap Choi
C.P.O. Box 10583
Seoul, Korea

Malaysia
Mr. Lim Tao Slong
No. 8 Jalan SS 7/6B
Kelana Jaya
47301 Petaling Jaya
Selangor, Malaysia

Mexico
Interamericana/McGraw-Hill de Mexico,
S.A. de C.V.
Cedro 512, Colonia Atlampa
(Apartado Postal 26370)
06450 Mexico, D.F., Mexico

New Zealand
McGraw-Hill Book Co. New Zealand Ltd.
5 Joval Place, Wiri
Manukau City, New Zealand

Portugal
Editora McGraw-Hill de Portugal, Ltda.
Rua Rosa Damasceno 11A–B
1900 Lisbon, Portugal

South Africa
Libriger Book Distributors
Warehouse Number 8
"Die Ou Looiery"
Tannery Road
Hamilton, Bloemfontein 9300

Singapore and Southeast Asia
McGraw-Hill Book Co.
21 Neythal Road
Jurong, Singapore 2262

Spain
McGraw-Hill/Interamericana de Espana, S.A.
Manuel Ferrero, 13
28020 Madrid, Spain

Taiwan
Mr. George Lim
P.O. Box 87–601
Taipei, Taiwan

Thailand
Mr. Vitit Lim
632/5 Phaholyothin Road
Sapan Kwai
Bangkok 10400
Thailand

Venezuela
Editorial Interamericana de Venezuela, C.A.
2da. calle Bello Monte
Local G–2
Caracas, Venezuela

Nurturing Yesterday's Child
ISBN 1–55664–258–X

Library of Congress catalog card number: 90–82875

Editing: Agnes McIvor, Kanata
Design: Dennis Boyes, Q.E.D. Design Associates, Toronto
Photography: Brian Boyle, Toronto
Index: Beatrix Robinow, Toronto
Typesetting: Type Aesthetics, Mississauga
Film and Printing: Book Art Inc., Toronto

Printed in Hong Kong by Book Art Inc.

10 9 8 7 6 5 4 3 2 1

TO NINA

PREFACE

The Academy of Medicine of Toronto was most fortunate to be the recipient of the magnificent private collection of Dr. T.G.H. Drake following his death in 1959. Being a paediatrician, he focused on the care and well-being of children, but the artifacts in his Collection overflow into general medical history.

With its vast scope and emphasis on children, the Collection is unique, unparalleled in any museum of medical history in North America, perhaps in the world. It encompasses about 3000 artifacts, 1500 rare books, 1000 prints, 1000 coins and medals, and all the child welfare stamps issued until Dr. Drake stopped collecting in the 1950s (about 1000 album pages). All relate to medicine and/or children.

Dr. Drake wanted his treasure to be cherished, kept as an entity, and made available for viewing, study, and research. Keeping his wishes in mind, his widow, Nina, made the final choice of a home for the Collection.

When Nina Drake brought this legacy to the Academy, a small group of volunteers was assembled to work with her. The authors were among them.

Dr. W.E. Swinton, the honorary curator of the museum, suggested that a book be written. He had been Principle Scientific Officer of the British Museum (Natural History) for many years, and from 1958 to 1960 was both President of the Museums Association of the United Kingdom and Chairman of the International Council of Museums. After coming to Canada he joined the staff of the Royal Ontario Museum and was its Director from 1963 to 1966. Thus we decided to heed his advice.

The purpose of the book is twofold: to put the artifacts into historical perspective and to help the Collection become better known, locally, nationally, and internationally. Such a collection deserves widespread attention.

No attempt has been made to write a comprehensive history of infant care. The text has been guided entirely by the contents of the Collection. Interrelated objects — artifacts including prints, stamps, and coins — have been grouped and discussed under appropriate topics against the historical background outlined by the documents and books within the Collection. General medical historical statements are based on Abt-Garrison's *History of Pediatrics.*[1]

The Collection contains items from a broad spectrum of interests. The authors have freely consulted specialists in various fields to ensure, to the best of their ability, the accuracy of information given. However, they themselves are interested amateurs and make no pretence at being expert in any particular area. They would therefore be pleased to receive corrections and suggestions from those who are more knowledgeable. This would greatly benefit the museum.

1. Garrison FH (1923). Reissued separately with an appendix on the history of pediatrics in recent times, by AF Abt (Philadelphia: WB Saunders, 1965).

ACKNOWLEDGEMENTS

Many people have contributed to various aspects of this work during the time it has taken to bring the book into being.

In the early years Kodak Canada Inc. gave film, Benjamin Film Laboratories provided developing services, and Phyllis Grightmier took the pictures to make basic reference photographs for research and writing. Hannah grants provided seed money and research assistance.

Molly Harrison, a colleague of Dr. Swinton's, suggested the format for the chapters. Ian Montagnes, Neale Wheeler Watson (Nantucket), and Susan Barrable offered considerable encouragement and guidance as we floundered in the initial stages.

Specialists from the Royal Ontario Museum have responded generously when advice was sought, particularly Peter Kaellgren, Nicholas B. Millet, and John Hayes. Barbara Philippaki (Athens) and Homer A. Thompson (Princeton) provided helpful information. David Brown, Charles Roland, George Wallace, G.R. (Pat) Paterson and Bill Seidelman offered invaluable assistance. Mariana Brown, Till and Irene Davy, Lindsay Leonard, and Geoffrey Stagg translated German, Latin, French and Italian excerpts.

Betty Mannett deserves special mention for her willingness to type, re-type, and type again our changing manuscript. Over the years no one could have been more consistently helpful than Nina Drake.

The Collection has resided at the Academy of Medicine, Toronto, and we are indebted to the Academy and the staff, especially Sheila Swanson and her library assistants. Felicity Pope, the museum curator, has been available to consult and to share her expertise in out-of-hours preparations for photographing artifacts. Support from the Drake Volunteers has been considerable: Peggy Clarke's persistent study of the prints coupled with her keen interest has been of great benefit. Friends of the Museum, among them Agnes Kossack, have responded whenever approached for help.

Working with designer Dennis Boyes, photographer Brian Boyle, editor Agnes McIvor, and indexer Beatrix Robinow to produce this book has been a pleasure.

Without generous financial support from the following organizations and individuals the book could not have been published.

Associated Medical Services Incorporated and
Hannah Institute for the History of Medicine

Jackman Foundation

The Hospital for Sick Children Foundation

The McLean Foundation

The W. Garfield Weston Foundation

Canadian Occidental Petroleum Ltd.

Mead Johnson Canada

Helen Geagan

Irmingard Hoff

Mary Jackman

Marjorie MacDonald

Elaine Mitchell

Lois Wightman

For all the assistance above mentioned, the authors are immensely grateful. To others who helped along the way but whose names have not been included, we offer equally sincere thanks. However, no acknowledgements would be complete without thanking our husbands and families for their continual encouragement, patience, and understanding during the past fifteen years.

CONTENTS

THEODORE GEORGE HARWOOD DRAKE, M.B.
(1891-1959)

"Don't let them break up my diamond," was the repeated plea of the late Dr. Theodore Drake during his final illness in 1959. His diamond was his Collection, begun in the late 1920s when he was doing graduate work in London, England, and continued throughout his life.

Best known for research that led to the production of the nutritious cereal, Pablum, Theodore Drake had many facets to his energetic life.

Born in Webbwood, Ontario, between Sudbury and Sault Ste. Marie, Theodore George Harwood Drake was the only child of a railway engineer. The family moved to North Bay, where Theo received his primary and secondary school education. During these years his parents built a cottage on nearby Lake Talon, a property that figured prominently in Theo's life. Over the years, derived mostly from the sands around the cottage, he built up a notable collection of North American Indian artifacts.

His parents scrimped and saved to send Theo to the University of Toronto, where he obtained his M.B. in 1914. After interning for a year at Toronto General Hospital, he joined the British army and served mostly on hospital trains in France.

On his return to Canada, he decided to live where general practitioners were financially successful (so judged by their regular vacations in Florida). Thus, he spent a rugged four years practising medicine in Caron, Saskatchewan, west of Regina. His savings enabled him to return to Toronto to do graduate work at the Hospital for Sick Children. His aptitude for, and interest in, biochemistry as it related to children won him a Rockefeller Foundation fellowship to study in Boston, and later a scholarship to Europe.

It was during his sojourn in England, about 1927, that he discovered the feeding bottle that launched his paediatric collection. After an evening out with friends, while waiting for a bus outside an antique shop in London, the young doctor saw in the window a blue and white, transfer-printed vessel, shaped like a submarine. Sure that it was a feeding bottle, he hurried back the next morning, purchased it, and rushed home to clean off the layers of dust. That bottle was the first of more than 250 such feeders that he would acquire in his lifetime.

Back in Canada, in 1928 he was appointed to the clinical and research staff of the Hospital for Sick Children and to the Department of Paediatrics, University of Toronto. His research in cooperation with Dr. Frederick Tisdall under Dr. Alan Brown, the chief physician, led to the production of Pablum in 1934. This nutritious, well-balanced, and easily digested cereal was produced and marketed world-wide by the Mead Johnson Company and for decades was the foremost infant (and invalid) food.

Nutritional research continued to occupy Dr. Drake. His interest in the enrichment of refined food extended beyond cereal to include such staples as bread, with particular emphasis on the addition of vitamins A and D. He was awarded the Order of the British Empire for working with the Royal Canadian Air Force during World War II, planning the nutritional content of the food parcels sent to the troops overseas. Following the war he worked with William McLean of Canada Packers Company providing food parcels for the United Nations Relief and Rehabilitation Administration.

In 1949 Dr. Drake succeeded Dr. Tisdall as Director of the Research Laboratories at the Hospital for Sick Children, a position he held until retirement.

Research at the hospital was only one of his responsibilities. His love of children was reflected in the devoted care he gave to his young patients. He was an astute diagnostician and a superb teacher. He developed good rapport with his students and enjoyed listening, discussing, advising, and even assisting with their financial concerns. As a shrewd investor himself, he encouraged his students to be thrifty with their limited funds. Many of his former students recall enjoying his delightful sense of humour and his hospitality, frequently at his home and sometimes at his cottage.

At the hospital Theodore concentrated on research, the care of children, and the training of paediatricians, but at home he spent his time working on his collection and his garden. In winter, with gardening in abeyance, he wrote articles about various aspects of the Collection, using his own rare books as references. His two "worlds" overlapped when he took exciting artifacts, usually new acquisitions, to the laboratory to show his coworkers and when he invited them to the house to view his collection or to see his rare irises.

These viewings began only after Nina Johnstone arrived at the house. Theodore had been testing foods at the orphanage where Nina was raised. When a position opened up in the laboratory at the hospital, the matron of the orphanage recommended Nina for the job. Theo's parents were living with him and his wife, who was chronically ill, so Nina moved into the house to help. Theo took Nina to work at the hospital every day, where she trained as a laboratory technician. He encouraged extra studies to develop her mind and prepare her to manage her own affairs. She, in turn, managed his house and took a keen interest in the Collection. As she cleaned and polished pieces in preparation for display, some of the drab, black artifacts, hitherto unrecognizable, became gleaming silver treasures. All this enabled Theo to share his "diamond" with his friends.

One of the authors vividly remembers being invited to tea at the Drake home in the early 1950s. At that time Theodore was Chairman of the Museum Committee of the Academy of Medicine, a committee on which he had served for years. After viewing the Collection under the watchful eye of Nina, visitors were free to tour the house, a veritable museum. Every room was completely furnished and furbished with antiques except the bathroom and the kitchen, where Theo tolerated modern equipment. Beside his Elizabethan four-poster bed, his bedtime reading rested in the old oak cradle that is in the Collection. Tea followed the tour, and the writer found herself sitting in the library beside shelves laden with urinals!

Acquisitions continued to arrive, largely through a few carefully chosen dealers in England with whom Theo had arranged that all reasonably-priced artifacts pertaining to his interest be shipped to him. Only very expensive items such as silver, rare books, and children's furniture required his prior approval. The arrival of a crate was an exciting occasion. Nina recalls a delight reminiscent of Christmas during the unpacking. For weeks following the arrival of a new shipment, they often restricted their menu to bread and cheese in order to honour the invoice.

After years as a widower, Theo eventually persuaded his devoted and supportive companion to marry him, and since his death she has continued to devote herself to the care and preservation of her husband's beloved "diamond," now a part of the Museum of the History of Medicine at the Academy.

Because there are many infant cereals available today, Pablum no longer enjoys the popularity it did a few decades ago. Conversely, the renown of the Collection has grown, and it is probable that present and future generations will remember Dr. Theodore Drake's name as a result of this remarkable gift to posterity.

Ah! c'est un Fils, Monsieur
[Ah! It's a Boy, Sir.]
Coloured engraving by
C Baquoy (1721-1777)
After JM Moreau Le Jeune (1741-1814)
Paris, 1776
35.0 × 26.2 cm

HISTORICAL BACKGROUND

. . . my purpose here is to doe them good that have most nede, [that] is to saye children.

Thomas Phaer. *The Boke of Chyldren.* 1550, preface [p. 2].

It is a melancholy but indisputable truth that of all patients, children are most neglected.

CA Struve. *Domestic Education of Children.* 1802, p. 58.

As the twenty-first century approaches, parents of a baby born in Canada expect the child to survive through infancy and beyond. In the past, high infant mortality was accepted as a hard fact of life, and the only counterbalance was the uncontrolled birth rate. Sadly, this is still true of some countries in the twentieth century. Reading the literature and examining the artifacts that tell the story of child care through the ages reveal that the changing expectation for survival had a marked influence on the attitude toward children.

Cited above are just two statements that draw attention to the concern for children which was prevalent for a long time. Not all children were as welcome as the infant boy in the painting, *Ah! c'est un Fils, Monsieur.* Child abuse, so openly discussed today, is not new. For centuries unwanted babies in India and China were drowned; in Athens and in Rome such infants were exposed—left to die or to be picked up by some passerby who might wish to rear a strong-looking child to serve as a slave. In Rome babies were sometimes deliberately maimed as a means of attracting charity; this condition seemingly was considered preferable to death. In Egypt and Babylon these practices were unknown; the fertile valleys of the Nile, Tigris, and Euphrates rivers produced an abundance of food so that what poverty existed was bearable, and children were not such a burden.

Coexisting with the practice of infanticide, however, were considerable care and affection in raising children. In Ancient Greece breast feeding was the custom; if the mother was unable to suckle her infant, she was expected to bring a wet nurse into the home for about two years. Attention was given to raising children in a system of harmonious development of body and spirit.

In Egypt it was believed that a bevy of goddesses presided over the birth and rearing of the child. Maternal feeding, or if necessary wet nursing, was customary in the earliest days. In the Alexandrian period (336–323 BC) ladies seldom nursed their own infants but contracted slaves to feed them, first on breast milk, later on cow's milk. There was a regular daily delivery of the best cow's milk, and unpunctual delivery was severely punished.

Many nursing bottles of ancient date continue to be found in children's graves in Greece, Cyprus, and Italy, but not to our knowledge in Egypt or in Palestine. In the latter it was considered the primal duty of a mother to nurse her offspring; if this was not possible or if twins were born, a wet nurse was employed for two or three years. No bottled nourishment was given; usually a child was nursed or it was doomed to die. However, sucking directly from the udder of a cow or goat was not unknown.

The first author to deal specifically with diseases of children was Soranus of Ephesus,[1] whose work of the second century set a pattern of care followed for hundreds of years.

Woodcut depicting Feeding
Metlinger, *Regimen of health for young Children* 1550
6.1 × 5.1 cm

Child drinking from vessel, referred to by Metlinger as an "emly" (little bucket).

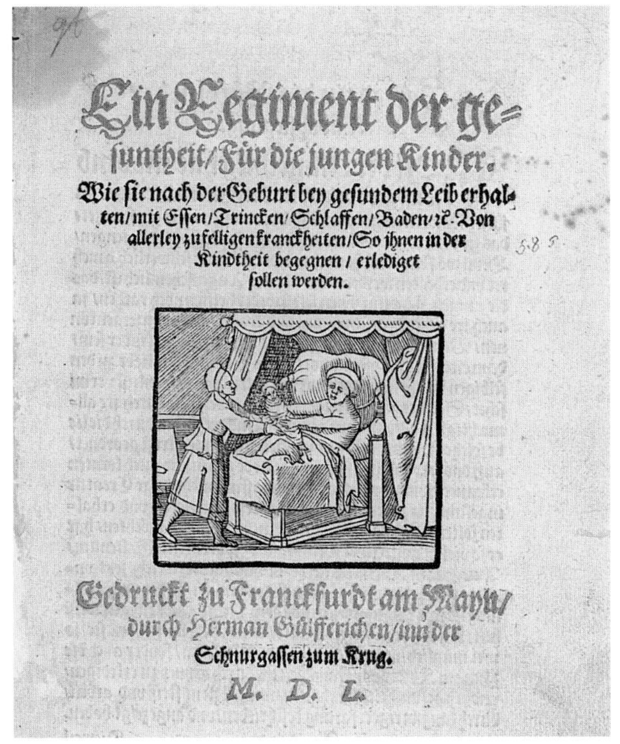

Ein Regiment der ge-
sundtheit/ Für die jungen Kinder.
Wie sie nach der Geburt bey gesundem Leib erhal-
ten/ mit Essen/ Trincken/ Schlaffen/ Baden/ rc. Von
allerley zufelligen kranckheiten/ So jhnen in der
Kindtheit begegnen/ erlediget
sollen werden.

Gedruckt zu Franckfurdt am Mayn/
durch Herman Gülfferichen/ inn der
Schnurgassen zum Krug.
M. D. L.

Title page
Metlinger, *Regimen of health for young Children* 1550
18.5 × 14.2 cm

[How to keep them healthy after birth with eating, drinking, sleeping, bathing etc. How to administer help for many a random sickness encountered in childhood.]

Printed at Franckfurdt am Mayn by Herman Gülfferichen at Schnurgassen zum Krug, MDL

During the Middle Ages little was recorded to suggest any particular concern for children, and their care continued as before. When later portrayed by artists, they were depicted as adults in miniature, dressed in cumbersome clothing; thus, they were expected to behave maturely. Childhood was a perilous transitional period, which many did not survive.

The increased number of books available from the late fifteenth century onward reflects the impetus given to publishing by the introduction of movable type. The field of health care produced its share of books, and a few focused on children. The earliest of these *De Infantium Aegitudinibus et Remediis,* by Paolo Bagellardo, first appeared in 1472. The Drake Collection boasts one copy published in Latin in Padua in 1487, and a German translation from Leipzig published in 1607. Only one year after Bagellardo's first printing came Bartholomaeus Metlinger's *Ein Regiment der gesuntheit fur die jungen Kinder,* Augsburg, 1473.[2] It was the first time such a book was written in the vernacular for laiety, especially for parents. A later edition contains charming woodcuts of mothers with babies and young children.[3]

The first English guide to rearing children, written as a addendum to his *Regiment of Lyfe,* was Thomas Phaer's *The Boke of Chyldren,* published in 1545.[4] Four sixteenth-century copies are in the Collection, as well as a 1955 reprint. The highly regarded French contemporary of Phaer, Ambrose Parey (1510–1590), wrote voluminously on health care in general and devoted several sections specifically to children.[5]

These fifteenth- and sixteenth-century writers dealt with feeding: breast feeding, wet nursing, dry nursing (artificial feeding), and weaning; with daily care: bathing, swaddling, clothing, rocking, and exercise; and with ailments and illness: diarrhoea, constipation, teething, rashes, fevers, scrofula, smallpox, and plague. Their advice reflected the prevailing beliefs of their time, beliefs held with little change throughout the Middle Ages and beyond.

Notes

1. Soranus, a Greek physician was born at Ephesus and lived during the reigns of Trajan (AD 98-117) and Hadrian (AD 117-138). He practised in Alexandria and subsequently in Rome and was chief representative of the school of physicians known as "methodists." Two of his treatises are extant: *On Fractures* and *On Diseases of Women*. (*The Encyclopia Britannica* XI ed. vol. XXV New York: The Encyclopedia Britannica Company, 1911, p. 430). Information in the text is taken from Abt-Garrison's *History of Pediatrics.*
2. Metlinger, 1473. The 1473 copy in the Drake Collection has no title page. The 1550 printing bears the cited title and contains woodcuts.
3. It is interesting to see it reported that Bagellardo (1472) and Metlinger (1473) wrote two of the first three medical books to go direct from the author's desk to the printer, published without the customary patronage of court or other high-ranking officials (Demaitre L. The Idea of Childhood and Child Care in the Middle Ages. *Journal of Psychohistory* 1977; 4:4, p. 461-490).
4. Phaer, 1550. *The Regiment of Lyfe* is a translation of a book by Jean Goeurot, 1530. Phaer added to it and called it *The Boke of Chyldren.*
5. Parey, 1649. In translating the works of the well-known French surgeon Ambroise Paré in 1649, Thomas Johnson designated the author as Ambrose Parey. Since this is the book of reference for this work, Johnson's spelling is used throughout.

Tendresse Maternelle
[Maternal Affection]
Stipple engraving by Armand St. Gilles
After Ruabien
France, early 19 C
31.0 × 22.5 cm

MATERNAL NURSING

> Wherefore as it is agreing to nature so it is necessary and comely for the own mother to nource the owne child. Which if it may be done, it shall be most comendable and holsome...
>
> Thomas Phaer. *The Boke of Chyldren,* 155.

The foregoing statement of Phaer's was not in keeping with the advice of his Italian predecessor, Bagellardo,[1] who, against popular opinion had promoted the use of a wet nurse by all who could afford it. However, it did conform with the belief of his German forerunner, Metlinger:[2] no consideration was given to food other than breast milk, that of the mother being regarded as most advantageous; only if the mother's health prevented her from feeding her child should a wet nurse be sought, and then with great care.

The milk produced immediately following childbirth, called colostrum, was held suspect by many authorities, and was therefore to be avoided. Consequently, advice about the time to begin breast feeding varied from putting the child to suckle before cutting the umbilical cord, to withholding the breast for a month. Soranus of Ephesus in the second century had advised beginning 20 days after birth. Metlinger in the late fifteenth century advocated expressing milk for 14 days before presenting the breast to the infant; he suggested that a puppy could suck the milk. Some recommended that other children or the mother herself could perform this task.[3] A century later in France, Simon de Vallambert,[4] who assumed mothers would nurse their offspring, noted that his contemporaries' opinions about the delay in maternal nursing ranged from one to 30 days, and he preferred to start maternal nursing as soon as the mother's temperament returned to normal.

Other sixteenth- and seventeenth-century writings in the Collection support Phaer's belief in maternal nursing with varying arguments to strengthen it. Gallego de la Serna declared it most natural, most convenient, and most humane for all mothers to feed their own children with their own milk, producing the greatest benefit for the infants.[5] Parey expressed the wish that all mothers would nurse their own children, for their milk is nothing else but "the same blood made white in the duggs,"[6] James Primrose reinforced this a century later when he claimed it was best for the mother to nurse her baby because she had the same blood, background, and customs, which are transmitted with love.[7] In Paris, Francis Mauriceau proposed nothing but breast milk for at least two months, longer if possible, as "Beasts do shew us, that milk alone is sufficient to nourish an Infant, since that they so suckle five or six of their young ones..., without their taking any other Food for a long time after." Surprisingly, he stated at the same time, "We daily see that Children brought up by Hand, do commonly thrive as well as those that are suckled." Mauriceau was not in favour of maternal nursing if the mother had red hair. He believed such milk to be sour and stinking.[8]

Elizabeth Clinton, a Puritan mother of 18 children whom she had been persuaded not to suckle, remorsefully felt compelled to share her convictions in favour of maternal nursing when she was a grandmother. Most of her children died young — only one reached adulthood — and she attributed two infant deaths to the carelessness of wet nurses. Supporting her belief with Biblical references to Eve, Sarah, Hannah, and the blessed Virgin, she published *The Countesse of Lincolnes Nurserie*. She strengthened her stand with "It is ordinary with the Lord to give good stomach, health and strength, to almost all mothers who take this paines with their children."[9]

Much of Metlinger's book was in poetic form. It was not uncommon for scholars to promote principles of child-rearing incorporating their ideas in poetic works. One such sixteenth- and seventeenth-century authority was Scavole de Sainte-Marthe.[10] So impressed with Sainte-Marthe's wisdom and so enamoured of his poetry in his *Paedotrophia* was Dr. H.W. Tytler, that he vowed to reproduce the Latin writings in similarly engrossing English poetry. The resulting translation, published in 1797, makes delightful reading. As revealed in the following excerpt, Sainte-Marthe felt maternal nursing was essential for both the mother and the infant.

> But when the child within the cradle lies,
> Demanding aid with tears, and melting cries,
> Its ancient bounds th' o'erflowing moisture breaks,
> And, of itself, the helpless infant seeks;
> If then restrain'd, the liquor kills the pains
> The swelling Breast, and rages in the veins,
> Would force its way from ev'ry winding maze,
> And for th' ungrateful deed, the mother pays.
> Besides, since ev'ry milky fountain flows
> By the same seed from which the foetus grows,
> What kinder nourishment could Nature give?
> By what, so proper means, could infants live,
> As from this sacred source to draw their food,
> And, with their own, to mix their mother's blood?[11]

Luigi Tansillo, a Roman contemporary of Sainte-Marthe, wrote a long poem, *La Balia*, similar in its thrust — much in favour of maternal nursing, strongly opposed to wet nursing — and it too was first published in Italian in 1767. He blamed wet nursing for the weakened men of Britain, and praised Spain for not indulging in the practice.[12]

Agreeing with Gallego de la Serna and Primrose, Sainte-Marthe believed that as the blood flowed through the glands of the breast, it lost its red colour and turned snow-white. Like others of his time, he cited the exemplary behaviour of monsters such as boars and tigers as they feed their infant young.

And wilt thou, Woman! grac'd with gentlest mind,
Become more fierce than this terrific kind?
Say, does thy infant likeness touch thee not,
When, with complaints, he strains his little throat?
Will you not pity, and his wants relieve,
When still he begs what none but you can give?[13]

As a women has a "generous mind" Sainte-Marthe urged that she begin in pregnancy to give up other cares for the sake of preserving herself and her infant. Then when the baby is born,

Be nurse yourself, and ev'ry sinew strain
To keep that offspring, which you bore with pain.[14]

The eighteenth century brought forth diverse publications concerning breast feeding, both in England and on the Continent. With few exceptions these were long dissertations on the necessity and/or the desirability of maternal nursing. The reasons given were varied: for the health of the child; for the health of the mother; for the temperament of the child (many believed that characteristics passed from mother to infant in the milk); for the stability of the family (different nurses might pass antagonistic characteristics to different siblings, thus creating jealousy); for the emotional relationship of mother and child; for increasing the love of a husband for his wife, and simply because nursing is natural.

James Nelson, in the middle of the century, mentioned that it was the fashion to let children suck for only three or four months.[15] Most writers recommended a much longer period, even 18 months to two years, yet it was common for infants not to be breast fed at all, and quite usual for them to be in the care of a wet nurse.

Why was there such an increase in publications encouraging better child care in the eighteenth century? Infant mortality rates in some areas of England and France soared to around 80 percent. Apart from the personal loss felt by parents, the loss to the countries was vital. Soldiers and sailors were needed, yet babies died in the streets. Many of these deaths could be attributed to abandonment of the newborn; no effective method of birth control was known, and poverty dictated smaller families. But blame for early deaths was also directed to the prevalent and irresponsible use of wet nurses and the increased reliance on artificial feeding. The move to encourage mothers to return to natural feeding was the practical result.

The writers acted from several motivating influences. N. Brouzet, physician to the French king and the Royal Infirmary and Hospitals of Fontainbleau, felt that physicians lacked knowledge about infant diseases and were negligent in their responsibility to advise families about raising their children. Though, in his efforts to draw attention to the prevalent indifference to the "medicinal education of children," he wrote for all, he directed his essay particularly to doctors. Brouzet's writings reflected the lack of concensus among scholars of the time. Though he advocated maternal nursing, he wondered, with so many improvements on nature being made, why so much doubt was cast on other kinds of milk. Perhaps mother's milk was best, but a nurse might be healthier. Cow's milk was also suitable. And, he added, if the mother did not nurse her own child, she would be free to breed more often.[16]

One who did not fall into the category of negligent physicians, was John Astruc, Chief Physician to the King of France and Regius Professor of Medicine at Paris, who wrote:

I am sensible, that it is no easy matter to persuade mothers to suckle their children: however, it is incumbent on us to use our endeavours to induce them to perform this important duty, since the child with the milk it sucks, imbibes the manners and dispositions, as well as the peculiar qualities of the nurse's humours...wherefore, the mother, though perhaps not the best nurse in other respects, and where it is not inconsistent with some present disorder, is always preferable to a stranger;...'Tis also observable, that there is often neither parental love, nor good understanding amongst brethren; that they are of very different tempers, because they have suck'd different breasts; whereas, had they been nursed by their mothers, it might be the means to prevent dissensions in families too frequently observable. Moreover, it is cruel and unnatural in a mother, either out of self-love or indolence, to defraud her new-born babe (tender and helpless) of that milk which nature has provided for it, and which by instinct, it eagerly searches for, though not offered.[17]

Blanche de Castille nourisoit son fils St. Louis.*
Engraving by Voyer, senior
After Clement Pierre Maniller
(1740–1808)
France, 1775–1790
21.4 × 16.1 cm

Un jour une Dame allaita le jeune Prince, la Reine ayant apris cette action la blâme et dit; je ne veux pas que personne puisse me disputer le titre de mère.

[Blanche of Castille suckled her son St. Louis. One day a Lady nursed the young prince. The Queen having learned of this, reprimanded her and said, "I do not want anyone to be able to dispute my title of Mother."]

*Blanche of Castille was mother of Louis IX. (1226-70)

Not shown is a nineteenth-century lithograph by d'Aubert and de Junea after Tellier which depicts Blanche of Castille forcing a finger into the throat of her son, thus compelling him to regurgitate milk he had sucked from a stranger.

In the spirit of Elizabeth Clinton earlier, an anonymous author, directing comments to mothers, simply cried out in frustration against the paucity of writing on "well-regulated education for the management of children and the lack of importance attached to it."

For I must confess, it has often grieved me to see, the Gentleman spare no Expence in his Stable; not only have a Groom, but a Helper, and not only a Helper, but Stable Boys, trained up to the proper and careful Management of the Horses; whilst the Lady neglects her Children in the Nursery, and thinks every Expence too great, that belongs to her Children, or to those that attend them.[18]

In response to a request from a governor of the Foundling Hospital in London to provide the staff of that institution with guidance in the care of their charges, Dr. William Cadogan produced an extensive essay. Naturally there was no possibility in the institution for the infant's mother to suckle her child, but Cadogan did not lose the opportunity to lash out at society and mothers in high society in particular, who chose not to breast feed their own babies. He advised anyone to:

Look over the Bills of Mortality; there he may observe, that almost Half the Number of those who fill up that black List, die under five Years of Age; So that Half the People that come into the World, go out of it again before they become of the least Use to it, or themselves. To me, this seems to deserve serious consideration; and yet I cannot find, that any one Man of Sense and publick Spirit, has ever attended to it at all; notwithstanding the Maxim in every one's Mouth, that a Multitude of Inhabitants is the greatest Strength and best Support of a Commonwealth.[19]

Cadogan was convinced these deaths were not normal, but entirely due to mismanagement.

> ...it is ridiculous to charge it upon nature, and suppose, that Infants are more subject to Disease and Death than grown Persons; on the contrary, they bear Pain and Disease much better, Fevers especially, and for the same Reason that a Twig is less hurt by a storm than an Oak. In all the other Productions of Nature we see the greatest Vigor and Luxuriancy of Health, the nearer they are to the Egg or the Bud; they are indeed then most sensible of Injury, and it is Injury only that destroys them. When was there a Lamb, a Bird, or a Tree that died because it was young? These are under the immediate Nursing of unerring Nature, and they thrive accordingly. Ought it not therefore to be the Care of every Nurse and every Parent, not only to protect their Nurselings from Injury, but to be well assured, that their own officious Services be not the greatest the helpless Creatures can suffer.[20]

La Mère Nourrice à l'estaminet
[Mother nursing at the public house]
Des and engraved by J Dassonville
(flourished 1650–1665)
9.0 × 9.3 cm

He insisted that one of the remedies essential to improving the health of infants, was for mothers to nurse their own children; fathers should show concern and involvement by supervising the nursing themselves.

> When a Child sucks its own Mother, which, with a very few Exceptions, would be best for every Child, and every Mother, Nature has provided it with such wholsome and suitable Nourishment; supposing her a temperate Woman, that makes some Use of her Limbs; it can hardly do amiss.[21]

Cadogan also observed that lower class children in England, had a better chance of survival than those in high society.

> ...the Want of Superfluity confines them more within the Limits of Nature; hence they enjoy Blessings they feel not, and are ignorant of their Cause. The Mother who has only a few Rags to cover her Child loosely, and little more than her own Breast to feed it, sees it healthy and strong, and very soon able to shift for itself; while the puny Insect, the Heir and Hope of a rich Family, lies languishing under a Load of Finery, that overpowers his Limbs, abhorring and rejecting the Dainties he is cramm'd with, 'till he dies a Victim to the mistaken Care and Tenderness of his fond Mother.[22]

About the same time the great physician Hermann Boerhaave of Leyden, Holland, whose advice and teaching were sought by students from Britain and continental Europe, advocated strongly that mothers nurse their own children. He held up as an example, La Reine de France who nursed M. le Dauphin. Nursing, he believed to be compatible with good health; he accepted none of the suggestions that temperament and other characteristics were transferred through breast milk.[23]

The promotion of breast feeding was augmented by the general philosophy of the time. John Locke[24] in England and Jean Jacques Rousseau in France in accordance with their back-to-nature movement, advised mothers to breast feed; if given over to wet nurses, neglect and ill-health resulted. Rousseau believed that "should mothers once again condescend to nurse their children... a general reformation will presently result."[25] Abandoning his professed beliefs, Rousseau deposited each of this own five children in the Foundling Hospital.

L'Amour Paternel
[Paternal love]
Engraving by Le Bas (1707–1783)
After A. Brouwer
France
17.9 × 13.6 cm

William Buchan, in a book intended to show people what is in their own power regarding prevention and cure of diseases, deplored the tendency to decide by whim and caprice rather than reason how to feed an infant. "Nothing can be more preposterous than for a mother to think it below her to take care of her own child..." He conceded, however, in his first book that breast feeding was often impracticable because "women of delicate constitutions, subject to low spirits, hysteric fits, or other nervous disorders, make very bad nurses," and these complaints were so common among women of fashion and high station, that Buchan was convinced it was rare to find one, who, though willing, was really able to suckle her own child.[26]

With this last statement, Cadogan firmly disagreed, believing that: "the mother would...in most hysterical nervous cases, establish her own Health by it [breast feeding], tho' she were weak and sickly before, as well as that of her Offspring."[27] It would be necessary for her to nurse only four times in 24 hours, and all other chores for the baby could be carried out by a supervised servant. Half a century earlier Thomas Tryon had suggested that a mother should aim to establish a routine to suit her own convenience.[28]

Following Cadogan's example, Buchan advised fathers to insist on and to supervise breast feeding, but he went further: they should concern themselves in everything respecting the improvement of the child's body or mind. He added that "men generally keep at such a distance from even the smallest acquaintance with...the nursery...not so, however with the kennel or the stables."[29] Rousseau carried this to extremes and urged the father to be the teacher from birth to adulthood: "his mother is his only true nurse, so is his father his only true preceptor."[30]

Joseph Raulin[31] in Paris and Nicholas Rosen von Rosenstein[32] in Sweden, at about this time, were urging mothers to breast feed, and in cases where this was impossible, to choose wet nurses with the greatest care. Both believed what Astruc[33] had stated a quarter century earlier, that the qualities of the nurse would be passed on to the child.

In England, reflecting George Armstrong's[34] opinion as published in 1771, William Moss wrote in 1781: "There can be no doubt that the Mother's Milk is the only sustenance nature has designed for an infant at the time of his birth."[35] Michael Underwood fully agreed.[36] By the end of the century nature's influence was more remarkable as Seguin Henry Jackson proclaimed that no one ought to trifle with the human body, and mother's milk is best. He declared that "In man...should nature find her best and truest friend."[37]

The trend continued in France: Jean Huxham[38] urged mothers to breast feed for their own health and that of the baby; Landais in 1781 and Icart in 1784 also strongly advocated maternal nursing. Landais stated that doctors had always recommended this. Most of the writers expressed no concern about characteristics passed to the infant through the breast milk, but all advised the mother to nurse for health reasons.

In the early nineteenth century Buchan[39] again wrote about the care of children and quoted from Tytler's translation of Sainte-Marthe, and from Underwood, Cadogan, Locke, Rousseau, and others. So much did he treasure the work of Cadogan, then out of print, that he reprinted much of that book as an appendix to his own work. After 40 years of practice Buchan revised his former thinking and claimed that *many* mothers *will not* nurse, *few cannot.* He supported Rousseau's belief, as did Astruc and Landais, that having mothers nurse their own children would bring families closer together and would accomplish a moral as well as a medical reformation. By this time Buchan was a well-known authority whose influence was widespread; this particular volume of his writing was published in the United States. Other eminent authorities were in tune with Buchan's approach. In Germany, Struve was in full agreement: healthy mothers should nurse; mothers who are chronically ill should choose a wet nurse with great care.[40]

One Year of Marriage
Lithograph by de Villain
After Bellangé
Paris, mid 19 C
14.4 x 18.4 cm

John Herdman, in his unmitigated support of maternal nursing, urged mothers to assume more responsibility. They should trust themselves, not nurses, midwives, or doctors: "right or wrong, they inquire not" and they must inquire.[41] "In one word, the fit and the proper management of the infant state is to be found in the sure and unerring principle of *instinct.*"[42] One should treat children according to the pure dictates and intentions of Nature. Mother's milk is ready when the offspring requires it,... "the infant's necessity for food and the mother's ability to supply it exactly keep apace or correspond with each other."[43] "Even the milk of another woman is not a proper food for your infant; for it is foreign to his nature."[44]

As concern for the care of children increased and the mother's suckling was more generally recognized as the best possible method of feeding, more thought was given to easing her load. Tryon in 1695 and Cadogan 50 years later pressed for a routine best suited to the mother. Both Buchan and Armstrong about 1770, suggested a supplementary feeding at night to give her more rest. In 1792 Alexander Hamilton disapproved of the move toward absolute regulation of feeding times but warned that "every woman should avoid becoming a slave of her child, as many unguardedly do."[45]

Nineteenth century French authorities were still promoting nursing by mothers. One writer, Edward Protat, reported that happily most French women were returning to this "maternal tenderness" after a low point at the end of the previous century.[46] J.P. Harmond de Montgarny, in promoting artificial feeding more strongly than any other writer in the Drake books of the period, nevertheless stated that mother's milk is most suitable: *Il faut cependant convenir que le lait de la mère doit être la nourriture la plus analogue au tempérament et à la faiblesse de l'enfant.* [It must be agreed, however, that the mother's milk is the most compatible nourishment for the temperament and strength of the child.][47] The subject in France was sufficiently controversial in 1819 to enable a candidate to earn his doctoral degree by presenting a thesis on the advantages of maternal breast feeding.[48]

In Britain during the nineteenth century the whole field of infant care was still much under discussion. John Burns[49] and James Hamilton[50] both wrote promoting maternal breast feeding if possible, but admitted there could be exceptions. Burns pointed out that there was some dispute as to whether disease could be communicated by suckling, and this was cause for concern.

The Fashionable Mama
or *The Convenience of Modern Dress*
Des and engraved by James Gillray,
London, 1796
45.5 x 35.5 cm

Note picture on wall of "Maternal Love" and Royal Coach waiting outside.

Holy Family
Sepia wash
Etching by WW Ryland
After Eles Sirani (1638–1665)
London, 1764
27.0 × 21.0 cm

Madonna and Child
Etching by LP (late 16 C–early 17 C)
After Antonio da Correggio (1494–1534)
18.7 × 16.3 cm

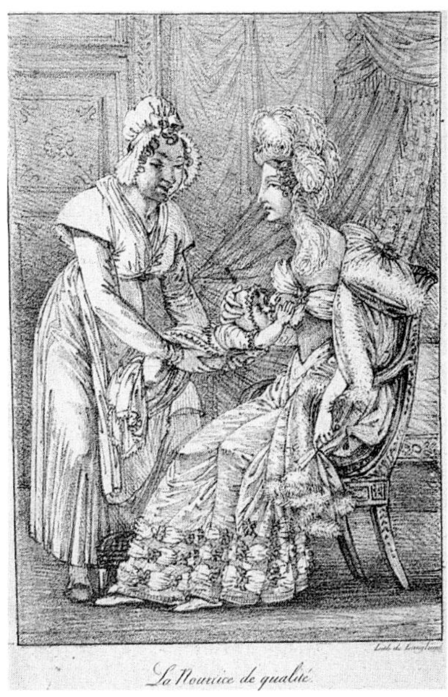

La Nourrice de Qualité
[The Nurse of Quality]
The Duchess of Berry, wet nurse to Henry V.
Count of Chambard, born Sept. 29, 1820
Lithograph by de Langlumé (fl. 1822–1824)
21.2 × 15.2 cm

Thomas Rowlandson,[51] poet and caricaturist, proclaimed the virtues of breast feeding and designated the lack of it as a common cause of death in *The English Dance of Death.*

In all the forms that Nature gives
To ev'ry work of her's that lives,
Whether in fashion weak, or strong,
That to the air brings forth its young,
Affection's first great Law applies,
To nurse their various progenies.

La Jeune Mère
[The Young Mother]
Engraved by AP Riffaut (1821–1859)
After J Verkolie (fl. 1657–1675)
France, 19 C
20.5 × 17.0 cm

He continued to point out that tigers and hyenas, even the wildest brutes, set us examples of the tender nursing of their young. He questioned whether such a woman could be found who would deliberately not provide the suckling's nurture, then concluded that such mothers do exist:

Yes, there are Mothers - yes, who dare,
Soon as it breathes the vital air,
While it unfolds its opening charms,
To yield it to a stranger's arms
And let the helpless babe be press'd
Unconcious to a stranger's breast ...
Does not the mind disgusted turn
When the tale's told, and frowning spurn
Th'unnatural mother, when she tears
From her full paps the Child she bears?
While thus to chance the bantling's hurl'd,
She gives her fondness to the world;
And, as she haunts where Pleasure reigns,
Forgets she felt a Mother's pains.

The poem later summoned the mother to visit the wet nurse and the child to see the result of her decision:

The foster-mother feels no more,
Than its own parent felt before:
Drown'd in inebriated sleep,
No vigils can the Drunkard keep.
— Death rocks the Cradle, as you see,
And sings his mortal Lullaby.

Though Protat assessed that most French women were relying again on maternal nursing, others did not support his opinion. Théodore Léger argued that Nature imposed the obligation to nurse the baby on one who becomes a mother. Each chapter in his book of medical advice begins with "Chère Jenny," and the style is personal, chatty, and sentimental.[52] In fact, in France, throughout the nineteenth century, the numbers of mothers nursing their infants did not increase, and the wet nursing business continued to thrive until World War I (1914–1918).

In England, John Roberton, in agreement with his French contemporary Léger, stated his position clearly:

> When the health of the female is good, ..., and her milk is plentiful, no excuse [for not nursing] is admissable, whatever be her rank in society; as it is just that she who determines not to suckle, ought not to become a mother.[53]

The same attitude is clear in the words of Walter Dendy:

> Indeed, every mother is guilty of lessening her own maternal dignity, who does not avail herself of that fountain of nutrition which nature has bountifully bestowed on her as the support and preservation of life.[54]

Writers later in the nineteenth century, particularly in France, dealt more with social problems concerning children: studies of foundlings, surveys of children's services, histories of institutions.

In this century the issue of breast feeding is still with us. Ambrose Bierce, in his *Devil's Dictionary* of 1911, offered the following definition of mammalia: "A family of vertebrate animals whose females in a state of nature suckle their young, but when civilized and enlightened put them out to nurse or use a bottle." Emmett Holt, in the eighth edition of his paediatric text claimed mothers' milk was best, but offered several formulae based on cow's milk as second best.[55] A former student of Holt and for many years Physician-in-Chief at the Hospital for Sick Children, in Toronto, Dr. Alan Brown[56] was a strong advocate of breast feeding. "Cow's milk is for calves" was his usual retort to anyone who questioned his stand.

The Mothercraft Movement, first established in New Zealand by Dr. Truby King in 1907, spread to other countries and opened in Toronto in 1931. Nurses trained in his methods helped mothers launch their newborn babies on a healthful routine based on breast feeding. A few decades later the La Leche League was founded in the United States and now functions internationally to provide information and encouragement to women who want to nurse their babies.

Today the choice between breast feeding and dry nursing is made more freely because of the vast improvements in infant formulas, but mothers must still consider the psychological impact of withholding the breast and the baby's possible intolerance of various alternatives.

Maternal nursing, by its very nature, does not stimulate the production of many artifacts. Nipple shields and breast cups are among the few. Recommended by Parey in the sixteenth century in France, nipple shields were well described.

> If when the child's teeth begin to grow, hee chance to bite the nipple of the Nurse's breast, there will bee an ulcer verie contumcious and hard to bee cured; because that the sucking of the childe, and the rubbing of the clothes do keep it alwaies raw; it must bee cured with fomenting it with Alum-water, and then presently after the fomentation putting thereupon a cover of lead, made like unto a hat, with manie holes in the top, whereat both the milk, and also, the sanious matter that commeth from the ulcer may go out; for lead it self will cure ulcers.[57]

Nipple shields and milk catchers
Upper: Three silver nipple shields
Left: 1797–1798
Centre: 1816–1817; diam: 5.7 cm
Right: 1803–1804
Lower: Three glass drip catchers
Centre: Leeka breast cup

Although comforting to both mothers and wet nurses and thought to be beneficial, the lead must have caused harm if used for prolonged periods. Wax, wooden, or leaden caps were recommended in directions to midwives, published in England in 1682,[58] and in Mauriceau's[59] publication in France. It was believed that they dried the nipples and encouraged matter and milk to pass away. Drawings in both of these seventeenth-century books resemble sketches shown by Parey. The nipple shields in the Collection are silver, early nineteenth-century pieces. Not always recognized for the purpose intended, they were sometimes put to other uses: one in the Collection has been converted into a tea strainer.[60]

Glass drip catchers, held by a binder over the nipple, caught dribbling milk. A variant of these was the Leeka breast cup, used in England until recently to collect milk for other babies in need of it. A similar device called a Woolwich shell was worn during pregnancy in an effort to correct inverted nipples.

Artists and artisans frequently portrayed the nurture of infants in paintings, prints, ceramics, sculptures, stamps, and medals. Some show the pleasure and contentment of mother and child, but a few emphasize the disdain felt by the high society mother in what she perceived as a demeaning role. Others depicted the concern and involvement of the father.

Lactasti Sacro Ubere
[Thou didst give milk from the holy breast]
Etching
After Carracci (1560–1609)
14.3 × 11.8 cm

Mother nursing swaddled baby
Engraving by Clemendt de Jonge
After C de Visscher
Amsterdam, 17 C
35.9 × 30.5 cm

Nursing Mother
Porcelain
Ludwigsburg
Germany, 1758–1793
Ht: 16.5 cm

Taylor's Wife
Porcelain
Chelsea-Derby
England, ca. 1780
Ht: 24.0 cm
See p. 52

Nursing mothers
Left: Porcelain, Europe, 1850
Ht: 18.4 cm
Right: Parian ware, England, ca. 1860,
Ht: 25.4 cm
Original by Sir Richard Westmacott
Reduced by G Peppercorn

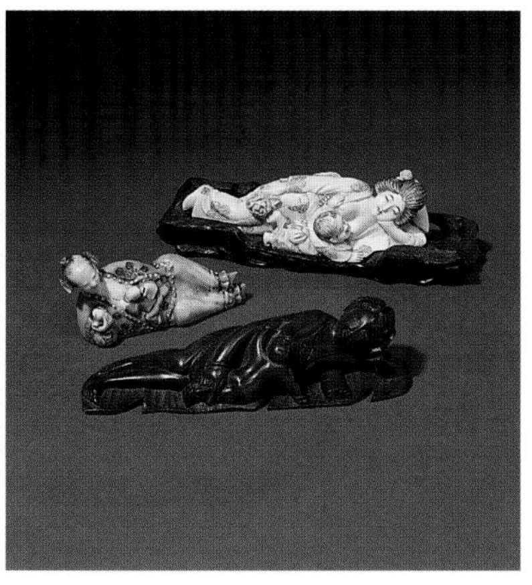

Oriental nursing mothers
Upper: Carved and painted ivory, Japan
Centre: Porcelain, Japan, 19 C
Length: 11.4 cm
The nursing mother, Hishimojan, represents the legendary devil of India, Hariti, who stole and consumed infants and children. Buddha reformed her by giving her the Zakuro or pomegranate, the emblem of fertility, as her special fruit.
Lower: Carved rosewood, China

Among Dr. Drake's favourites were the 18 Egyptian figures of Isis and Horus, dating from 1000 to 150 BC. The mother goddess, consort of Osiris, sits with their son, Horus, on her lap. The pose is classic: she sits with knees together, facing straight ahead, and proffers her left breast to the child. In portraying mother and child, in many cultures the artists often chose a goddess as subject.

Isis and Horus
Bronze
Egypt
Ht: 23.0 cm

Ancient terra cotta mother
Probably a goddess
Cyprus, 3 C BC
Ht: 10.2 cm

Pre-Columbian pottery mother
Knees flat in front and feet at the sides, a pose characteristic of an early period, probably Narjarit
Mexico, 500–400 BC
Ht: 16.5 cm

La Mère Imprisonée
[The Imprisoned Mother], 1902
Ht: 12.5 cm
Copied from the original bronze by Stephan Sinding, a Norwegian sculptor working in Paris, 1884

Ashanti incense burner
Supported by nursing mother
Bronze, Ghana, 19 C
Ht: 35.0 cm

Inuk nursing mother
Ht: 17.5 cm
In appreciation of the services of Dr. Drake as their medical advisor, the Hudson Bay Company commissioned an Eskimo carving in soapstone, 1956

Argentine Farmers[61]
Argentina, 580
Sept 20, 1948

Mother and Child
Portuguese India, RA 5
1948

Virgin and Child
Belgium, B466A
April 1, 1949
Painting by Van der Weyden (1399–1464)

Sometimes appeals for larger families were direct, and compliance was rewarded. The medal produced in Hitler's Germany was awarded to mothers of the state: bronze for three children, silver for five, and gold for 10.

Bronze German mother's cross
OBV: DER DEUTSCHEN MUTTER around swastika
REV. (not shown):
16 DEZEMBER 1938
45 × 36 mm

Poster
Lithograph by Henon
After Jean Droit, Paris, 1920–1929
[Without Children Today
No France Tomorrow!
No children
Without a birth and family policy
Join the National Alliance
They know how to get it]
73.6 × 56.2 cm

Bronze nursing mother
REV: (not shown) Bust of young girl
THERESE
1 MAI, 1899 G_1
81 x 53 mm

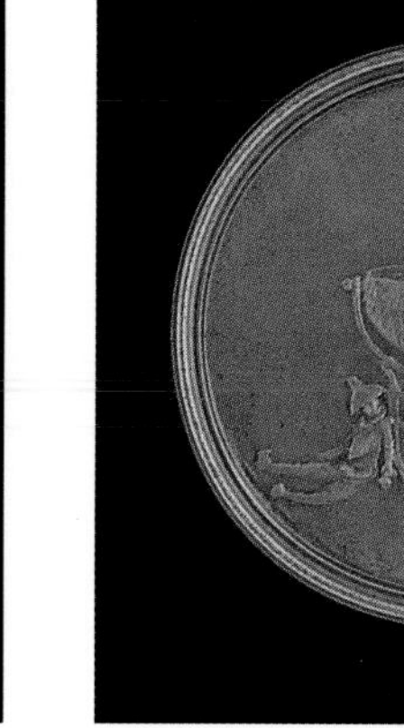

Bronze medal
HAEC SUNT MEA ORNAMENTA
[These are my jewels] HN
REV: Cradle with doll and toy horse
53 mm

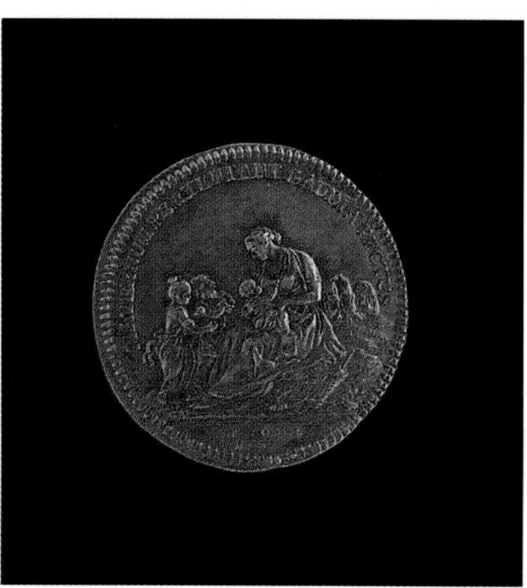

Bronze medal
LA BONNE MÈRE
[The Good Mother]
MATERNUM PERTENTANT GAUDIA PECTUS
[Joy fills a mother's heart] G.A.
REV: (not shown) Wreath of olive branches
34 mm

Notes

1. Bagellardo 1487.
2. Metlinger 1473.
3. A number of early writers recommended that the mother, during this postpartem waiting period, should suck her own milk. Ferrarius showed sketches of a long-spouted, bulbous glass device to facilitate this practice, (Ferrarius, O., *De Arte Medica Infantium*, BRIXIAE, F.&P. Mariam, 1577, p31), and Parey in his works of the same period showed a similar glass contrivance. He also suggested as alternatives that a mother "may let children or little whelps suck (her) breasts whereby they may draw out the milk that is fixed fast in (her) dugs..." (p 616). *The Turning Wheels*, a novel about South Africa, mentions the large number of puppies needed by the nineteenth-century trekking Boers to relieve the engorged breasts of mothers whose babies had died (Stuart Cloete, Houghton Mifflin, Boston, 1937). Obviously it was a method of expressing excess milk, used for some centuries.
4. de Vallambert 1565 (the first paediatric text in French).
5. Gallego de Serna 1634.
6. Parey 1649.
7. Primrose 1659.
8. Mauriceau 1683: (from the original 1668 edition in French, p 397.) A 1674 French printing is also in the Collection.
9. Clinton 1662:14.
10. Scavole de Sainte-Marthe lived 1536-1623.
11. Scavole de Sainte-Marthe 1797:11.
12. Luigi Tansillo, born ca. 1510 in the Kingdom of Naples. An English translation by William Roscoe, Liverpool: Cadell & Davies, 1800 is in the Collection.
13. Scavole de Sainte-Marthe 1797:15.
14. Scavole de Sainte-Marthe 1797:17.
15. Nelson 1753,
16. Brouzet 1755. (Translated from the original 1754 French edition)
17. Astruc 1746:17-19.
18. Author unknown. *Observations Upon the Proper Nursing of Children from a Long Series of Experience.* London: R and J Dodsley, 1761:17.
19. Cadogan 1748:6.
20. Cadogan 1748:6-7.
21. Cadogan 1748:14.
22. Cadogan 1748:7.
23. Boerhaave 1759: excerpted from M Van Sweeten. Commentary on Boerhaave's Aphorisims. Translated from Latin by M Paul.
24. Locke 1693.
25. Rousseau 1763:16.
26. Buchan 1769:3.
27. Cadogan 1748:14.
28. Tryon 1695.
29. Ruchan 1769:6.
30. Rousseau 1763.
31. Raulin 1769:160.
32. Rosen von Rosenstein 1776:1-2.
33. Astruc 1746.
34. Armstrong 1771.
35. Moss 1781:65.
36. Underwood 1784.
37. Jackson 1798:276.
38. Huxham 1776.
39. Buchan 1804.
40. Struve 1802.
41. Herdman 1807:8.
42. Herdman 1807:11.
43. Herdman 1807:72.
44. Herdman 1807:96.
45. Hamilton, A. 1792.
46. Protat 1803:10.
47. Harmond de Montgarny 1806:2.
48. Torrent 1819.
49. Burns 1811.
50. Hamilton, J. 1813.
51. Rowlandson 1815:34-47.
52. Léger 1825.
53. Roberton 1827.
54. Dendy 1833:21.
55. Holt 1917.
56. Dr Alan Brown, Dr Fredrick Tisdall and Dr Theodore Drake developed Pablum, a baby food that achieved world-wide use.
57. Parey 1649:610.
58. (Author unknown) *The English Midwife* 1682:265.
59. Mauriceau 1683,
60. Elizabeth Heathman, a collector reporting in *Keeping Abreast*, Vol I, No 3, 1974, claims that no other item in collections of infant feeders and related artifacts has been mistaken for so many different purposes as the blown glass breast cup, sometimes called a Leeka breast cup.
61. All numbers following stamps are those from *Scott Standard Postage Stamp Catalogue.*

La Belle Nourrice
[The Beautiful Wet Nurse]
Hand-coloured etching by Boissot
1790-1820
18.5 × 13.8 cm

WET NURSING

> Wherefore the true Mother, tho not the best Nurse, should ever be preferred before a Stranger. But because there are several that either will not, or cannot suckle their own Children, whether it be to preserve their beauty, as all Persons of Quality, and most of the Citizens do; or that their Husbands will not suffer them, nor be troubled with such a noise; or that being ill or indisposed, they cannot, there is then an Obligation to provide another Nurse, which should be chosen as convenient for the Child as may be.[59]
>
> Francis Mauriceau. *The Diseases of Women with Child and in Child-bed.* 1674, p 432

Mention has been made of wet nurses. They commonly substituted in the ancient world when mothers were unable to suckle their own children. In Greece this nurse was carefully chosen: preferably a Spartan, young, robust, and of good character. She was paid a living wage and stayed with the family about two years. In Egypt, if needed, a slave woman was taken under contract to nourish the baby on breast milk the first six months and on cow's milk for the next 18 months. This custom made it easy for Moses' mother, as told in the Bible, to play the role of wet nurse to her own son when he was found hidden in the bulrushes and adopted by Pharoah's daughter.[1] In Palestine a slave or hired woman with no other employment moved into the home, if necessary, for two or three years. She was carefully nurtured and pampered as one of the family; her sole duty was to suckle the nursling for whose fate she was held responsible.

When Datheus, a priest of Milan, announced the establishment of his home for abandoned children in 787, he simultaneously declared his commitment to procuring wet nurses to feed them.[2]

First sought as a necessity, these women became increasingly popular. In Europe women in high society worried about losing their trim figures, and, anxious to return to their active social lives, resorted to wet nurses. It was the fashionable way of life.

As opportunities appeared for women of the lower class to work in the food trades, silk manufacturing centers, shops, and service industries in the developing cities, wages rose sufficiently in excess of the cost of a wet nurse for these jobs to become attractive to young mothers. Wet nurses no longer served just the upper class; they were sought by all levels of society. High demand for their services encouraged unmarried girls to have a child so they could get into the business,

Birth notice
Proudly announcing twins, a son Robert and a daughter Hélène
France, 1892
Babies shown in the arms of a wet nurse reflect the importance of her position.

La Nourrisce [The Wet Nurse]
Engraving by Balathasan Moncornet
Paris, 1640–1660
15.7 × 11.7 cm
[This beauty, without artifice, sells what she pleases at the market and will be able to sell her milk easily when she becomes a wet nurse]

Wet Nurse
Pottery figure of a typical 16 C wet nurse, in the style of an early 17 C earthenware figure made at Avon, near Fontainebleau by Bertelemy de Blenod, a follower of the 16 C potter, Bernard Palissy, ?1792
Ht: 26.4 cm

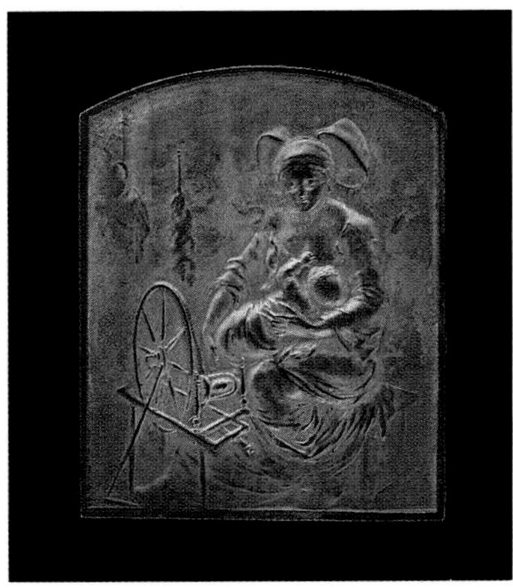

Silver medal of Wet Nurse
REV: (not shown)
Book, spool of yarn etc. left
6.4 × 5.2 cm

Nutrice in Napoli [Wet Nurse in Naples]
Watercolour
9.0 × 6.0 cm

La Nourrice [The Wet Nurse]
Lithograph, printed by Frick frère
Paris, 1850–1870
13.3 × 9.0 cm

and women with one baby to attempt to nurse a second.

Although many nurses moved into the home for extended periods of time, often the baby went to stay at the home of the wet nurse. As belief in the healthful benefits of the country air became widespread, more and more children were sent to the country. Nurses located closer to the city could charge more for their services. For the wealthy, personal interviews and frequent visits were possible; for the less fortunate, usually no personal contact occurred and supervision was limited. No doubt there were wet nurses who were needed and who were conscientious and satisfactory, but the system was open to abuse.

Though wet nurses existed elsewhere, most of the books, documents, artifacts, and prints in the Drake Collection relate to England and the continent, particularly France, where the practice reached its peak in the eighteenth century.

In France, the employment of the wet nurse, *la nourrice,* became so standard that hostels directed by *recommandaresses* were established, where nurses could register and stay until their services were assigned. Here, those in need of such services could come to make the necessary arrangements. Transportation to take babies and nurses to and from the country, to deliver payments and parcels, and to convey messages, was supplied by *meneurs.* A *meneur's* medallion was his badge of office.

The system appears efficient, but in both England and France the business became scandalous, to the detriment of both nurses and their wards. In the beginning of the eighteenth century, the two bureaux in Paris were operating so badly that government intervention was sought. In 1715 a declaration by the king established four bureaux in the city and introduced regulations for their administration and for the wet nurses. They were placed under the jurisdiction of the Lieutenant General of Police, who was empowered to appoint the *recommandaresses* [directors] and was made responsible for collecting fees. The offices were to be inspected each month by the courts.

Any nurse registering at the bureau had to have the facts about herself, her husband, and her own infant certified by her parish priest; similarly when returning home she had to present to her local curé a certificate of particulars about the nursling from the *recommandaresse.* She was forbidden to have two nurslings at the same time and was required to give notification by the second month if she became pregnant or if for any reason she could not nurse. If the baby died she was to submit a death certificate and she could claim back pay. Disciplines, fines, and punishments were outlined.[3]

Bronze medal
OBV: NUTRIX QUOQUE MATER. VIVER F.
[Nurse as well as Mother]
REV: MAISON CENTRALE DE NOURRICES, 1831
[Central Home for Wet Nurses, 1831]
35.0 mm

Bronze Meneur's identification badge, 17 C
OBV: MENEUR DES NOURICES DE L'HÔPITAL
[Meneur of Hospital Wet Nurses]
REV: DES ENFANS TROUVEZ DE PARIS
[Foundlings of Paris]
40 mm

Gradually, as hazards of the system and opportunites for abuse became apparent, changes were introduced. In 1727 the following amendments were made: nurses must accompany *meneurs* to feed babies en route; if requested by parents or guardians, nurses must return children within 15 days; the nurse was forbidden to transfer a baby in her charge to another nurse; nurses were punished if babies died through neglect. Money owed to the nurses could not accumulate beyond three months.[4]

Regulations were strengthened in 1737.[5] In 1740 an ordinance introduced a fine for nurses leaving Paris without a return certificate to be given to the parish curé, and for *meneurs* failing to provide a nurse with same.[6]

Because of frequent smothering deaths caused by overlaying, in 1756 nurses were forbidden to sleep in the same bed with a nursling but were made to provide a cradle or crib. They were fined 100 *livres* for the first offence and given "exemplary punishment" thereafter.[7]

A significant addition in 1762 was a compulsory examination of the nurse or baby by the official physician and surgeon, if requested by those specifically concerned.[8]

Lack of care and supervision of the four hostels operated by the *recommandaresses* led to corruption of morals and poor health among wet nurses. Consequently orders were issued by the king in July, 1769, for the four bureaux to cease by January 1, 1770, and for one central bureau to be established in Paris to house all country women who came for nurslings.[9] *Le Bureau de la Direction Générale des Nourrices* was to oversee the conduct of the entire wet nursing business.

Additional regulations were imposed on *meneurs*. Their transport wagons had to be in good condition and covered; supervisors had to sit front and back to prevent infants falling out.[10]

Voiture des Nourrices [Wet Nurses' Wagon]
Lithograph by C Motte after V Adam
Paris, 1825
12.1 × 20.4 cm

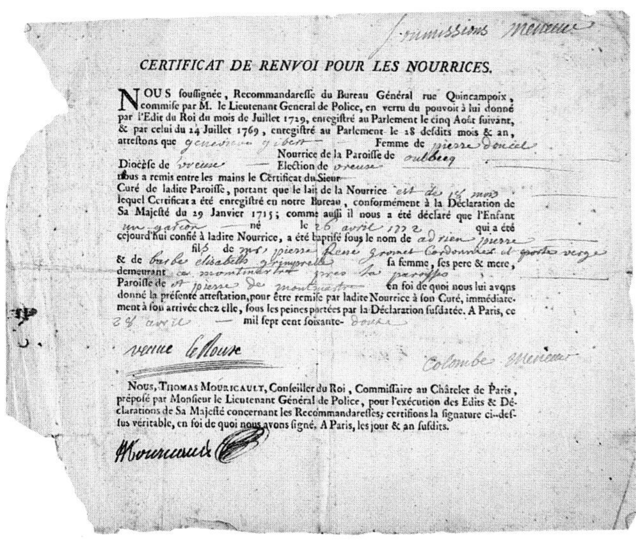

CERTIFICAT DE RENVOI POUR LES NOURRICES.

NOUS soussignée, Recommandaresse du Bureau Général rue Quincampoix, commise par M. le Lieutenant General de Police, en vertu du pouvoir à lui donné par l'Edit du Roi du mois de Juillet 1729, enregistré au Parlement le cinq Août suivant, & par celui du 24 Juillet 1769, enregistré au Parlement le 28 desdits mois & an, attestons que genevieve giber Femme de pierre doucel Nourrice de la Paroisse de oulbecq Diocèse de vreuse Election de vreuse nous a remis entre les mains le Certificat du Sieur Curé de ladite Paroisse, portant que le lait de la Nourrice est de 18 mois lequel Certificat a été enregistré en notre Bureau, conformément à la Déclaration de Sa Majesté du 29 Janvier 1715; comme aussi il nous a été déclaré que l'Enfant un garçon né le 26 avril 1772 qui a été cejourd'hui confié à ladite Nourrice, a été baptisé sous le nom de adrien pierre fils de mr. pierre rené gronet cordonnier et porte verge & de barbe elisabeth grimprelle sa femme, ses pere & mere, demeurant a montmartre pres la paroisse Paroisse de st pierre de montmartre en foi de quoi nous lui avons donné la présente attestation, pour être remise par ladite Nourrice à son Curé, immédiatement à son arrivée chez elle, sous les peines portées par la Déclaration susdatée. A Paris, ce 28 avril mil sept cent soixante-douze

veuve le Roux

Colombe meneur

Nous, THOMAS MOURICAULT, Conseiller du Roi, Commissaire au Châtelet de Paris, préposé par Monsieur le Lieutenant Général de Police, pour l'exécution des Edits & Déclarations de Sa Majesté concernant les Recommandaresses; certifions la signature ci-dessus véritable, en foi de quoi nous avons signé. A Paris, les jour & an susdits.

Mouricault

Return certificate for the wet nurses

On the back is an excerpt from the parish records signed by the priest, stating that the child died.

Office of Nurses
Hand-coloured aquatint
Paris, 1800
Published by W Sams, London, 1822
16.8 × 25.0 cm

Note meneur and charges in front.

Jean Lenoir, the Lieutenant General of Police in 1780, the year before publication of the above Code of Wet Nurses, estimated that, of the 20,000 to 21,000 infants born in Paris each year, about 700 were nursed at the mother's breast and an equal number by a wet nurse in the parental home; between 2,000 and 3,000 babies of well-to-do families were placed nearby with nurses whose integrity the parents could verify and whose fees were high because of their convenience.[11] By inference more than 16,000 babies a year were sent to wet nurses in the country whose qualities were dubious and whose supervision was not guaranteed.

According to the document shown, dated January 22, 1782, Lenoir commissioned Gabriel Gaillard to attend the gates of Paris each day to check the official certificates carried by nurses who were returning their charges home. Too many nurses had been returning children without reporting to any bureau director; some children could not be identified, and others could not be traced.

One of the problems frequently encountered by wet nurses was difficulty in obtaining their pay regularly. The Bureau undertook to guarantee nurses' wages and to collect from parents. Each year found hundreds of fathers imprisoned as ***debiteurs des mois de nourrice*** [debtors for monthly nursing fees]. In a letter published in 1786 mention is made of a concert performed the previous December by the Royal Academy of Music for the benefit of poor prisoners held for wet nurses' fees.[12] Other efforts to raise funds for such prisoners were not uncommon. The print, ***Maternal Nursing Encouraged*** was intended to stimulate maternal nursing as a means of avoiding the incurrence of these debts. In the background is the prison for those owing wet nursing fees.

The Bureau survived the Revolution, but imprisonment of fathers as debtors ceased. A law releasing those imprisoned for nonpayment of wet nursing fees was signed by Danton in 1792.[13]

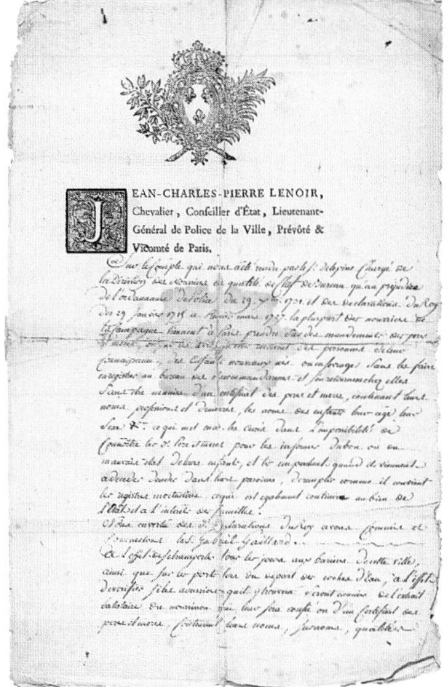

JEAN-CHARLES-PIERRE LENOIR, Chevalier, Conseiller d'État, Lieutenant-Général de Police de la Ville, Prévôté & Vicomté de Paris.

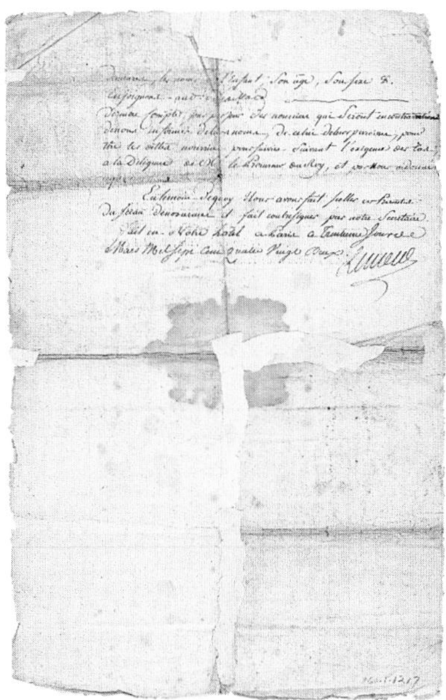

Appointment of Gaillard signed by Lenoir

L'Alaitement Maternel Encouragé [Maternal Nursing Encouraged]
Engraving by E Voysant (1746–1812)
After Antoine Borel (? 1743–1822)
Paris, 1784
24.2 × 37.0 cm
Written above prison entrance *Débiteurs des mois de nourrices* [Debtors for wet nursing fees]

It is apparent that in the average level of society nurses were hired with little care. This was not in accordance with the advice generally pronounced. Since early times stringent requirements for a good wet nurse had been recommended: she must appear healthy and robust; have borne and nursed a healthy child; have plenty of milk which flows readily through prominent nipples; be of an even temperament and of unquestionable moral character. She must lead a regular life and eat a good diet. Many other points were made by specific doctors, such as: no wine, spirits, tobacco, or sexual intercourse. In the seventeenth century, several writers damned redheads as being bad nurses. More and more specifications were added until the desirable nurse sought was so perfect as to seem unobtainable. A detailed list of specifications is offered by Rosen von Rosenstein, compiled in Sweden in 1764:

> Such a one ought to be naturally of a serene, chearful, sweet, and virtuous disposition. She ought to be between 20 and 30 years of age, to have lain-in a little before the child's mother, and also to be used to the nursing of children; she ought to be of a strong constitution, and not afflicted with any hereditary disease, that might be transferred to the child: free also from the scurvy: therefore her gums ought to be well examined, whether they are hard and firm. But above all other things, care should be taken, that she has not any venereal disorder, scabs, herpes, hard glands, etc. as these are indications that her humours are corrupted.
>
> A fat nurse is preferable to a lean one; but if one can be found, that nearly corresponds with the constitution of the child's mother, she will answer still better; she ought to be able to suckle the child at each breast, the nipples of which should be of a middling size. These ought also to be irritable, so that they grow erect by being gently stroked with your finger, which is a necessary quality to their giving milk. She ought to have good milk, and a sufficient quantity of it.
>
> Its goodness may be tried,
>
> 1. By its colour, which ought to be white or rather bluish.
> 2. By the smell, as it should be void of any.
> 3. By the taste, which ought to be quite sweet, and not by any means salt or bitter, . . . Its most healthy taste is like cows milk diluted with a little water, and sweetened with a little sugar.
> 4. By its consistence, because when thin it is always better than when thick: therefore a drop of it on your nail, ought easily to run off on inclining it: even on shaking the finger hastily, there ought not to remain the least white streak on your nail.[14]
> 5. By the touch, because not any pain ought to be felt, on letting a drop of it fall into the eye.
> 6. With rennet, for if the milk gives much cheese on coagulating it, you may judge it to be good for nothing.
> 7. By keeping it for several hours in a glass, because if it then gives much cream it will also prove bad. The same is to be observed upon weighing the milk, for the more cream it gives the lighter it will be found.
> 8. By the age, because the older the milk is, the thicker and more unhealthy it will be; therefore, when the choice of two nurses can be made, the one of 30 years of age, and her milk one month older than that of the mother, and the other at the age of 20 years only, and her milk 6 or seven months old, we then ought to give the preference to the first, provided they both agree in other circumstances. . . .

It is not only necessary to procure a nurse with the above-mentioned qualities, but she ought also to observe a healthy and regular diet, in order to make the child thrive better; therefore it is necessary that she should have a large and airy chamber, free from any draught of air; it ought to be equally and tolerably kept warm, often swept clean and neat, in order to avoid any bad smell, as also to prevent the nurse and the child from getting the itch; she ought not imprudently to expose herself to the cold; and except when it cannot be avoided, she ought always to cover her breasts very well, and if they should at any time grow cold, then she ought to omit suckling the child until they are grown warm again, otherwise the child will get the catarrh at the nose, and cough: however in my opinion, she ought not by any means to keep continually in the chamber with the children; on the contrary, she ought to have free access to the other rooms whenever she pleases, and there perform any kind of gentle exercise. I have myself known the milk of a good nurse spoiled by such a confinement, which by moderate exercise in the house, from one room to another, was restored again in a fortnight's time. She ought to have a sufficiency to eat, and that at certain hours: small beer [weak][15] may be drank at pleasure, but this should be neither sour, new, or stale, and not to be drank, by any means, when drawn over night. Wine, brandy, ale or coffee, ought by no means to be given her; . . .[16]

Compare the above with the specifications outlined by Phaer two centuries earlier:

. . . ye must be well aduised in takyng of a nource, not of ill complexion and of worse maners: but suche as shalbe sobre, honeste and chaste, well fourmed, amyable and chearefull, so that she may accustome the infant vnto mirth, no dronkarde, vicious nor sluttysshe, for suche corrupteth the nature of the chylde.

But an honest woman, (such as had a man childe last afore) is best not within twoo monethes after her delyueraunce, nor aprochyng nere vnto her time againe. These thynges ought to be cõsidered of euery wise person, that wyll set their chyldren out to nource. Moreouer, it is good to loke vpon the milke, and to se whether it be thicke & grosse, or to muche thinne and watry, blackysshe or blewe, or enclinynge to reddenesse or yelowe, for all suche are vnnaturall and euill.

Likewyse when ye taste it in your mouthe, yf it be eyther bitter, salte, or soure, ye may well perceyue it is vnholsome.

That milke is good, that is whyte and sweete, and when ye droppe it on your nayle, and do moue your finger, neither fleteth abrode at euery stering nor will hange faste vpon your nayle, whẽ ye turne it downeward, but that which is betwene both is best.[17]

In 1759 Boerhaave simplified the specifications by urging that the choice be based entirely on the health of the nurse, but apparently his criteria did not achieve general acceptance.

It was sometimes the priest who evaluated the quality of the wet nurse's milk. In G.J. Witkowski's book, published in 1898, a print shows a priest carrying out such an inspection: a porringer on the bureau is ready to catch a sample. According to the text, this wet nurse was a nun. A similar examination was used to ascertain whether a nun had been pregnant.[18]

Involvement of the priest in the wet nursing business has already been indicated: he signed the nurse's registration certificate; he monitored the arrival and departure of babies in his parish. Shown is a certificate such as a priest signed to indicate a child was nourished and cared for by a particular nurse (or that said child had died at that home). The same documental form was adapted for secular use soon after, signed by an offical rather than a priest.

Fig. 97.

A priest assesses breast milk for wet nursing.
Witkowski, p. 176

Certificates showing records of nurslings.

[I the undersigned priest of Pailhard en Ardeche certify to have seen at the house of the widow of Pierre Entrepangle of my parish the one named Jean Baptiste Badin, age about eleven years 4 months . . . child from the said Hôtel-Dieu, who was doing well at the time I was there.

At Pailhard, this thirtieth day of October, 1793

Sent cloth and had clothing made. I have paid the nurse for five months ending the first of December, 1793 17 livres, 10—]

HOTEL-DIEU DE VIENNE EN DAUPHINÉ.

N°.
N°.
N°.
N°.

JE soussigné Curé de Pailhard en ardeche certifie avoir vu chez la veuve de pierre Entrepangle de ma Paroisse le nommé jean baptiste Badin

enfant dudit Hôtel-Dieu, qui est bien tenu; en foi de quoi j'ai fait le présent.
A Pailhard ce trentième
jour du mois d'octobre 1793

[I the undersigned priest of – first officer of . . . certify to have seen at the home of dear Antoine de Bos – of my parish, the one named Anne Yallouis who is making a good start. The nurse asked for her to be baptized. The nurse will care for her in this municipality. Child of the said Hôtel-Dieu who at the time I was there . . . ?

At Montels, 27 November, 1793

I have paid the nurse for eight months ending the first of December, 1793 . . . 32 livres, 5—]

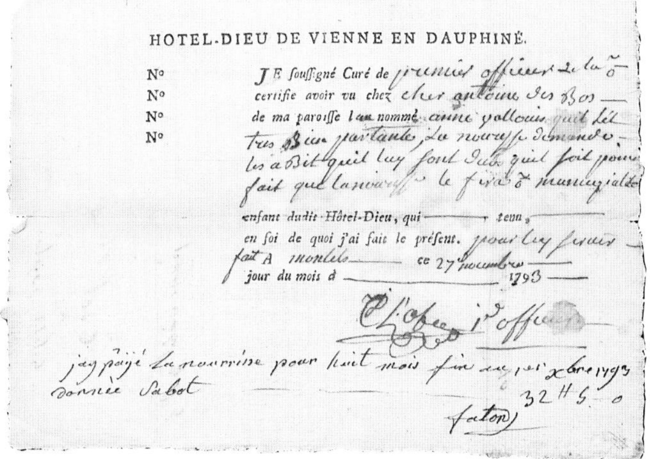

HOTEL-DIEU DE VIENNE EN DAUPHINÉ.

N°
N°
N°
N°

JE soussigné Curé de premier officier de la certifie avoir vu chez cher antoine des Bos de ma paroisse la nommée anne yallouis

enfant dudit Hôtel-Dieu, qui tenu, en foi de quoi j'ai fait le présent.
A Montels ce 27 novembre
jour du mois d 1793

j'ay payé la nourrice pour huit mois fin au 1er xbre 1793
32 # 5 0

In practice, the choice of the wet nurse fell to the father, who, when the need arose, visited the bureau to hire a nurse. A story on file from 1814 describes such a scene: a father is interviewed by the director:

> *Tenez-vous au pays? — Non. . . pourvu que ce ne soit pas une Lorraine. . . il y a un vilain proverbe sur les Lorraines. . . Ah! je ne me soucierais pas d'une Normande; elle donnerait du cidre à mon enfant. . . c'est trop rafraichissant. je ne veux pas non plus d'une Picarde; elles ont mauvaise tête; elles se disputent pour un rien, et cela échauffe leur lait. On dit que les Bourguignonnes sont trop les gentilles avec les hommes. . . cela n'est pas rassurant. . . Je ne désire pas une Bretonne. . . Je craindrais de prendre un Champeroise. . . Du reste, le pays m'est indifférent.*
>
> [Do you insist upon a certain region?
> No. . . provided that she's not from Lorraine. . . there is a nasty proverb about the natives of Lorraine. . . Ah! I would not care for a Norman, she would give cider to my infant. . . it is too stimulating. I don't want one from Picardy; they are bad tempered; they quarrel over nothing, and that overheats their milk. They say that Burgundians flirt too much with men. . . that isn't reassuring. . . I don't want a Breton. . . I would be afraid to take one from Champagne. . . Otherwise I don't care which region.][19]

LA NOURRICE

La Nourrice [The Wet Nurse]
Engraving
France, 1750–1790
8.3 × 10.5 cm

[The way Licidas rushes to see if you have milk, it would seem the rake is interested in the baby. And I would bet, Philis, that he has fathered it.]

The above excerpt illustrates the fastidious concerns of an anxious father about to take a wet nurse into his home.

Through the ages, talents, temperaments, and characteristics of the wet nurse were considered, because it was believed that they could be passed on to the nursling through the milk. Phaer quotes a classical authority of the second century:

> And Phauorinus the Philospher (as writeth Aulus gellius) affirmeth that if the lambes be nourished with the milk of goates, they shall haue course wolle, like the heare of goates: and if kiddes in like maner sucke vpō shepe, the heare of them shall be softe lyke wolle. Wherby it doth appeare, that the mylke and nourishyng hath a marueylous effect in chaunging the complexion, as we se likewyse in herbes and in plantes, for let the seede or ympes be neuer so good and pure, yet if they be put into an vnkinde earth, or watred with a noughty and vnholsome humour, either they come not vp at all, or els they wyll degenerate and turne out of their kynde,. . .[20]

Michelangelo, born in 1475, was nursed by a stonemason's wife with whom he lived for several years. It was widely believed that his sculpting abilities were derived from his nurse's milk.[21] Ambrose Parey (1510–1590) expressed concern about passing undesirable characteristics from nurse to nursling.

> If the Nurs bee squint-eied, shee cannot look upon the childe but side-waies, whereof it commeth to pass that the childe beeing moist, tender, flexible, and prone to anie thing with his bodie, and so likewise with his eie, by a long and dailie custom unto his Nurse's sight, doth soon take the like custom to look after that sort also, which afterwards hee cannot leav or alter.[22]

Only a few decades later Mauriceau warned, in choosing a nurse, one must consider her manners and temperament, for her humours will be passed on . . . "as the nurse is, so will the Child be, by means of the Nourishment which it draweth from her; and in sucking her, it will draw in both the Vices of her Body and Mind . . ."[23]

Nothing prevented a man from choosing a nurse to his personal liking; promiscuity was a hazard to be confronted and must have put a strain on many marriages.

One unhappy situation was recorded in 1773 by Madam Mallard, former wet nurse of the Dauphin, when she was petitioning for a legal separation. As a result of her husband's debauchery and unfaithfulness in her absence, she returned to a disintegrating family with debts which depleted her savings. Adding to the difficulties shared by all wet nurses, she had become inolved in political intrigue at court; this brought criticism and damage to her reputation.[24]

Nurse in Normandy
Lithograph by C Motte (1785–1836)
After F Grenier
13.2 × 16.4 cm

A biography of Guy de Maupassant refers to the incredible resemblance between Guy and his "frère de lait," the son of his wet nurse. Guy's mother was very angry about the inference, not because of her husband's infidelity, which she readily accepted, but because she had proudly nursed Guy herself for all but a few days of his suckling period.[25]

Promiscuity was also a problem in England. A ballad of 34 four-line verses, written in 1743, tells the story of a poor wet nurse supplanting a sad wife of riches. The wife retaliates:

By thee abandon'd must I bend
  Beneath thy Nurse's Scorn?
No; live with me thyself, and send
  To her thy Youngest born.[26]

Some fathers coming to the *Bureau des Nourrices* might request a wet nurse in the country to whom they could send the newborn. A print in the Collection portrays a father presenting a baby at the Wet Nurses' Office.[27] The practice of sending the baby away provided artists with a variety of subject material: the new country home and travels to it; separation and reunion scenes, of the child and the parents or of the child and the wet nurse, and visits of parents to the country. Similarly poignant scenes depict nurses leaving family homes after long service. Wet nurses' portraits were also popular.

La Nourrice [The Wet Nurse]
Lithograph by Mlle Formentin
After AH Le Prince
Paris, 1824
15.0 × 20.0 cm

La Nourrice [The Wet Nurse]
Sepia aquatint des and engraved by JB Le Prince (1734–1781)
France
14.5 × 18.0 cm
Le Prince was among the first to develop the process of aquatint.

La Nourrice [The Wet Nurse]
Engraving by Charles Courtry, 1846–1897
After Pieter de Hooch, 1629–1681
Paris
13.2 × 16.2 cm

A Visit to the Child at Nurse
Mezzotint engraving by Wm. Ward
(1762–1826)
After George Morland
England, August 20, 1788
38.6 × 47.6 cm

Visite à la Nourrice [Visit to the Wet Nurse]
Lithograph after F.S.
Paris, 1840–1860
16.0 × 11.5 cm

Les deux Nourrices l'une perlant l'autre
[Two Wet Nurses, the one mimicking the other]
Hand-coloured engraving by Le Vachez
After Carle and Horace Vernet
France, mid-19 C
24.6 × 34.6 cm
(cf. porcelain figure of *The Tailor's Wife*, p. 24)

Le Départ de la Nourrice
[The Departure of the Nurse]
Engraving by JB Simonet (1742–1813)
After JB Greuze (1725–1805)
Paris, 1780
36.0 × 26.2 cm
The mother gives a last kiss to the baby she may never see again as the wet nurse takes the infant off to the country.

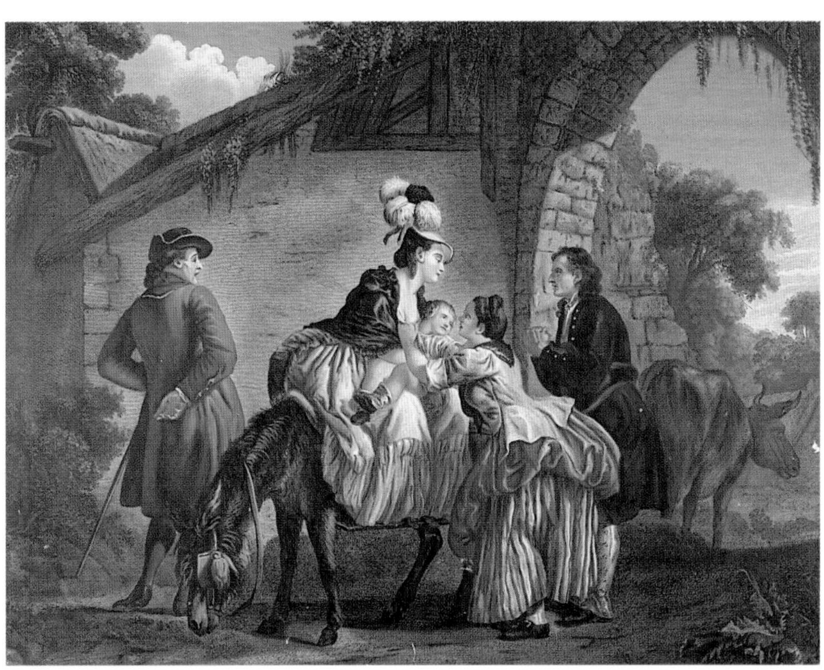

Goody-bye to the Wet Nurse
Coloured engraving
After Etienne Aubry (1745–1781)
? France, 1780–1790
34.5 × 44.9 cm

The etching of *La Nourrice sur Place* appeared with an article by Amédée Archard. "La Nourrice sur Place" tells of the manoeuvrings of a wet nurse who comes from the country to a wet nursing position in Paris. It describes, deprecatingly, her manipulation of the parents to elevate her position, increase her pay, and extend her freedom. The frightened parents grant her every wish. The pampered girl returns to her farmer husband and convinces him to have more children to keep her in business in order to secure a better family estate. Others in the village follow her example.[28]

Another story in the Collection brings to life the impressions of a sibling when a baby was sent to the country. A little girl tells of going by train with her mother to visit the little brother she has not seen. She was at her grandmother's when he was born; because of her mother's frail health the infant was sent immediately to a peasant wet nurse. After a long walk from the station the girl is astonished to see a baby as small as a doll and unable to walk. During the visit the nurse milks a cow to make pap for the baby. The girl returns home but the brother does not come back until he has learned to walk well.[29]

La Nourrice sur Place [Wet Nurse in the Nursling's Home]
Coloured etching by Paul Constant Soyer (1823–1903)
France, 1840
14.0 × 10.0 cm

Les Frères de Lait, one of a collection of stories, depicts the popular, romantic view of wet nurses in France in the nineteenth century. Paid by the government, a needy young couple takes in a foundling; the wife breast feeds him, and they raise him with their own son in a happy relationship. Just as adopted children often do today, the boy later finds his own father.[30]

Many accounts related to wet nursing in France are among the documents. These indicate that in the late eighteenth century a wet nurse charged from 18 *livres* to 50 *livres* per month for feeding, according to her proximity to Paris and the status of the nursling. Bills list a number of other charges, among the most frequent of which are shoes, bonnets, and shirts. Prices of the first two vary enormously from less than a *livre* to several *livres*, but the shirt value is fairly standard, about one *livre*. Apothecary costs are also listed.

One file deals almost exclusively with an infant Alexandre in Paris in the 1790s. He is supported by Citizen Bouillainviliers, and nursed by Citizen Hachette. One bill for four months of wet nursing is 120 *livres*, and sundry charges bring the total to 158 *livres*. There is a New Year greeting card from the child to his parents, expressing gratitude for his wellbeing. There are receipts for bills paid years after their due date and letters from Hachette to Mr. Bouillainviliers begging for payment.[31] A corresponding file on Hachette gives a fairly complete picture of her caring for other infants.[32]

Another nurse in Paris, femme Dufour, also commanded good wages: in 1768 and January of 1769, she received 50 *livres* a month; in April, 1769 and into 1770 she received 30 *livres* a month. This decrease in pay no doubt indicates that the baby was weaned in April but remained in the care of the nurse.[33]

Accounts for foundlings of 1759 suggest a much lower charge for wet nursing, but the lack of mention of a timespan makes calculation impossible.

Many wet nurses were employed in institutions: hospitals and foundling homes. Accompanying prints show such nurses at an orphanage and in a maternity ward, and a cartoon portrays nurslings on strike, protesting conditions in maternity hospitals in mid-nineteenth-century France.

Une Visite à Bébé [A Visit to Baby]
Hand-coloured lithograph
After Mès
Late 19 C
37.0 × 54.3 cm

Postcard in aid of orphans
[Bench of wet nurses at the Saint-Valery Orphanage]
Etching by Paul Delance
Paris
16.16 × 22.1 cm

La Visite à la Nourrice [The Visit to the Wet Nurse]
Lithograph, printed by d'Aubert & Cie
Paris, mid–late 19 C
22.5 × 22.5 cm

[Come now, kiss papa, my dear little one! He does not want to, today but ordinarily he is very easy-going! Just the day before yesterday, his mother came to see him with your cousin with the moustache, and he kissed him immediately.]

Children of the upper classes were attended in elegant fashion and their nurses held in high regard. Special chairs were commonly used for nursing, some of which appear in the illustrations.

A note from Paris in April 1664, sent to Fontainebleau, regarding the wet nurse who was proceeding there to rearrange accommodations for herself and the Spanish chambermaids of the queen, was signed by Colbert, finance minister to Louis XIV. Both the responsibility given her and the attention of the high-ranking minister, suggest the respect with which the position was regarded.

Nobility and royalty rewarded their wet nurses in many ways. Madam Mercier, wet nurse to the Duke of Brittany and his brother (Louis XV), and her husband were given positions in court; her eight children were granted high status. Some of her honours are in the Collection: a medal, a coloured sketch of her coat of arms, and a draft of the proposal to ennoble her.[34] Also wet nurse to the Duke of Brittany, Madam Renoux, was given a certificate declaring she had had the honour of nursing the young duke in 1705.[35]

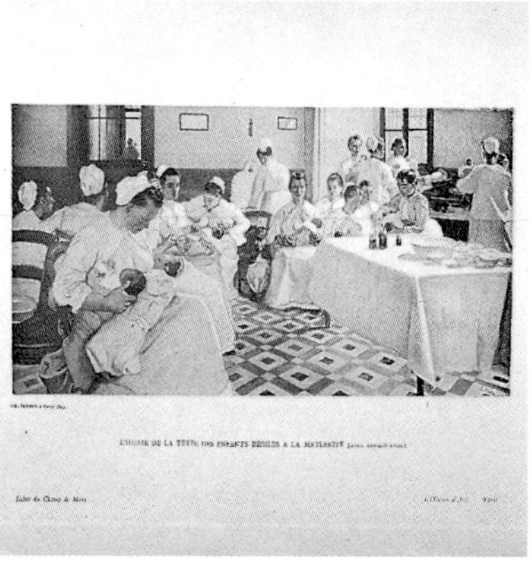

L'heure de la tétée des enfants débiles à la maternité [Feeding time for the sickly children in the maternity ward]
Des and lithographed by Ernest-Ange Duez
Paris, late 19 C or early 20 C
15.3 × 27 5 cm

Revolté à l'Hospice de la Maternité [Strike at the Maternity Hospital]
Lithograph by de Lemercier
After FE Chaponnier
Paris, 1840–1860
16.5 × 19.4 cm
Nous ne tetrons plus jusqu'à la dissolution des chambres [We will suck no more until Parliament dissolves.]

Walnut conversation chair
France, Abbaye de Roselande, Nice
1585–1600
Ht: 78.8 cm

Oak nursing chair
England, late 17 C
Ht: 82cm

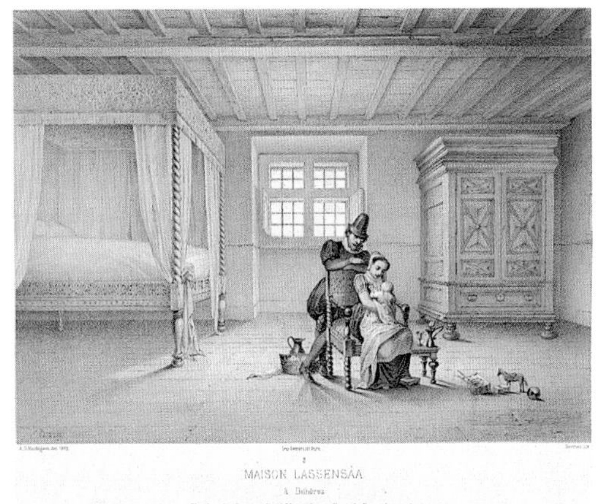

La Maison Lassenáa à Bilhères [Lassenáa house at Bilhères]
Lithograph by Sonnier after AC Houbigent
Paris, 1855
21.5 × 29.5 cm
The room where Henry IV, born 1553, was breast fed by Jeanne Fourcade, Femme Lassenáa

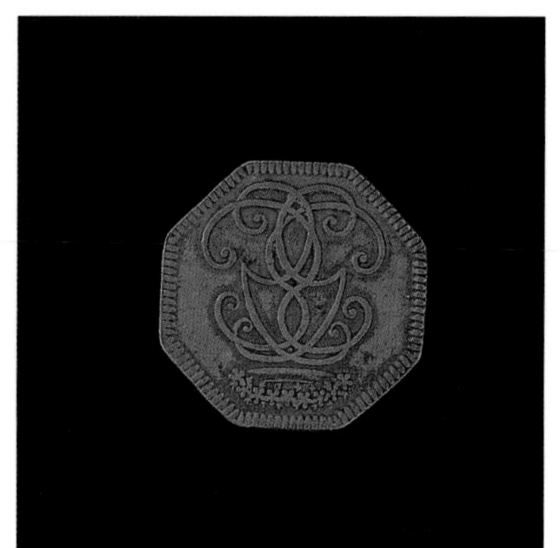

Madame Mercier medal
Bronze
OBV. and REV.
Minimum width: 12.7 cm

A Paris le 3e auril 1664.

Je vous escris ce mot pour vous dire que Madame la Nourrice s'en allant a Fontainebleau pour quelques accomodem. qui sont a faire dans son logement et dans celuy des femmes de chambre Espagnoles de la Reyne, Il est necessaire que vous dressies au plustost un memoire au juste de tout ce a quoy montera cette despense, et que vous me l'envoyes, afin qu'apres l'avoir fait resoudre, je puisse vous mander d'y faire travailler en diligence.

Colbert

à Mr Bruault, cons. du Roi, Commandant tous les travaux

Instructions from Colbert to a Wet Nurse

Prints of royal wet nurses depict them dressed in fashionable grandeur. Examples include: a nurse who fed the Duke d'Anjou (not shown); one who fed the eldest son of Philip V of Spain; and one who fed Charles, Duke de Berry (grandson of Louis XIV).

Nourrice de Monseigneur Le Duc de Berry
[Wet nurse of H.R.H. the Duke of Berry]
Engraving
France, ca. 1687
23.2 x 17.7 cm
[I have reason to be proud for having the exceptional good fortune of mingling my milk with Royal Blood.]

Nurse to Royalty
Wet Nurse of H.R.H. the Prince of Asturias
Infante of Spain eldest son of Philippe V.
King of Spain, and of Gabrielle of Savoye,
born August 25, 1707
Engraving
Published by Chez Bonnart
Paris, 1708–1710
25.0 x 18.0 cm

Madam Poitrine was nurse to the Dauphin, Louis Joseph, born October 22, 1781, son of Louis XVI and Marie Antoinette. While nursing the prince she became obese from lack of exercise; his health deteriorated and her overweight was blamed. At age 33 she retired on a pension of 6000 *livres*, of which 500 was revertible to each of two daughters and 800 to a son. She was exceedingly beautiful. A wash drawing appeared in France about 1782 and from this an engraving entitled "L'Amour Maternelle" was produced.

Mme Poitrine
Original wash drawing in sepia tones by Jean Anton de Peters (1723–1795) artist to the King of Denmark.
France, ca. 1782
17.6 x 13.8 cm

L'Amour Maternelle
[Motherly Love]
Engraving by Chevillet (1760–1780)
After de Peters
France, 1782
42.3 x 31.5 cm

[Dedicated to Madam Elisabeth Gouël de Villebrune, wife of Mr. de Peters, painter of His Majesty the King of Denmark and of His Royal Highness, Prince Charles, Duke of Lorraine, Governor of the Low Countries, Grand Master of the Teutonic Order of Knights]

The care of royal babies was very well documented, for example, that of the Duke of Bourgogne, son of Louis XIV and father of Louis XV, born at Versailles in August, 1682. His nurses, one each for suckling, rocking, holding, and walking the elegantly dressed prince, are pictured in an article which tells his story from birth to age 10 and lists the dozens of attendants and the costs of having them. Among all of these living at court, were nine ladies, *femmes de chambre pour veiller*, who watched over the child, one each night in rotation. From this group were chosen *la berceuse* (for rocking), *la teneuse* (for holding), and *la promeneuse* (for walking). Not only is *la nourrice* described, but also *la seconde nourrice;* the first received 2295 *livres*, the second 1695 *livres*. The second also served as one of the nine bedside guardians.[36]

With no royal connections, but famous nonetheless, the mythological Roman heroine, Pera, rescued her imprisoned father, Cimon, from certain death. Left to starve, he thrived. Learning that his daughter fed him her breast milk, the authorities rewarded her love and devotion by granting his release. This story was immortalized as The Grecian Daughter, Filial Piety, and Roman Charity. It is depicted on the accompanying German coin, and in English pottery.

Wet nurses were extensively used in England, but the business never developed into the vast organization that existed in France. The French experience was an example available to the English, and presumably they benefitted from it. But how the parishes in England compared with those in France regarding the care of the infant poor is difficult to assess. Statistics in general are not comparable.

It was in the mid-eighteeth century that the efforts of Thomas Coram to get the deserted children off the streets of London culminated in the establishment of the London Foundling Hospital (see Foundlings, Chapter 5). Wet nurses were hired to service that institution; other children were sent to nurses in the country. In 1748, Cadogan was recommending that mothers should take their own children from the foul air of London to the fresh air of the country during their suckling period.[38]

Filial Piety
Bronze medal, 1692
OBV: DIE ROMERIN IHRN VATER LIEBT DURCH IHR BRUST SIE IHM NAHRUNG GIBT. [The Roman woman loves her father; she gives him nourishment through her breast.]
REV: DIE STORCK UNS LEHRN WIE WIR SOLN EHRN UNSR ELTERN WERTH AUFF DISER ERDT. [The storks teach us how we should honour the worth of our parents on this earth.][37]
44 mm

Jonas Hanway agitated during this same period for intervention to save the lives of the thousands of infants born in workhouses. Some of these infants remained with their mothers, while others were sent to parish houses to be raised. In 1763, of the total number of infants born in the workhouses or received under 12 months of age in the parish houses throughout the city of London, there remained living by the end of 1765, at best, 7 in 100 in one parish, at worst, none in many parishes. In one parish, of 133 children aged three or under, either born in or received into the workhouse in 1765, 54 left with their mothers; of the 79 remaining, 73 died before the end of 1766, and none reached the fifth birthday. Hanway attributed the availability of such studies to an act of June, 1762, which made it necessary to keep registers of the infant poor under four years of age. He pointed out that these appalling statistics resulted from the nation's unwillingness to pay half a crown a week for the nursing of each child.[39]

Filial Piety
England, Staffordshire, ca. 1820
Ht: 19.6 cm

Hanway's efforts resulted in an act being passed in 1767, obliging parish officers of London and Westminster to send infant poor to be nursed in the country, at proper distances from town. James Hamilton reported that before the law was passed an average of no more that four percent of infants received into the workhouses reached their first birthday; afterward 84 percent did so, and of those who did not, most died during the first three weeks, while they were kept in the workhouse.[40]

Generally speaking in France and England in the seventeenth and early eighteenth centuries, writers advocated maternal nursing as first choice but recommended wet nursing with little hesitation. Cadogan[38] in England and Astruc[41] in France represented those who were basically opposed to voluntary wet nursing. Boerhaave[42] (Holland), Raulin[43] (France), Buchan[44] (Great Britain), and Rosen von Rosenstein[45] (Sweden) were typical advocates of exercising great caution in turning to the wet nurse. Toward the end of the eighteenth century, Icart[46] (France) and Underwood[47] and Moss[48] (England), in tune with their contemporaries, cautioned against the hiring of wet nurses unless absolutely necessary and then begged the use of extreme care in making the choice. Moss was emphatic in urging that children who must have a wet nurse should have that nurse at home where the family could supervise. A few, of whom Huxham[49] (France) and Herdman[50] (England) are examples, went so far as to condemn wet nursing entirely.

The majority opinion of the late eighteenth century, prevailed into the nineteenth. Struve[51] (Germany) and Protat[52] and Léger[53] (France) were strong proponents of the attitudes objectively summed up by John Roberton[54] (England) in 1827. Though believing that a mother in good health who elected not to suckle her child ought not to become a mother, he accepted that substitutes were sometimes necessary, the best being a wet nurse. He cautioned that it was impossible to hire the affection of a mother and that while the faults of wet nurses were many, to condemn them *en masse* accomplished nothing. He believed they could not be eliminated, and so must be chosen with great care.

During the nineteenth century, young women looking for wet nursing positions advertised freely in newspapers. Two such advertisements appeared alongside reports of the Battle of Waterloo in *The Times*, London, June 22, 1815.

Notes

1. *The Bible*, Exodus 2:5-90.
2. Aucoc ca. 1878: 266-267.
3. Declaration du Roy. Portant règlement pour les Recommandaresses, et les Nourrices. Donné à Versailles, le 29 Janvier, 1715 (960.1.1088).
4. Déclaration du Roy. Concernant les Recommandaresses et Nourrices. Donné à Versailles, le premier Mai, 1727 (960.1.1018).
5. Arrêts de la cour du parlement..., Du 19 Juin, 1737 (960.1.1018).
6. Ordonnance de Police, Paris, le 13 Février, 1740 (960.1.1004).
7. Sentence rendue en la Chambre de Police du Chastelet de Paris. le 23 Juin, 1756 (960.1.1002).
8. Drake 1935:53.
9. Déclaration du Roi. Concernant les Recommandaresses et Nourrices, et l'etablissement d'un Bureau Général dans la Ville de Paris. le 28 Juillet, 1769 (960.1.1021).
10. *Code des Nourrices* ou recueil des Déclarations du Roi, arrêts du Parlement, ordonnances et sentences de police; concernant des Nourrices, des Recommandaresses, de Meneurs et Meneuses. Paris, 1781
11. Lenoir 1780.
12. Letter published in 1786. Names of correspondant and recipient are not known.
13. A series of documents demonstrates the rapid progress leading to the final law of Sept. 2, 1792, which released all fathers imprisoned for wet nursing debts. (Loi qui met en liberté tous les Prisonniers pour mois de nourrice, du 2 Septembre, 1792, l'an quatrième de la Liberté, No. 2433)
    a) Government to give financial assistance to poor fathers confined in Paris, signed by Louis [XVI] (Loi, Relative aux secours à donner aux pauvres pères de famille détenus pour mois de nourrice, Donnée à Paris, le II Décembre 1791, No. 1457) (960.1.1056)
    b) Government to give financial assistant to similar fathers outside Paris, signed by Danton (Loi, Relative aux Citoyens détenus pour mois de nourrice, du 15 Août 1792, l'an quatrième de la Liberté, No. 2176) (960.1.1060)
    c) No bodily constraint to be exercised for debts of wet nursing fees, signed by Danton. (Loi, Portant que la contrainte par corps ne pourra être exercée pour dettes de mois de nourrice, donnée à Paris le 25 Août 1792, l'an 4 de la Liberté, No. 2222) (960.1.1064)
    George Jacques Danton was a major revolutionary leader, a Jacobite who became president of the provisional executive council of the new government, and in this capacity signed the laws passed during this period.
14. The nail test for milk consistency was first mentioned by Soranus of Ephesus in the second century and remained popular with only slight variations for many centuries.
15. Small beer is a weak brew made with the liquor from a second sparging of the malt grain.
16. Rosen von Rosenstein 1776:2–3.
17. Phaer 1550:5–6.
18. Witkowski, 1898:176.
19. Le Bureau des Nourrices La Grande Ville, 1814 (960.1.1384).
20. Phaer 1550:3–4.
21. Hayens (n.d.):65.
22. Parey 1649:610.
23. Mauriceau 1683:369
24. Memoire à consulter et consultation pour la Dame Mallard, Nourrice de Monseigneur le Dauphin, à Paris MDCCLXXIII (1773).
25. Steegmuller 1949:6
26. *The Wife and the Nurse: A New Ballad.* London: 1743, vol 16, 5.
27. Le Bureau des Nourrices, engraved by Coupe after A. Desemme, France, 1814. TDPA 274
28. Published in "Les Français peints par Euxmêmes, 1840" [The French portray themselves] (960.1.1381). Another article from the same source depicts "La Sage-Femme" [The Midwife] (960.1.1382).
29. Stahl (n.d., 19C).
30. de la Madelaine 1847:17–125.
31. Re child Alexandre (960.1.1116–1141).
32. Re Citizen Hachette (960.1.1165–1181).
33. Re Nourrice Dufour (960.1.1192).
34. Re Mercier (960.1.1288(b) and 960.1.1289(a)).
35. A handwritten document declaring that Madam Renoux was retained by the Duke of Brittany for eight months and breast fed the infant Duke for two and one-half months. Signed by Duchess de la Motte, wife of the Field Marshall and their secretary, Madame Robillarts, and stamped with their seal, 17th August, 1705 (960.1.1309).
36. Magasin Pittoresque, La Nourrice, La Berceuse, La Teneuse, La Promeneuse de M. le Duc de Bourgogne, collection d'estampes et de dessins historiques de M. Hennin (960.1.1383).
37. Storks have been celebrated from ancient times for the affection which they display toward their young, and also have the reputation — although not so well founded — of showing great regard to their aged parents (Chambers Encyclopedia, 1906).
38. Cadogan 1748.
39. Hanway 1767:50–52.
40. Hamilton, J 1813:35–56.
41. Astruc 1746.
42. Boerhaave 1759.
43. Raulin 1769.
44. Buchan 1769.
45. Rosen von Rosenstein 1776.
46. Icart 1784.
47. Underwood 1784.

48. Moss 1781.
49. Huxham 1776.
50. Herdman 1807.
51. Struve 1802.
52. Protat 1803.
53. Léger 1825.
54. Roberton 1827.
55. Etat de Recette et de Dépense de l'institut de Bienfaisance pour les Mères-Nourrices, 1787 (960.1.1036)
56. Décret de la Convention Natonale... 1794 (960.1.1049).
57. Ordonnance concernant les Nourrices, Seureuses et Gardeuses et les personnes qui s'entre mettent pour leur confier des enfants, Paris, le 1er fevrier, 1878 (Prefecture de Police) (960.1.1363)
58. *British Medical Journal.* April 7, 1860, 273.

Silver medal
By Genèvieve Granger
OBV. and REV.
E: *I argent 5*
L: 75 mm

DRY NURSING

L'ancienne Société royale de médecine de Paris a distribué, dans sa séance publique du 1.ere septembre 1789, par la bienveillance de M. Decrosne, alors lieutenant de police, une somme de deux mille francs en médailles d'or, à quinze auteurs de mémoires qui lui avaient été adressés, sur les avantages de l'allaitement artificiel.

Ces excellens et précieux mémoires réunissent tout ce qu'on peut désirer sur cet important objet. Ils sont faits par des médecins et des chirurgiens de réputation, et par des pères tendres et éclairés. Il me suffira d'en donner ici les noms pour avoir l'idée de ce que peut être leur travail, et y prendre toute la confiance qu'il mérite.

[The ancient Royal Society of Medicine of Paris has distributed at its public meeting of September first, 1789, through the largesse of Mr. Decrosne, then Lieutenant of Police, a sum of two thousand francs in gold medals, to 15 case history writers who had been approached by him regarding the advantages of artificial feeding.

These excellent and valuable reports brought together all that one could wish on that important topic. They were done by doctors and surgeons of repute, and by caring and enlightened fathers. It is enough for me to give their names here to convey the idea of their work and to inspire from it the confidence which it deserves. (Underwood and Armstrong, English doctors mentioned frequently, were among the eminent names listed.)]

J.P. Harmand de Montgarny.
Félébriologie. 1806, p. 3.

Any method of feeding an infant other than breast milk, mother's or nurse's, is considered dry nursing. It can begin at birth, at the time of weaning, or be given in supplementary fashion during breast feeding. Usually when human milk was unavailable or in short supply, animal milk was sought. Various animals were chosen for the purpose: ass, goat, sheep, mare, and cow.

In some circumstances these animals nursed infants directly, and in this capacity legends credit the wolf, the hind, the lion, and the bear. Romulus and Remus, legendary founders of Rome, believed to have been suckled by a wolf, were depicted on coins of the Republic and Imperial periods. In Greek mythology, Telephus, son of Hercules, exposed as an infant by his grandfather, survived because he was suckled by a hind. Zeus is reputed to have been nursed by a goat, and Paris by a bear. Mazzini's book, *Il Bambino nell'arte,* includes an Etruscan stella which portrays a child suckled by a lion, and a picture of Telephus being nursed by a hind.[1]

A nineteenth-century French coin depicts a child feeding from a wolf. Romulus and Remus are also shown in nineteenth-century pottery and on twentieth-century stamps, again being nursed by a wolf.

The cantique of St. Geneviève tells another survival story. When Geneviève de Brabant, falsely accused of being unfaithful to her absent soldier husband, was sentenced to death, her devoted servants instead released her with her infant son in a forest. A hind regularly fed her son and eventually led her hunting husband to her side.

Madonna of the Bowl
Etching by Annibale Caracci (1560–1609)
Rome, 1606
12.5 × 16.4 cm

Putting infants to nurse directly from the teats of animals, previously mentioned as occurring in Palestine, was also a practice in Europe. Raulin in 1769, F. Baldini in 1786, Protat in 1803, and Léger in 1825, recommended direct suckling, particulary with asses or goats, the latter seemingly more cooperative. Baldini suggested an instrument with a piece of tubing be fastened to the animal teat. Through this a child could suck and avoid the risk of suffocation. C.M. Gardien, 1807, reported that in l'Hôpital d'Aix where the administration raised goats to supply the infants, each goat soon came to recognize her nursling and voluntarily went to straddle the appropriate cradle, ready to feed.[2] Léger recorded a similar story.[3] Pierre Rambaud reported that goats came to know the babies so well that each would run to her nursling when she heard its cries.[4] *Le Guide Maternel*[5] contains a lovely print of a child nursing directly from a goat.

She-wolf suckling Romulus and Remus
Italy, 213
1929–1942

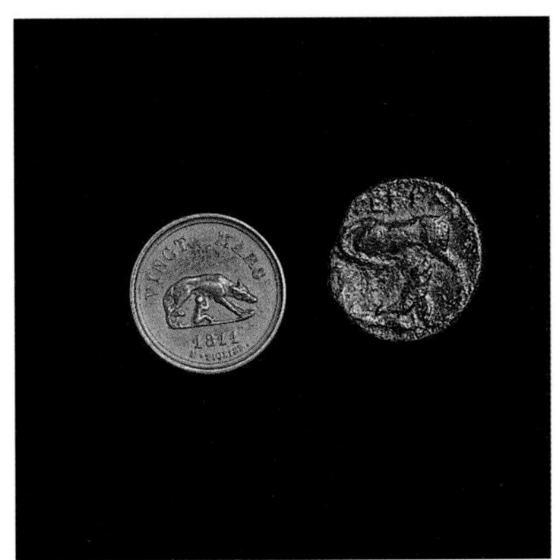

Coins depicting animals giving suck to infants

OBV: (not shown): NAPOLEON P.J.C. ROI DE ROME around bust left

REV: VINGT MARS 1811
N. TIOLVER
France, bronze, 1811
16 mm

OBV: (not shown): Head of Athena Alea Facing

REV: TETEA
Infant Telephus suckled by a hind
Greece, Arcadia, Tegea, 370–240 BC
17 mm

OBV: (not shown): Head of Rome
Jug in background

REV: SEX. PO (M) F (OSTULUS)
Wolf (right) suckling the twins, fig tree with birds shepherd Faustulus (left)

Republican Rome, silver, 137 BC
16 mm

OBV: (not shown): ANTONINUS AUG PIUS P.P.TR.P around bust right

REV: She-wolf in cave feeding Romulus and Remus
Imperial Rome, Bronze, AD 138
33 mm

Romulus and Remus,
Pottery, England, Staffordshire, ca. 1820
17.5 cm × 16.4 cm

La Chèvre est douée d'un instinct tout à fait maternel
[The goat is endowed with a keen maternal instinct]
Lithograph by Thierry Frères
After D. Fragonard

From Dr. Bergonier. *Le Guide Maternel.* Paris, 1842, p. 281

Cantique de Sainte Geneviève
[Song of Saint Geneviève]
Fabrique de Pellerin, Imprimeur-Libraire à Épinal
61.5 × 35.8 cm

In recommending animal milk at the turn of the nineteenth century, Struve in Germany favoured cow's milk, fresh and still warm, preferably taken from the same animal. He felt it would be most useful if the child could be positioned to draw the milk immediately from the teat of the animal, as no qualities would be lost and the sucking would promote good digestion. But he admitted to attendant difficulties.[6]

In 1827 in London, Roberton stated that to his knowledge feeding directly from an animal had never been thought of in his country, but might be advisable under peculiar circumstances.[7] In retrospect, in eighteenth- and nineteenth-century Europe when the wet nursing business became so corrupt and the importance of cleanliness and sterilization was not yet understood, direct nursing from animal dugs might often have been safer than the dry nursing available at the time, or the use of some wet nurses.

When an infant was unable to get enought breast milk, it was common to substitute animal milk: ass's, goat's, or cow's. Ass's milk, being most like human milk, was preferred, but its scarcity and high cost led later authorities such as Armstrong,[8] Moss,[9] and Struve[10] to recommend goat's or cow's milk. Many others, among them Hugh Smith,[11] made no attempt to rate the milk of different animals. Cow's milk eventually came into popular use, but opinions about its preparation varied: fresh and unheated, carefully warmed without boiling, boiled, sweetened with sugar or honey, not sweetened, diluted with boiled water, or undiluted.

From the days of Sainte-Marthe at the turn of the seventeenth century into the nineteenth century, writers encouraged giving infants some type of supplementary feeding, usually with a particular preference. As more and more mothers chose not to nurse their own children, and because many wet nurses were known to be deleterious, the authorities became increasingly critical and outspoken about feeding practices, especially in the infant's early months. A few, notably Cadogan[12] and Herdman,[13] condemned artificial feeding altogether.

> No other Woman's Milk can be so good for her Child; and dry-nursing I look upon to be the most unnatural and dangerous Method of all; and, according to my Observation, not one in three survives it. To breed a Child in this artificial Manner, requires more Knowledge of Nature, and the animal Oeconomy, than the best Nurse was ever Mistress of, as well as more Care and Attention than is generally bestow'd on Children: the Skill of a good Physician would be necessary to manage it rightly.
>
> [Dr. Cadogan]. *An Essay upon Nursing and the Management of Children*, 1748, p. 25.

Harmand de Montgarny's report, quoted at the beginning of this section, shows the effort of the Royal Society of Medicine of Paris to evaluate the success of artificial feeding in 1806. He was favourably impressed by the numbers of healthy children raised by hand.

For as long as the feeding of children has been a topic of concern, the variety of ideas expressed has been manifold. Opinions relate to when and how to wean, when supplementary feeding should begin, what should be fed, and how the food should be presented to the baby.

Ancient Greeks believed in weaning babies between 6 and 18 months of age. Soranus of Ephesus, in the early second century, recommended gradual weaning while introducing other foods, as opposed to abrupt weaning precipitated by using unpalatable, bitter, or malodorous substances on the nipples. The Romans, represented by Galen, supported these views.

Metlinger, in fifteenth century Germany, advised weaning when the child could walk and talk.[14] A century later in France, Parey related weaning to teething, for "they [the teeth] are prepared of nature for no other purpose than to chaw the meat." This resulted in most being weaned in the second year, many in the 18 to 20 month range. Parey directed that, at the appropriate time, the nurse remove the teat little by little, and "then let the teat bee anointed or rubbed with bitter things, as with Aloes, water of the infusion of Colacynthus, or Wormwood, or with Mustard, or Soot steeped in water, or such like."[15]

Shakespeare most likely reflected the prevalent habit of the period in the words of Juliet's nurse, as she recalled to the mother, the weaning of her little girl:

'Tis since the earthquake now eleven years;
And she was wean'd – I never shall forget it –
Of all the days of the year, upon that day:
For I had then laid wormwood to my dug,
When it did taste the wormwood on the nipple
Of my dug, and felt it bitter, pretty fool,
To see it tetchy, and fall out with the dug!

William Shakespeare. *Romeo and Juliet.*
Act I, Scene 3.

Such sudden weaning must have been a commonly recurrent practice, yet the majority of writers in the books of the Collection endorsed a gradual process beginning at various ages, often related to teething, and advancing to different foods. Many, Herdman (1807) among them, condemned the use of distasteful substances on the teat to precipitate weaning. No doubt the lack of sufficient breast milk frequently determined the timing of supplementary feeding as well as weaning.

Except for the few who simply advised weaning when necessary, (Mauriceau, 1668; Armstrong, 1771; Moss, 1781), most writers from de Vallambert (1565) to Underwood (1784) advised long nursing periods from close to a year to two years.[16] Huxham (1776), who suggested breast feeding for at least three months, was an exception. From his time on, the usual recommendation was a short period of six months or less,[17] although James Hamilton in 1813 still urged breast feeding for nine to 12 months. The trend to shorter nursing periods parallelled improvements in artificial feeding.

Whether on breast or animal milk, at a time dictated either by custom or by hunger, a baby was given other food, and the first addition was commonly some type of gruel or broth.

It is easy to become confused about various gruel-like preparations. Basic gruel is the liquid obtained by straining a mixture of water (sometimes milk) and oatmeal, which has been boiled. A more elaborate gruel is made by using broth instead of water, or by flavouring with herbs, spices, and perhaps onion.[18]

To convert gruel into caudle, a little wine, brandy, or ale is added. Dorothy Hartley in *Food in England* quotes a twelfth century manuscript describing such a hot soup wine.[19] Six cook books, which date from 1734 to 1816, recommend wine, but suggest the substitution of ale, to make brown caudle. These recipes use oatmeal, mace, wine (ale), lemon, nutmeg and sweetener.[20]

Caudle cups
Left: Tin-glazed earthenware
England, 1755–1760
Capacity 375 cc

Right: Silver, London 1679–1680
Capacity: 300 cc

A good Way to make Caudle

To four full Quarts of Water, you may put a Pint of whole Oatmeal; let it boil very slow for five or six Hours at least; then strain it out, and put to two Quarts three large Blades of Mace, a full Pint and a half of White or Rhenish-wine; and make it sweet to your Taste: And just as you take it off the Fire, slice in a Lemon, from which all the White is cut, which is apt, by lying long, to make it bitter; just the Yellow of the Peel may be put in. A little Salt does very well in Caudle, but is not often us'd.

Several Hands [one author identified as Mary Kittelby].
A Collection of above Three Hundred Receipts in Cookery, Physick, and Surgery; for the use of all Good Wives, Tender Mothers and Careful Nurses. 1734.

Tin-glazed pottery posset pots
Upper left: for several servings
England, Last quarter 17 C
Capacity: 4100 cc

Lower left: for children
England, Lambeth delft, late 17 C–early 18 C
Capacity: 375 cc

Upper right; for adults
England, late 17 C–early 18 C

Lower right: for children
Continental, 18 C

Caudle was served chiefly between or before meals, often to tide one over until meal time (especially travellers), and to soothe the sick. According to *the Oxford Dictionary* it is "given to sick people, also to their visitors." Mothers would have had no hesitation in giving it to an infant.

Posset was a popular supper dish, recommended for the sick and considered suitable for babies as well. It is what today we call a custard, highly flavoured with wine (sack or ale) and spices. Compilation of a number of recipes dating from 1671 to 1801 summarizes the ingredients as follows: eggs (whole or separated); cream and/or milk; sugar; sack, brandy, Canary wine, sweet wine, or gooseberry wine; nutmeg and perhaps whole spice; cinnamon or mace; possibly lemon, and sometimes bread, biscuits, or biscuit cake. Caution against boiling the custard, lest it curdle, is mentioned.

Glass syllabub pot
Capacity: 150 cc

To make a Posset[21]

Take the yolks of twenty eggs, then have a pottle [a measure for liquids, about one-half gallon] of good thick sweet cream, boil it with good store of whole cinamon, and stir it continually on a good fire, then strain the egg with a little raw cream; when the cream is well boiled and tasteth of the spice, take if off the fire put in the eggs, and stir them well in the cream, being pretty thick, have some sack in a posset pot or deep silver bason, half a pound of double refined sugar, and some fine grated nutmeg, warm it in the bason and pour in the cream and eggs, the cinamon being taken out, pour it as high as you can hold the skillet, let it spatter in the bason to make it froth, it will make a most excellent posset; then have loaf sugar finely beaten, and throw on it good store.

To the curd you may add some fine grated manchet, [the finest kind of wheaten bread] some claret or white-wine, or ale only.

Robert May. *The Accomplisht Cook, or the Art and Mystery of Cooking.* 1671.

Recipes also advise pouring the custard mixture into the sack from a height, one even suggesting mounting the table to do so! The recipe from 1671, recommends serving in a posset pot, others in posset glasses[22] or glass syllabub pots.[23]

The recipe to be served in a syllabub pot, though called a sack posset, is indeed a syllabub. Such nutrient is not cooked and consists of cream, sugar, wine, spices, and perhaps orange or lemon.

> Take a mutchkin [a measure for liquids, about three-quarters of an imperial pint] of sweet cream, half a mutchkin of white wine, and the juice of a lemon; sweeten it to your taste with fine sugar; put in a bit of the pairing of a lemon, and a piece of cinnamon, if you chuse; whisk it very well, and as it rises, take it up with a spoon.
>
> Mrs. MacIver. *Cookery and Pastry,* 1774.

Panada resembles a gruel in which bread is substituted for the oatmeal; butter, sweetener, spices, and often wine are added.

> Cut all the crust off a penny loaf, slice the rest very thin and put it into a saucepan with a pint of water, boil it till it is very soft and looks clear, then put in a glass of sack or Madeira wine, grate in a little nutmeg, and put in a lump of butter the size of a walnut, and sugar to your taste, beat it exceeding fine, then put it in a deep soup dish and serve it up. – N.B. You may leave out the wine and sugar, and put in a little good cream and a little salt, if you like it better.
>
> Elizabeth Raffald. *The Experienced English Housekeeper,* 1780.

In Ancient Greece some infants were put to suckle before the umbilical cord was cut; others were withheld as long as 20 days in the belief that early breast milk was valueless and indigestible. Interim nourishment containing ingredients such as honey, butter, flour, and goat's milk or wine was the forerunner of pap or panada. Pap is a gruel adapted for infant feeding, strictly speaking, wheat flour mixed with milk or water. In practice it was not uncommon to add wine or beer, and the product became a caudle.

The use of pap was controversial, some condemning it, some regarding it as an acceptable supplement to milk. The criticism was based on fears that: (1) it would be given to settle a disturbed infant, to the exclusion of more nourishing milk, (2) it would be used by a wet nurse who was trying to hide the fact that her milk supply was drying up, and (3) the wet nurse would use it to stretch her milk supply to nurse, and be paid for, two infants, without being discovered.

De Vallambert in 1565 included pap as one of a number of mixtures to be given at the time of weaning. He stated that nurses sometimes added egg yolk, then put it into the child's mouth with their fingers. Parey in the seventeenth century, stated, "Pap is the most meet food or meat for children: because they require moist nourishment, and it must be answerable in thickness to the milk, that so it may not bee difficult to be concocted or digested." He proceeded to give directions for its making of baked wheat flour mixed with boiled milk.[24]

Astruc (1746) in Paris warned against the infant being glutted with pap, while Cadogan (1748) in London absolutely condemned its use along with panada and gruel. Brouzet (1755) recommended making pap with the flour of wheat malt and made a strict rule that "children at the breast ought only to have milk, panada, or pap made with malt."[25] J. Ballexserd (Paris), spoke strongly against pap in 1762, blaming death in infancy on unboiled pap, wet nursing, and swaddling clothes. He advocated action to prevent the spread of the use of pap, then softened to approve it if made from fermented and germinated meal and if cooked.[26] Raulin (1769) feared too much pap, too much wheat, and too little cooking, and discouraged its use before seven months. C.D.G. de Claubry classified pap as being very dangerous to children.[27] Contrarily, in 1781, William Moss criticized the English habit of supplementing the breast milk for newborns with a panada, as he considered both bread and sugar indigestible. Moss noted that many children could not tolerate bread; he therefore favoured the French use of pap.[28] In 1807, Herdman in London, condemned panadas and gruels and recommended weaning to milk and broth.[29] The same year Gardien stood firm by his belief that pap and panada were good supplements for infants, pap being best if well prepared. He attributed the widespread criticism of pap to poor preparation.[30] James Hamilton (1813) among others, felt that small daily amounts of pap or panada were important to facilitate later weaning.[31] The strongest proponent of dry nursing in general was Harmand de Montgarny, who in 1806 placed its value as second only to maternal nursing, claiming its many advantages had been overlooked. As good evidence of its nutritional value, he quoted the case of Elie Mesnard, who ". . . avait nourri treize enfans avec le lait de vache, dont onze étaient encore vivans en 1764 le plus age ayant 52, et le plus jeune 32." [. . . had raised 13 children on cow's milk; 11 were still living in 1764, the oldest being 52 and the youngest 32.][32] This was an outstanding record for 13 siblings on any kind of nourishment in the early eighteenth century. The quote from the same author at the beginning of this section indicates that authorities were attempting to promote artificial feeding, at least in France, and awarding medals to eminent writers on the subject. The particular awards mentioned were authorized by the chief of police, who was responsible for the control of wet nursing. This was obviously an attempt to reduce the use of wet nurses.

As late as 1842 Bergonier advocated the superior pap introduced by Brouzet a century before, that is: boiled pap made from fermented or germinated meal.[33] German physicians, according to Alfred Vogel, felt the best substitute for mother's milk was Liebig's soup; wheat flour, malt meal (from a brewery), potassium bicarbonate, water, and cow's milk – all heated to boiling and strained. Again, Brouzet's superior pap.[34]

From the middle of the eighteenth century most writers agreed on one principle: children were being crammed or glutted; it was time to stop overfeeding. At the same time there was protest, from mild rumblings to loud outcries, against the use of wine and beer in infant's food, though sometimes small beer was a noted exception. Small beer was the brew allowed in unlimited quantities to wet nurses (see p. 45).

The increased demand for milk brought a new problem to the fore, namely tampering with the milk before it was sold. Moss believed that for small infants cow's milk should be diluted with water to simulate human milk. But to advise about dilution was difficult.

> As milk is frequently mixed with water by those who sell it, it cannot be said, with any degree of exactness, what proportion of water must be added to the milk to reduce it to a suitable consistence: but, if the milk be good, about one part milk, and two parts water,* will do very well, to give at the first.
>
> *. . .the water must have boiled. . .

William Moss. *An Essay on the Management and Nursing of Children*. 1781, p. 86.

Apparently in mid-eighteenth-century England, the watering of milk was a common offence.

As early as 1701, in Paris, concern for the quality of cow's milk being fed to adults (including nursing women) and children, was expressed in an ordinance of September, made public through town criers in November. Cows were being fed the dregs of barley piles from breweries and the spoilage left at the starch works. The Lieutenant General of Police sought advice from the Faculty of Medicine.[35]

During the nineteenth century the adulteration of milk became a scandal in France. In February of 1902 an issue of *L'Assiette au Beurre*[36] was devoted to the topic. A number of prints from the magazine, done by well-known caricaturists, are in the Collection.

In the mid-nineteenth century the same difficulty was prevalent in Germany, particularly in large cities. According to Alfred Vogel, "The milk obtained from general dealers is always far from being satisfactory, and it is absolutely necessary for one to be present at the milking and feeding of the cow, until he has become satisfactorily convinced of the honest dealings of his milk purveyor. . . It will be cheaper in the end to procure milk from the country at an extra cost than to employ a wet nurse."[37]

Once the desired milk was obtained, however, it was not easy to feed it to an infant. Spoons or spouted feeders were a possibility from birth, but many felt the sucking bottle was better because it exercised facial muscles much as in children at the breast. Precursors of the nipple were far from satisfactory. They included rags, rags stuffed with sponge, chamois or leather pricked with holes or sewn with large stitches in the fashion of a glove finger, with or without stuffing. Probably the most successful, though not always available, was the dried cow's teat.

Struve, in 1802, praised the nipple-shaped sponge as being a substitute that enabled the child to satisfy the need for sucking. In 1860 Vogel emphasized that such sponges, which were secured over the neck of a bottle with a piece of gauze, should be changed several times daily and were best preserved in pure cold water.

Illustration from L'Assiette au Beurre
[The Patented Poisoners, The Falsifiers of Milk]
30.0 × 24.5 cm

Illustration from L'Assiette au Beurre
[The Innocents
Are you almost finished drinking? You are going to drown your milk, worse they will say you've diluted it from within.]
26.3 × 20.0 cm

Struve had felt that the nipple-shaped sponge would mean getting rid of "those disgusting little sucking bags, the favourite remedy of nurses, for exercising the mouths of children in suction."[38] Such bags, according to Vogel, were prepared by mixing pulverized sugar-crackers with sufficient milk or water to make a dough. A small ball was then tied in a linen rag and put in the child's mouth. Fungus infections of the mouth were a frequent result, and Vogel was among the many who banned the use of sugar teats completely.[39] Their demise would certainly have been hastened by the advent of the rubber nipple, and especially by its adaptation as a soother or pacifier. Probably the strongest factor in determining the trend to use artificial feeding in early infancy was the invention of the rubber nipple, patented in America in 1845 by Elijah Pratt.[40] In 1860, Vogel went on to say that "Children drink very readily out of the perforated caoutchouc caps [India rubber nipples] which lately have become so popular, and which are especially recommendable on account of their cleanliness."[41]

Pewter bowl
Germany, 18 C
Capacity: 80 cc

For steeping infants' sponge nipples and/or sucking bags

Further evidence of the widespread use of the new nipple was indicated by J.H. Walsh, Professor of Clinical Medicine, Dorpat, Russia, who in 1858 recommended that sweetened, diluted cow's milk be given to newborn infants from a feeding bottle with an India rubber nipple varnished white, "now generally sold for the purpose."[42]

Increased impetus to artificial feeding was soon to come with the development of pasteurization and knowledge of sterilization. These influences all combined to make substitute feeding easier, more efficient, cleaner, and safer.

When discussing ancient vessels, their exact use is often in question. The development of those seemingly used for feeding is an interesting study. Earliest designs with a handle and a spout, resembling a tea pot, persisted for several thousand years; the top, usually open for filling, was sometimes closed over with a strainer; clay was the common material, and craftsmanship in its moulding and decorating was often very skilled. No apparent features were incorporated to facilitate cleaning; it was a long time before consideration was given to the type of nourishment, the need for cleaning, and the preference of the infant.

The best preserved of ancient vessels came from children's graves where they were intended to give solace in the afterlife. The earliest in the Collection are from Cyprus.

Dating from the fifth to third century BC are examples of black glazed ware, the pride of Athenian potters, and a Laconian pot banded in black and red with pattern between. As with other artifacts, Greek feeders found their way to the colonies. Two rare feeders from Sicily are shaped like a mouse and a cow. Another from Sicily has an unusual loop handle between the mouth used for filling the vessel and the spout. Of two others found in Italy, one is a fine example of Etruscan black glazed pottery with a strainer moulded in the top; the other is an oddity, Greek brown glazed clay with white incised decoration which may have been added later. It is interesting to speculate about the history of the feeder found in a Roman cemetery in Luxembourg in 1862.

Greek pottery feeders from Cyprus
Upper right: 1800–1600 BC
Lower right: 1500–1200 BC, capacity: 140 cc
Note strainer moulded in top

Others: 8–6 BC
Upper centre: black on buff
Lower centre: biochrome ware, capacity: 175 cc
Note bulbous knob on spout for tying nipple.

Upper left: black on buff, capacity: 195 cc
Lower left: black on red ware

Pottery feeders
Upper: cow and mouse, Greek from Sicily, ca. 300 BC
Cow, capacity: 210 cc
Has not been used

Lower: 5 C – 3 C BC
Left: Laconi, Sicily
Capacity: 90 cc

Centre: Athens, black glaze with red reserve
Capacity: 38 cc

Right: Athens, black glaze on red clay
Capacity: 40 cc

Note varied relationships between handle and spout.

Pottery feeders
3 C BC and later
Upper centre: Greek found in Sicily, 3 C BC
Capacity: 300 cc

Left: Greek found in Italy
Capacity: 140 cc

Right: Etruscan, Italy, 250 BC
Capacity: 125 cc

Lower centre: Roman, found at Moestroff, Luxembourg, AD 1 C – 3 C
Capacity: 50 cc

A Roman glass feeder found in Cyprus is very delicate, in striking contrast to later pottery examples. The Arab jug-like vessel of heavy pottery with a trussed spout appears crude in spite of careful decoration.

Preceding the fall of the Roman Empire and following its dissolution, maurauding hordes roamed Europe, leaving devastation behind. It was hundreds of years before settled communities again developed a reasonable standard of living, with household articles of a quality and quantity to survive. Meanwhile, the horn of a cow with chamois or some soft material tied over the end as a nipple, was a common vessel for dry nursing. A number of physicians in the eighteenth century continued to recommend the horn as an alternative, if not preferred, vessel for feeding infants. Among them was Rosen von Rosenstein whose Swedish work of 1764 first appeared in English in 1776.

Glass feeder
Roman found in Cyprus, AD 100–200
Capacity: 250 cc

> If we cannot procure any nurse, and the mother cannot suckle her child, then we must accustom the child to suck by means of a little instrument, or sucking bottle (called Biberon), which is universally used in Easter-Bothnia [sic] with great advantage; but this machine ought always to be kept clean: it is to be made of horn, the smaller end of which may be fastened to a tanned skin of a cow's teat, or if that is not to be procured, we may use any other thin skin, pierced with many small holes. Pour in this as much cows and goats cream (unboiled) as you think the child will use at once, dilute it with water, and sweeten it with a little sugar.

Nicholas Rosen von Rosenstein. *The Diseases of Children and their Remedies.* 1776, p. 3.

The Industrial Revolution saw the mass production of household items: pottery and porcelain feeders, especially in England, are prime examples. Of 222 feeding bottles in the Collection, over half are blue and white transfer-printed, submarine-shaped, pottery (1830–1850). One such was Dr. Drake's first purchase. These feeders have a circular opening in the top of the body which can be corked; one end is flat, the other extended, narrowing to a small hole, with a bulge or rim for securing a nipple. The original parchment sewn like a glove finger, is still attached to one, and the original chamois, to another.

Pottery feeder
Near East, 13-14 C
Capacity: 200 cc

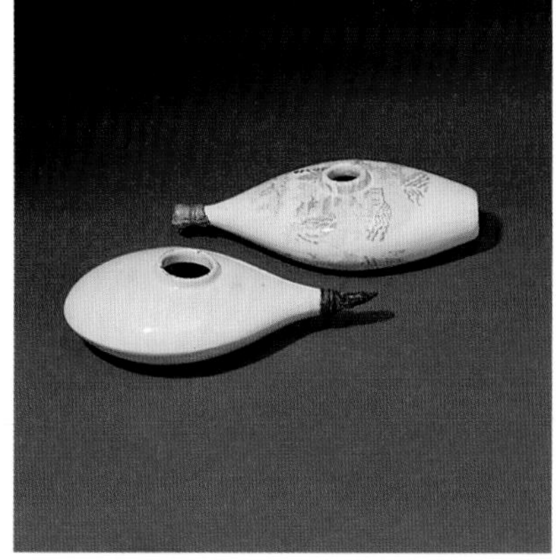

Submarine-shaped pottery feeders
England, Staffordshire, ca. 1840
Capacity: 190 cc

Note chamois nipple upper and parchment nipple lower.

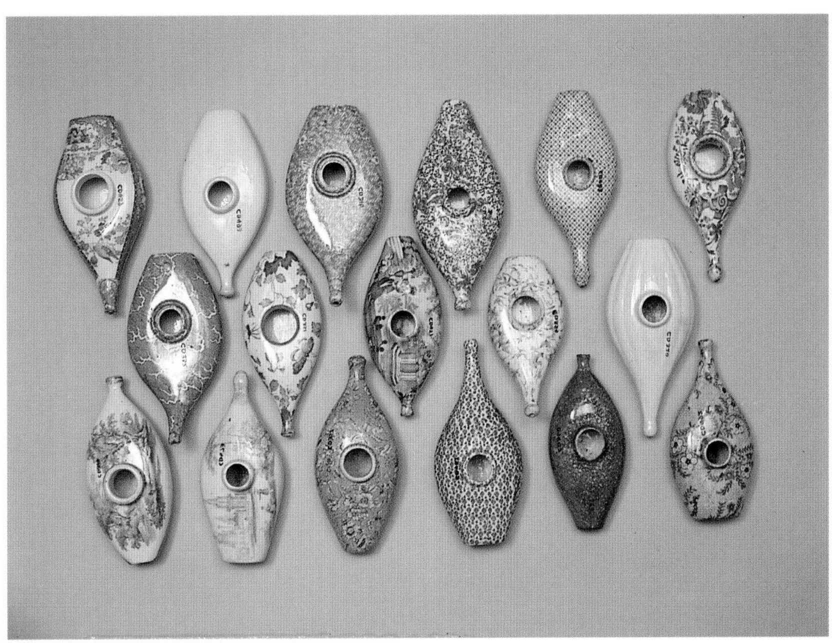

A sampling of English feeding bottles
1830–1850
Capacities: 120–280 cc

Transfer-printed, submarine-shaped pottery feeders
England, 1830–1850
Left: Copeland and Garret, Late Spode, marked, Tower Pattern
Capacity: 240 cc

Upper: Copeland and Garret, Late Spode, marked, Botanical Pattern
Capacity: 210 cc

Right: Overall stylized floral pattern
Capacity: 220 cc

Transfer printing on a ceramic surface was first used at the Battersea Enamel Works in 1753 and the process credited to John Brooks. This involved spreading an engraved copper plate with ink prepared from one of the metallic oxides, then printing the design on transfer paper, which, while the pigment was still wet, was pressed on the ceramic surface leaving an imprint. Its potential for mass production was soon realized. In 1756 John Sadler and Guy Green (Liverpool) established the Printed Ware Factory; they printed on Liverpool tiles, local pottery and porcelain, and wares from over 500 factories. Robert Hancock developed underglaze printing at Worcester in 1759, initially in cobalt blue. Caughley, Spode, and Wedgwood set up their own printing departments, and considerable rivalry resulted. Engravers, with their own plates, were lured from one establishment to another: Hancock from Worcester to Caughley, Thomas Lucas and James Richards, from Caughley to Spode.

By the mid-nineteenth century vast quantities of underglaze blue had been produced, decorated in many styles: classical landscapes, chinoiserie, and naturalistic motifs. Leading potteries used the same basic shape, but decoration varied: Davenport, an overall blue floral pattern called Marine Chintz; Wedgwood, pastoral scenes called Harbour Series; Old Leeds, a Chinese scene; Copeland and Garret, Late Spode, Botanical design and Tower pattern. These pieces were available at prices the rising middle class could afford, such as a shilling for a bottle.[43,44]

Transfer-printed, submarine-shaped pottery feeders
England, 1830–1850
Left: Old Leeds, Chinese scene
Capacity: 220 cc

Centre: Wedgwood, Harbour Series pattern with blue rose border
Capacity: 160 cc

Right: Davenport, Marine Chintz
Capacity 200 cc

Submarine-shaped pottery feeders
England, 19 C, Salt-glazed stoneware, bust of Queen Victoria
Capacity: 300 cc

Green and white transfer-printed, ca. 1830
Capacity: 275 cc
Imprinted with Hannah, and the following:
Morning Song
Give me O Lord thy early grace
Nor let my soul complain
That the morning of my days
Has all been spent in vain

Note reproduced chamois nipples.

Novelty feeders were not unknown. One commemorating Queen Victoria is stoneware. The green and white transfer-printed bottle covered with a stylized floral pattern and bearing a moralistic *Morning song* such as might be expected on a sampler or a *Band of Hope* plate[45] of the same century, is personalized with *Hannah*. Dr. Drake always felt this bottle had been made by a potter for his own daughter.

Examples of more costly submarine-shaped feeders are porcelain with gilt edged openings and naturalistic decoration of ferns and flowers.

Most of the 36 glass feeders in the Collection are English from the mid-nineteenth century, and are submarine-shaped. An earlier example with enamelled design is European. Others, including several from North America and Europe are conical or flask-shaped.

Porcelain feeders
England, 19 C
Upper: Capacity: 210 cc

Lower: Capacity: 160 cc
Note reproduced chamois nipple.

Glass feeders
Upper left: Bohemia or Germany, 1750–1800
Capacity: 350 cc

Upper right: North America, 1872
Capacity: 275 cc

Lower: England, 1850
Capacity: 100 cc

Twenty-four eighteenth-century pewter feeding bottles are English, French, and Dutch, with two Swiss and one Chinese; they too, are conical or flask-shaped. It is significant to note that Struve stipulated that bottles ". . .ought not to be made of pewter, nor even have a pewter or leaden top, which infants put into their mouths: such utensils ought always to be constructed of glass. . ."[46] Concern for lead poisoning was not generally advocated in 1802.

Eight silver feeders include two submarine type: one with a hinged lid for filling is plain except for chased decoration surrounding the opening; the other is engraved in stripes of geometric pattern on the upper and lower surfaces with borders of floral chasing.

Pewter/glass feeders
Left: China, 19 C

Left centre: Germany, late 18 C
Capacity: 175 cc

Right centre: Switzerland, 18 C

Right: France, England, or Holland, 18 C
Capacity: 200 cc

Silver submarine feeders
Upper: Edinburgh, 1800, maker M+C°
Capacity: 90 cc

Lower: Birmingham, 1860, maker Geo. White
Capacity: 145 cc

Various styles of spouted feeders for infants and/or invalids, in pottery and porcelain, represent many makers. For a time pewter was also used. Silver was frequently selected by those who could afford it. Some authorities identify infant feeders by the presence of a ridge to hold the nipple on the spout; some consider invalid feeders to be the larger size.

Spouted feeders
England
Left: Pewter, 18 C, crown with I.D.K. above Tudor rose
Capacity: 135 cc

Centre: Silver, London, 1885
Capacity: 310 cc

Right: Pewter, late 19 C
Capacity: 250 cc

Spouted feeders
Left: Creamware, Leeds, ca. 1760
Capacity: 100 cc
Note bird form.

Upper: Tin-glazed pottery, England, 18 C
Capacity: 500 cc

Right: Porcelain, Ireland, Belleek, 1863–1891
Capacity: 200 cc

Lower: Blue transfer-printed, tin-glazed pottery, Staffordshire, 19 C
Capacity: 112 cc

Tin-glazed, spouted pottery feeders
Left: France, Moustiers, 1686–1728
Capacity: 300 cc

Centre: England, 1660–1692
Capacity: 270 cc

Right: France, 18 C
Capacity: 270 cc

Spouted porcelain feeders, Germany, 19 C
Left: 1860–90
Capacity: 150 cc

Right, capacity: 88 cc

Among the silver feeders, several are spouted, the most significant being a Hugh Smith milk pot, 1790. It is described in detail in his book and was highly recommended for use by Underwood (1784), who cautioned people to keep it clean, and by Jackson (1798), who advised fine linen or vellum be properly fastened over the spout:

> This pot is somewhat in form like an urn; it contains a little more than a quarter of a pint; its handle, and neck or spout, are not unlike those of a coffee-pot, except that the neck of this arises from the very bottom of the pot, and is very small; in short it is upon the same principal as those gravy-pots which separate the gravy from the oily fat. The end of the spout is a little raised, and forms a roundish knob somewhat in appearance like a small heart; this is perforated by three or four small holes: a piece of fine rag is tied loosely over it; through which, by the infant's sucking, the milk is constantly strained. (The model of this milk-pot is left with Mr. Morrison, at the Three Kings, in Cheapside, for the benefit of the public.)
>
> Hugh Smith. *Letters to Married Women.* 1767.

Pottery pots of the same design were produced in quantity and made such feeders available to the Middle Class.

As more devices were developed for presenting artificial nourishment to children, more opinions came forward as to the ideal means of doing so. In England, Armstrong (1771) suggested a horn, boat, or spoon, the last being the best. Moss (1781) advised a machine of horn or tin, a spoon, or a boat, stipulating that the first induces some to eat. Jackson (1798) recommended the feeding pot or glass horn, no spoon or boat. In France, Léger (1825) advocated the spoon, biberon, or bottle, rating the spoon as most convenient. Thinking that sucking on an artificial teat causes intake of air, Léger hesitated to recommend bottles or biberons, but he conceded that the bottle used in Italy, having a hollow tube reaching to the bottom, was preferable. In Italy, F. Baldini had earlier recommended such a biberon with a sponge tightly held in place by a screw-on top.[47] H. Ley approved sucking bottles as being the best substitute for the breast and indicated that nipples made from a dried cow's teat, vellum, parchment, or chamois leather were all in common use. Because such nipples engendered problems of collapsing and uncleanliness, in 1836 he began advising the use of silver nipples.[48] An advertisement for items patented in Paris in May, 1827, outlines the advantages of nipple shields and biberons with detailed instructions for their use and care.[49]

Hugh Smith feeders
Left: Creamware, Wedgwood, ca. 1800
Capacity: 200 cc

Right: Silver, London, 1790–1791

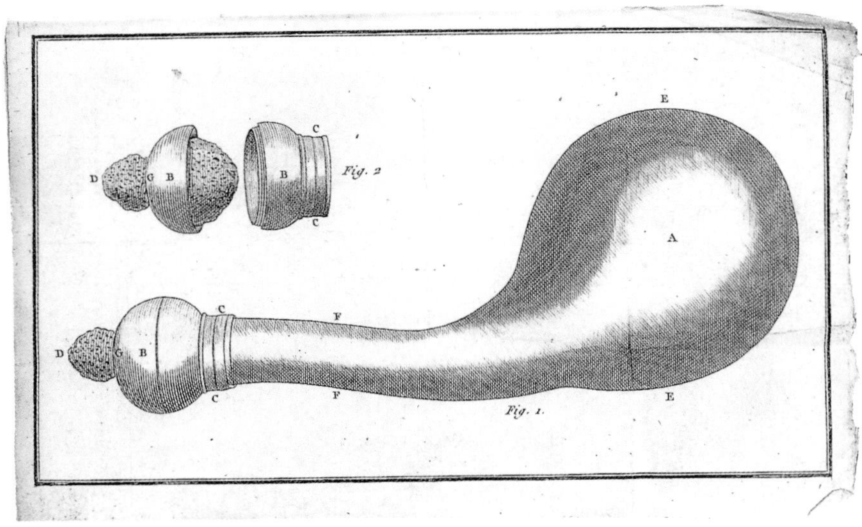

Biberon as described by Baldini (b. ca. 1750)

The boats referred to by some, became popular vessels for feeding any of the soft foods introduced in the months of infancy. Most commonly used for serving the controversial pap, they became known as pap boats. Their popularity in eighteenth- and nineteenth-century England is indicated by the presence in the Collection of over 200 of that era. Of 158 porcelain and pottery examples, 88 are blue and white transfer-printed. Many are plain pottery with white or cream glaze; a few are porcelain. Factories of Minton, Davenport, Wedgwood, late Spode (Copeland, and Copeland and Garrett) are represented — the same factories that produced nursing bottles.

Pottery pap boats
England, late 18 C – 19 C
Left: Transfer-printed, Copeland and Garrett, late Spode, 19 C
Capacity: 85 cc.

Upper: Transfer-printed, Copeland, late Spode, 19 C
Capacity: 80 cc.

Right: Transfer-printed, Davenport, 19 C
Capacity: 88 cc.

Lower: Wedgwood, late 18 C – early 19 C
Capacity: 88 cc.

Porcelain pap boats
England 19 C
Upper: Crown Derby, ca. 1800
Capacity: 130 cc.

Left: Capacity: 85 cc.

Right: Minton
Capacity 110 cc.

Nine pap boats are pewter, all are English, eight are eighteenth-century. Forty-three are silver, most of them English, made in the eighteenth or nineteenth centuries, but six are from elsewhere: Scotland, Ireland, the Netherlands, India. Though the pap boat was most popular in England, it was obviously not limited to that country. Of the silver pap boats a large number are a simple undecorated style; later pieces are more ornate. An unusual European example, reminiscent of a pap spoon, is a small fish with blue eyes, imported into England in 1902. The usual pap spoons recommended as alternatives to pap boats have a large covered bowl, a hinged lid, and a pouring spout.

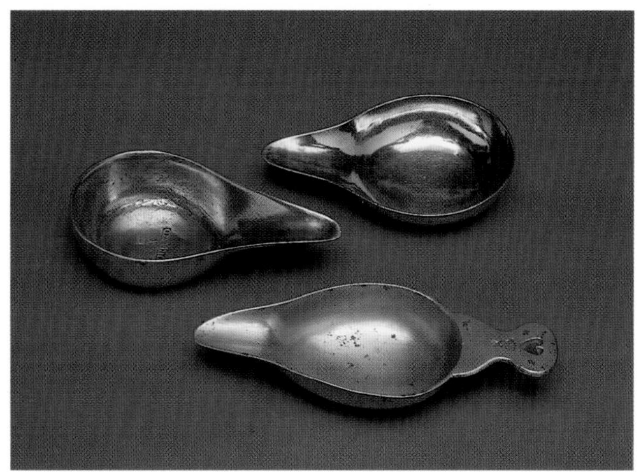

Pap boats
England
Left: Pewter, 1825

Right: Britannia standard, London, 1719
Capacity: 95 cc.

Lower: Pewter, 18 C

Silver pap boats and pap spoon
England
Undecorated, 18 C
Left: London, 1780
Maker: Hester Bateman
Silver gilt interior
Capacity: 110 cc.

Right: London, 1756
Maker [F.W.] [Fuller White]

Decorated, 18–19 C
Upper: London, 1829–1830, egg and dart beaded edge.

Lower: London, 1769–1770, maker: Samuel Massey, floral repoussé.

Pap spoon
London, 1823, maker [CR]
Capacity: 45 cc.

Silver pap boats
Outside England
Upper left: Silver gilt, Edinburgh, after 1759
Maker R.G.

Upper right: ? Calcutta, 1790–1810
[Hamilton & Co. from Inverness, Scotland, established a company in Calcutta]
Capacity: 170 cc.

Lower right: Netherlands, imported into France, 19 C, 83.3% silver

Lower left: Europe, imported into England in 1902
Capacity: 13 cc.

It is apparent, noting the various feeding approaches described, how overfeeding or stuffing the infant was easily accomplished. Food was simply poured into the mouth. Such practices were prevalent in the eighteenth and nineteenth centuries, and many did not consider babies well fed until they had regurgitated and been fed again. Quoting Sir John Pringle, William Moss wrote, "Children are always observed to thrive best when they posset or throw up freely."[50]

La Jeune Nourice
[The Young Wet Nurse]
Engraving
France, 1780–1850
16.5 × 11.0 cm

Note the veilleuse in use.

Spoon-feeding Baby
Etching by Jacques François Amand (1730–1769)
France
12.0 × 8.0 cm

A means of keeping food warm was the pap warmer or *veilleuse* [night light] which operates on the principle of a double boiler, often with facility for holding a candle on the lid. Harold Newman in *Veilleuses 1750–1860* makes frequent reference to the veilleuses in the Drake Collection. On the cover of his book and described as "probably the rarest English food warmer" is the most precious one in the museum; Chelsea, red anchor mark about 1758.[51] Others shown in Newman's book, because it is so highly regarded, are noted in the captions.

Porcelain pap warmer
Paris, 19 C
Ht: 20.3 cm

A complete pap warmer consists of: *pedestal* or base, usually cylindrical, with an aperture at the bottom large enough to allow a godet to pass through; *godet* or vessel for oil, either open or resembling a spirit lamp; *liner*, a bowl for hot water fitting into the top of the pedestal; *pannikin*, a bowl fitting into the liner to hold the food; and *lid* topped by a finial often designed to hold a candle. Since most were made of pottery, few have survived in their entirety. Not all originally possessed a liner. Of the veilleuses in the Collection, there are 45 with two parts or more, and many separate pieces.

The eighteenth-century pap warmers are predominantly English earthenware, but several are French, Italian, Swiss, and Dutch, and some are porcelain.

The pedestal of an early food warmer of brown-glazed red clay decorated in slip with green and yellow flowers, is crudely spherical with a square godet aperture closed by tying on a square door; it has only one sturdy loop handle. It is marked in slip "16 Dec. 1751 I H" and is probably Staffordshire. Other early English pottery warmers have a tortoise shell glaze, and have survived whole or in part.

Porcelain pap warmer
England, Chelsea, 1758
Ht: 35.6 cm
(Newman, p. 35)

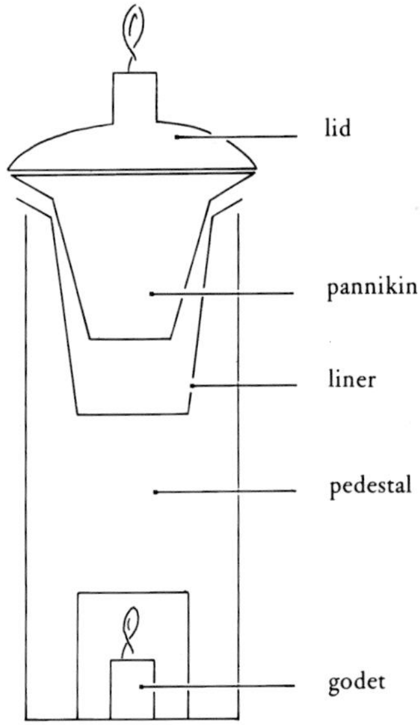

Cross-section of complete veilleuse

Glazed earthenware pap warmers
England, 18 C
Left: Whieldon, ca. 1760

Centre: Staffordshire, Dec. 16, 1751
Ht: 18.5 cm
(Newman, p. 42)

Right: Leeds, ca. 1770

Creamware pap warmer, four pieces
England, Leeds, late 18 C
Ht: 26 cm

The earliest English delft veilleuse piece is a pedestal only, 1750–1760, noted in Newman's book as being similar in form to other delft-ware warmers in the Collection, but unique among all known delftware pedestals in its random floral decoration.[52] The other eight delft-ware veilleuses are typified by the centre of the three blue and white ones shown opposite: the cylindrical base is footed, has a godet aperture topped in a double ogee curve, above which projects, about two-thirds up the pedestal, a male mask concealing air vents. An identical mask is opposite. On each side and at the level of the masks is a heavy, solid scroll handle, below which are three lugs at about one inch intervals. The pannikin has two shell-shaped handles and sits on a projecting flange over the base. The lid, also flanged, has a socket finial to carry a candle. The veilleuse is tin-glazed, very pale blue earthenware with cobalt blue decoration. Bands of blue surround the base top and bottom, are interrupted by the handles on the pannikin, and are complete on the edge of the lid and around the candle holder. Feather-like swags and trailing flowers encircle the top of the pedestal, and a similar pattern borders the aperture. A more stylized but similar design borders the lid. All handles and lugs are touched with blue. Some delft pieces are identical to this, while others vary slightly.

Unusual in the Collection are two European veilleuse pedestals (below), one with its lid.

Creamware veilleuses[53] were popular in England in the late eighteenth and early nineteenth century. Several from Leeds, Wedgwood and Minton are characterized by: elegant loop or scroll handles, sometimes twisted, sometimes foliate, often grooved; pierced patterns above the aperture and elsewhere on the pedestal, in floral, foliate, or geometric shapes. Several of these have the maker's marks.

Pottery pap warmer pedestals
Europe, 18 C
Left: Majolica, Faenza, Italy, late 18 C
Ht: 22.5 cm
(Newman, p. 67)

Right: ? Switzerland, ca. 1765

Pap warmer and pedestals
England 18 C
Left: Tin-glazed earthenware, 1750–1760
Ht: 16.6 cm
Unusual overall, Chinese style floral decoration (Newman, p. 30)

Centre: Tin-glazed earthenware, Lambeth
Mid-18 C

Right: Porcelain, Lowestoft, ca. 1773.

Pottery pap warmers
England
Left: Minton, dissembled to show its parts
Early 19 C

Right: A similar Wedgwood, creamware, assembled with spirit lamp seen in the godet
Late 18 C
Ht: 25 cm.
(Newman, p. 51)

American versions are a combination of tin and white pottery as in Samuel Clarke's Pyramid Food warmer, consisting of tin pedestal and liner with white pottery pannikin and lid, or the all-tin bubby pot of the Pennsylvania Dutch.

As children advanced beyond the age for food of gruel consistency, the common vessel used for solid foods was the porringer, and for drinking, the mug. Porringers in the Collection are of pewter, pottery, horn, and brass. Similar vessels with incised markings for measuring ounces are believed to be bleeding bowls.

Pottery mugs were plentiful in all classes of society, but among the affluent silver mugs were common christening gifts and often passed from one generation to the next, so that many survive.

Those in the Collection evolve from simple, undecorated cups, through some incised with bands, to elaborately decorated pieces. This evolution is illustrated by examples from the seventeenth, eighteenth, and nineteenth centuries.

As lead poisoning gradually became recognized, pewter feeding vessels fell into disuse. Though silver, porcelain, and pottery porringers and mugs are still popular, indestructible and inert plastics have taken over much of the market. Even the commonly used glass feeding bottles of the earlier twentieth century have been largely replaced by efficient plastic bottles. Today, although breast feeding is fairly common in the first three months, it is much less so beyond that age, and many types of artificial feeding are available. To those raising infants since the middle of this century, the variety of formulae offered in the stores is overwhelming. Most parents rely on the guidance of physicians in choosing the one best suited to their child.

Pap warmers, 19 C
Left: Transfer-printed pottery, England, Staffordshire
Ht. of pedestal: 23.0 cm
Note tin liner

Right: Samuel Clarke's Pyramid Food Warmer
United States, late 19 C
(Newman, p. 197)

Pewter porringers
England
Upper: Mid-18 C, base marked "Britannia"
Note lid designed to serve as a trivet.

Lower: London, 17 C
Capacity: 200 cc

Pottery porringers and mugs
Europe
Left porringer: Brittany, Quimper HR, La Hubaudière & Co., late 19 C
Capacity: 370 cc

Right porringer: Copper lustre ware, Hispano-Moresque, 16 C
Capacity: 270 cc

Mugs: Transfer-printed, England, 19 C
Capacity, left: 130 cc
right: 170 cc

Silver mugs
England
Left: London, 1781–1782. Plain with 2 bands of incised rings on body, ringed foot, flattened scroll handle
Capacity: 120 cc

Centre: London, 1827, maker: A.B. Savory Heavily decorated with repoussé, baluster body with floral decoration above and below strapping, flared pedestal base, serpentine and floral twisted handle.
Capacity: 135 cc

Right: London, 1692–1693. Plain with ringed foot and grooved scroll handle
Capacity: 105 cc

Most of the prints in which an infant is being fed, show the baby on a nurse's lap. When a child could sit reasonably well, he would be fed, and later would feed himself, in a high chair. Dr. Drake collected children's furniture.

Almost an exact duplicate of the ash high chair shown opposite was pictured in "Furniture in the Nursery"[54] described as being in Ann Hathaway's cottage, Stratford-upon-Avon. The author wrote: "No other example of a turned child's chair is recorded of such elaborate design." Therefore, the acquisition of this piece gave Dr. Drake immense pleasure. It is doubtful that any such joy came to the occupant, however: the loading of the structure with turnery, much of which is deep-cut, would not increase the comfort. One wonders if this "torture chamber" was specifically designed to force a youngster to sit up straight, for it would appear to be the only way to sit in it.

An elaborately carved and turned, caned high chair of Charles II period is a piece worth featuring.

High chair
England 17 C
Walnut, Charles II period
Ht: 110 cm
Caned seat and back, back caning original

Vertical supports and stringers twisted
Joint blocks carved

Cross piece halfway up front legs, top of back, and finials carved with crowns
Restraining bar, adjustable footrest

This chair is branded in several places with RP, the maker's initials, probably Richard Price, who in 1678, was sworn in as joyner to his majesty's wardrobe.

High chairs
Left: Oak, England, 1650
Ht: 112 cm
Carved solid back, turned legs and arm supports, grooved apron, straight stringers at floor level

Centre: Walnut, Tuscany, ca. 1600
Minimal carving on finials, back and leg stringers, and apron

Right: Ash, England, ca. 1600
Heavy knobs and movable rings between back rungs. All pieces turned except restraining bar and footrest.

A walnut high chair and a similar tall table are in William and Mary style. Such a table, with its locking drawer, is sometimes pictured in a nursery. Did it harbour a treasured silver porringer? It is an ideal size for this purpose.

The eighteenth-century oak high chair shows ingenuity on the part of its maker: though simply decorated, its elaborate design enables the seat with arms attached to be raised and lowered.

High chairs, because of their limited and specific use and their high sentimental value, were treasured. As a result, old ones are more readily available than low chairs like those pictured on page 310, which are adaptable to general use and so wear out.

Children's furniture
Late 17 C and early 18 C
Left: Walnut high chair, England, William and Mary, 1690–1700
Ht: 110 cm
Caned seat and back, back caning original, turning throughout, carving on arched headrest, adjustable footrest missing

Centre: Walnut table, England, William and Mary, Late 17 C

Right: Oak high chair, England, 18 C
Turned arm supports, fiddle-shaped back panel, height of seat adjustable with arms attached.

Notes

1. Mazzini 1933.
2. Gardien 1807:Vol 3, 543.
3. Leger 1825:179.
4. Rambaud 1915:7.
5. Bergonier 1842. As well as a standard copy of this book there is in the Collection an elegant copy bound in green velvet, with cream silk moiré end papers, and ornate gilded metal corners, lock, and title plaque. It is inscribed by the author as a gift to her majesty, Empress Eugenie.
6. Struve 1802:241.
7. Roberton 1827.
8. Armstrong 1771:148.
9. Moss 1781.
10. Struve 1802.
11. Smith 1767.
12. Cadogan 1748:25.
13. Herdman 1807.
14. Metlinger 1473.
15. Parey 1649:611.
16. Breast feeding periods advised were: de Vallambert (1565), 20–24 mo; Sainte-Marthe (early 17th C), 8 mo; Astruc (1746), 18–24 mo; Cadogan (1748), 12 mo; Brouzet (1754), 15–16 mo; Raulin (1769), 1–2 yr; Underwood (1784), 12 mo.
17. Breast feeding periods recommended: Icart (1784), 6 mo; Struve (1802), 6 mo; Herdman (1807), 3–6 mo.
18. Kitchiner 1838.
19. Hartley 1954:558. (This book is not part of the Drake Collection.)
20. The cookbooks quoted in this section are not part of the Drake Collection, but are among those collected by Nina Drake, widow of the late T.G.H. Drake.
21. "Captain Bath Making Posset" is an illustration included in Reid, 1871.
22. May 1671.
23. Smith 1772.
24. Parey 1649:610.
25. Brouzet 1755:112–113.
26. Ballexserd 1762:89.
27. de Claubry 1783:224.
28. Moss 1781:93.
29. Herdman 1807:96.
30. Gardien 1807:539–541.
31. Hamilton 1813:40.
32. Harmond de Montgarny 1806:2–30.
33. Bergonier 1842:308.
34. Vogel 1885:47.
35. Ordonnance de Monsieur le Lieutenant General de Police, Rendu à l'encontre des Laitieres pour la mauvaise nourriture des Enfans (960.1.1005).
36. At the turn of the twentieth century, a magazine called *L'Assiette au Beurre* (satirizing those who lived off the fat of the land) was published in Paris for a decade, by a group of free-thinkers who did not hesitate to point out malpractices of the government and prominent individuals. As the magazine was constantly in trouble, several issues were impounded, and in 1902 editor Delaney was imprisoned. To help support him during his confinement, contributing artists sold some of their works. Copies of the magazine are very rare. (Stanley Applebaum, *French Satirical Drawings from "L'Assiette au Beurre"*, New York, 1978).
37. Vogel 1885:48 first German edition published in 1860.
38. Struve 1802:243.
39. Vogel 1885:51.
40. Bullough V.L. Bottle Feeding: An Amplification. *Bulletin of the History of Medicine* 1981;55(2):256–259.
41. Vogel 1885:50.
42. Walsh 1858:272.
43. Coysh 1970.
44. Williams-Wood C. Transfer Printing's Artful Aid. *The Antique and Collectors Guide*, February 1979.
45. See p. 297 for further references to Band of Hope plates, and pp. 301–3 for samplers.
46. Struve 1802:242.
47. Baldini 1786:139.
48. Ley 1836:208–209.
49. Artificial Feeders and Nipple Shields as invented by Madam Breton, midwife (960.1.1327).
50. Moss 1794.
51. Newman 1967:33,35.
52. Newman 1967:30 (Fig. 2).
53. A common outgrowth of the food warmer, and particularly popular in creamware in the nineteenth century, was a teapot with a rounded bottom, replacing the pannikin.
54. Symonds, R.W. Furniture of the Nursery *The Antique Collector*, May-June, 1949:98.

Le Tour [Revolving Receptacle]
Original Watercolour by Herman Vogel
? France, 1889
19.5 × 15.5 cm

Note mother ringing the bell to notify those within that she is leaving her baby.

FOUNDLINGS

The Foundling's Hymn

Our Light, our Saviour is the Lord,
For nothing need we care:
The mighty Lord is our support
What have we then to fear.

When Parents deaf to Nature's Voice
Their helpless Charge forsook;
Then Nature's God who heard our cries
Compassion on us took.

Continue still to hear our Voice,
When unto thee we cry;
And still the Infant's Praise receive,
And still their Wants supply.

Frequent mention has been made of the neglect of children, their abandonment, and the high mortality rates among infants. It was in Rome that the first laws to protect children were passed. In the early days of the Republic, population growth was encouraged: bachelors were taxed, and all male infants not malformed and all first-born girls were to be raised. Later, however, attitudes changed and unwanted children were thrown into the Tiber.

With the advent of Christianity and the belief that a child had a soul, more attention was given to preserving and caring for children. In 315, in an effort to eradicate infanticide, Emperor Constantine issued an edict declaring all foundlings to be slaves of those who chose to rear them, defining punishment for parents who abandoned offspring, and giving them the right to sell newborn infants. Only a few years passed before this last provision roused opposition and was disallowed.

Frontispiece
Foundling Hospital's Hymnal
Psalms, Hymns and Anthems used in The Chapel of the Hospital for the Maintenance and Education of Exposed and Deserted Young Children. Foundling Hospital. 1774.

(see p. 111)

In circumstances of poverty when no effective means of birth control was known, practices of exposure, infanticide, and the sale of children waxed and waned but remained widespread. Gradually public sentiment developed a more humane attitude. The state began to take some responsibility, and the church even more, for the welfare of the needy and the children. As a result of decrees issued by the Councils of the Roman Church in the fifth and sixth centuries, mothers unable to care for their children could leave them in a receptacle at the church door. In the early nineteenth century L. Aucoc referred to a marble shell for receiving infants, which had been installed near the church door at Trèves (Germany) in the seventh century.[1] His treatise also mentions a house next to a church in Milan, bought by Archbishop Datheus in 787 and used as a hospice for foundlings, the first one on record. The basic purpose of this home was to save the souls of children born in adultery who might otherwise die without baptism. The charter included the provision of wet nurses and the teaching of a trade to prepare the children for making their way as free citizens.

Spedale degli Innocente[2]
[Hospital of the Innocents]

Florence, designed by Brunelleschi (1429)
Photograph, Italy, 20 C
19.3 × 25.3 cm

Porte de la Maison des enfans trouvés à Cordoba
[Entrance of the Foundling Hospital at Cordoba]
Spain, 15 C
Des and lith by Asselineau (1808–1889), Paris, 19 C
28.4 × 19.0 cm

Procession of the reliquary of Ste. Geneviève
17 C scene in square of Hôtel Dieu (Foundling Hospital) with Church of Ste. Geneviève in background
Engraving published by Michel Direx, Paris, late 18 C – early 19 C
15.5 × 21.2 cm

Orphanage and the Amstel Bridge
Amsterdam, 18 C
Coloured engraving and etching
Published by Daumont
Paris, 19 C
24.0 × 38.0 cm

Note backward printing of title for projection with a zygrascope.

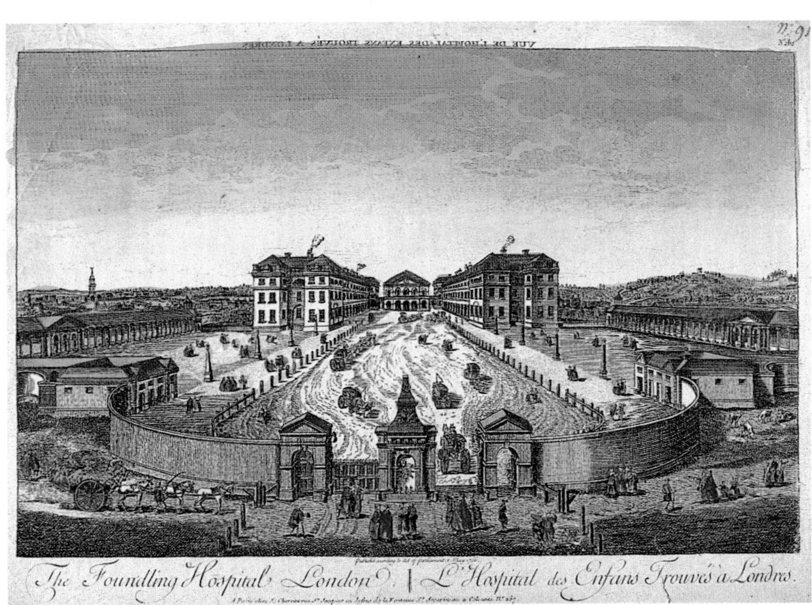

The Foundling Hospital, London
L'Hôpital des Enfans Trouvés à Londres 1756
Coloured etching, published by J. Chereau
Paris, mid 19 C
25.5 × 41.0 cm

Note again backward title for use in zygrascope.

Not for some time was the example of Datheus followed, but from the eleventh century on, many such asylums were operated in England and on the continent. One of the notable advances of the Middle Ages was the success of the church in reducing abortion and infanticide. It was not uncommon for such institutions to have a revolving receptacle in which a mother could place her child, before hurrying to a secluded vantage point to observe the turning process that took the infant inside. This mechanism was called a *tour* in English as in French. Though most infants who were abandoned were illegitimate, some born to parents too poor to raise another child were disposed of in the same way. Several prints show the heartbreak of such a separation.

L'Enfant Abandonné
[Abandoned Child]
Lithograph by C. Motte (1785–1836)
France
25.5 × 33.2 cm

Enfants Trouvés: le tour, extérieur et intérieur
[Foundlings: the revolving receptacle, outside and inside]
Engraving by Henri Pottin (1820–1864)
After a 17 C engraving
France
24.0 × 38.0 cm

Remord [Remorse]
Engraving and etching by Alberto Maso Gilli
France, 1875
27.7 × 21.9 cm

An atypical reaction from those within is depicted in a political cartoon in which a child was abandoned on the doorstep of the Duke and Duchess of Buckingham in Pall Mall. Observing that the infant bore no resemblance to the exclusive group present, they chose to send it to the workhouse immediately.

Commonly those abandoning infants left with them a token of identification and some contribution toward their future care. Booklets containing documents entitled "Documents Concernant des Enfants Trouvés" give the story of two abandoned children. On December 10, 1761, Marie-Joseph was left with his baptismal medal, a little note, and 20 *écus* (silver crowns totalling 60 *livres* in value) on the steps of Saint Esprit Hospital in Besançon. The document is a copy of the Police Commissioner's report as taken in evidence at the hospital in the presence of the Sisters of Charity. On February 3, 1778, Jean François was received at the Foundling Hospital at Dôle, also in the diocese of Besançon. A small cross and 100 *livres*, 10 *sous* for wet nursing fees were in the bundle. His story was extracted from the Registers of the College Church and the Parish of Dôle. Both booklets have the baptismal medals on their ribbons mounted on the inside cover. To see these flimsy relics adds poignancy to the stories.

The Foundling or L'Enfant Trouvé, a Sample of Roman Charity!—and the misfortune of not being born with marks of "the Talents" — "What! a Relation to the Broad Bottoms! O, Sainte Marie! why there's not the least Appearance of it!—therefore take it away to the Workhouse immediately"

Coloured etching by James Gillray
London, May 19, 1808
23.5 × 34.7 cm

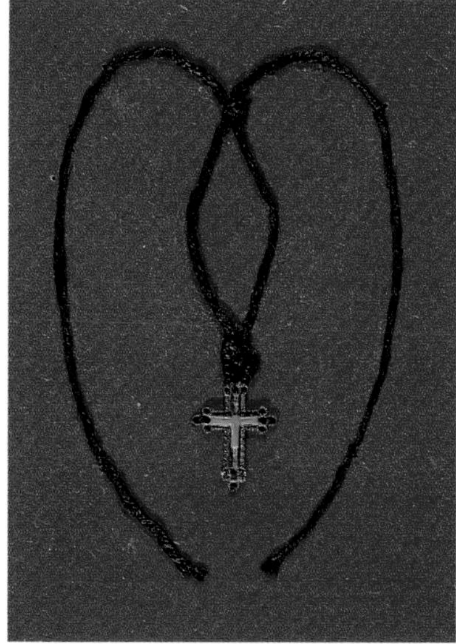

Medal from the Document of Jean François, 1778

Born Jan. 22, baptized and removed from home by the vicar, Jan. 23, and taken to a wet nurse

Received at the Foundling Hospital at Dôle, Feb. 3

L: 18 mm

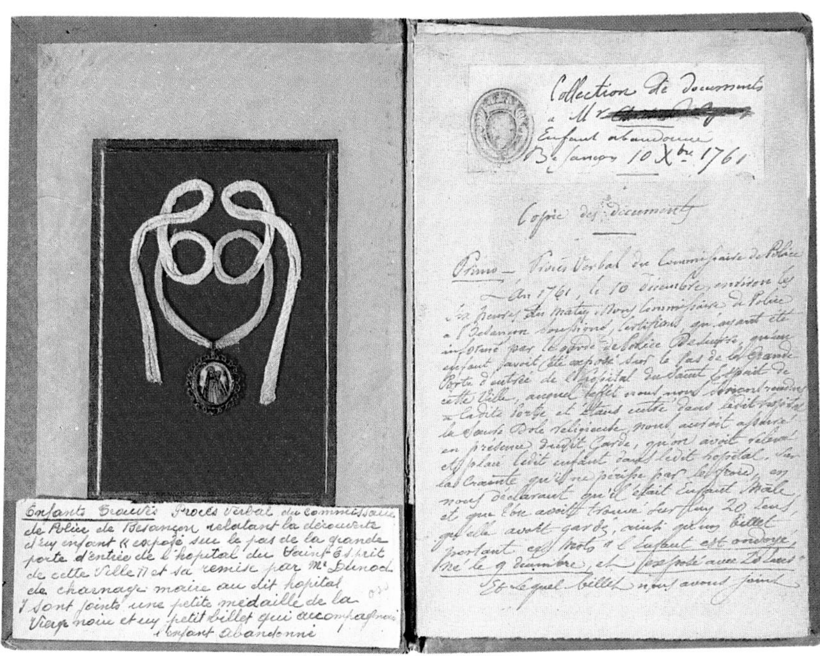

Medal and Document of Marie-Joseph, 1761
Born Dec. 9, found abandoned on the steps of Saint Esprit Hospital, Besançon, Dec. 10
L: 19 mm

By the twelfth century shelters had been established in France, including those in Marseilles, Montpellier, and Bordeaux. Support of these homes fluctuated with public opinion. Were they justified on the grounds that they reduced abortion and infanticide, or did they encourage promiscuity and irresponsibility? In 1365 the Bishop of Paris founded the Hospital of Saint Esprit for the care of foundlings; in 1445 Charles VII forbade the same hospital to admit foundlings, in the interest of customs and morals. In 1536 Francis I founded the House of Enfans-Rouges to raise the poor infants whose parents died at Hôtel Dieu. Five years later, by declaration it was ordered to receive also the infants, orphans, and poor of Paris and surrounding villages.[3] A history of the establishment of L'hôpital des Enfans Trouvés published in 1746, describes the first house run by a charitable lady, opened in 1638.[4] In no time the numbers were overwhelming, and servants developed a business selling the infants to beggars to incite the benevolence of the public, to wet nurses to keep up their milk supply or to substitute for a loss in a family, or to magicians to be used in their shows. Such people were usually unconcerned about baptism. The abuses were soon known and in the same year the hospice was moved and placed under the care of a person of piety. Because funds were limited and numbers great, they chose to raise the strong and abandoned the others. In 1640 Vincent de Paul, who believed in life for all, gathered a group of pious ladies who wished to care for abandoned children and established a foundling home in a castle given by the king.

St. Vincent de Paul
Clay, France, 17 C
Ht: 19.0 cm

Twice more the children were moved, until in 1670 L'hôpital des Enfans-Trouvés found a home where it still operated when this history was written. Its usefulness is seen in the numbers admitted: in 1670, 312; in 1745 more than ten times as many. By this latter date, Vincent de Paul had been made a saint and his name lives on today, connected with works of charity.

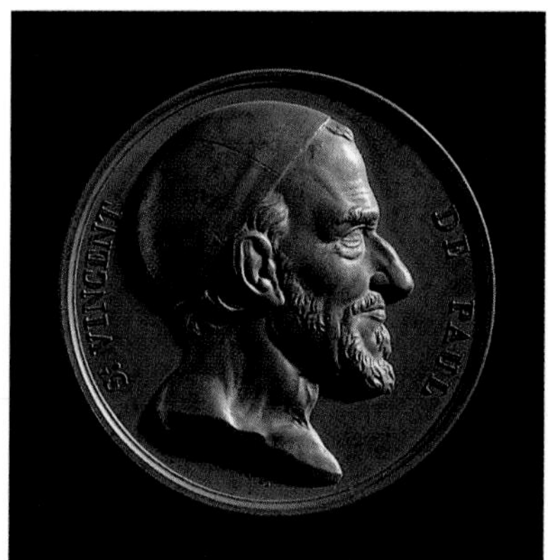

St. Vincent de Paul
Bronze medal
OBV: ST. VINCENT DE PAUL bust right
REV. (not shown): oak wreath around inscription
51 mm

St. Vincent de Paul
Coloured engraving by Auguste Alexandra
Boudran, fl. 1859–1866
After Claude Jacquand (1804–1878)
France
19.5 × 15.5 cm

Note 1640 on collection box

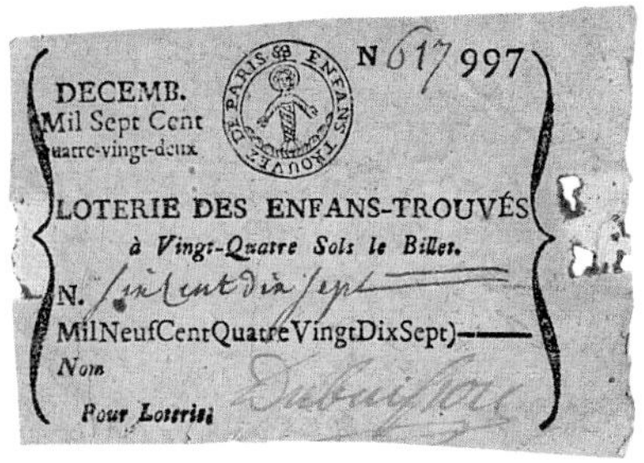

DECEMB.
Mil Sept Cent
uatre-vingt-deux
N 617997
LOTERIE DES ENFANS-TROUVÉS
à Vingt-Quatre Sols le Billet.
N.
MilNeufCentQuatreVingtDixSept)——
Nom
Pour Loterie

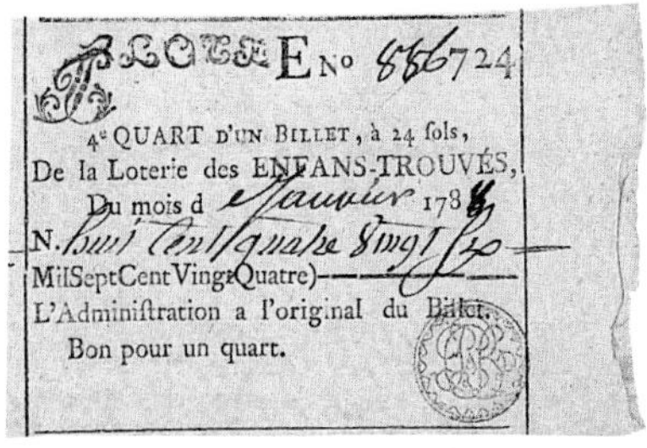

LOTERIE No 886724
4e QUART D'UN BILLET, à 24 fols,
De la Loterie des ENFANS-TROUVÉS,
Du mois d Janvier 178
N.
MilSeptCentVingtQuatre)——
L'Adminiftration a l'original du Billet.
Bon pour un quart.

Lottery tickets of 1782 and 1788

Reflecting the emphasis placed on baptism is a declaration of Louis XIV in 1698 and repeated in 1708, renewing an edict of Henry II, 1556. This stated that women who had concealed their pregnancy and the birth of a child who died must themselves die without receiving the holy sacrament.[5] One reason for leaving proof of identity with an abandoned child was to avoid such accusation.

In the interest of efficiency and better care for children, Louis XIV united the Foundling Hospital, the General Hospital, and the House of Enfans-Rouges. This Home in Paris grew rapidly; in 1780 there were 5600 admissions.[6] Though many infants were sent to wet nurses in the country, considerable numbers were raised in the hospital.

In a declaration of December 25, 1719, the King announced the continuation and extension of a five-percent sales tax levied in Paris and the suburbs for the benefit of the General Hospital and the Foundling Hospital, for a second four-year period.[7,8]

The view of a fund-raising publicity stunt by M. Coustard de Massi during an aerial show of June 24, 1784, shows the beneficiary, the Foundling Hospital, Paris, in the background. At the bottom of the picture are two addresses from which prints of the event may be purchased. Evidence of other efforts to raise funds for foundlings is seen in a variety of lottery tickets.

Les Enfans Trouvés [Foundlings]
Des and lith by Jean Henri Marlet
France, 1831
17.5 × 26.4 cm

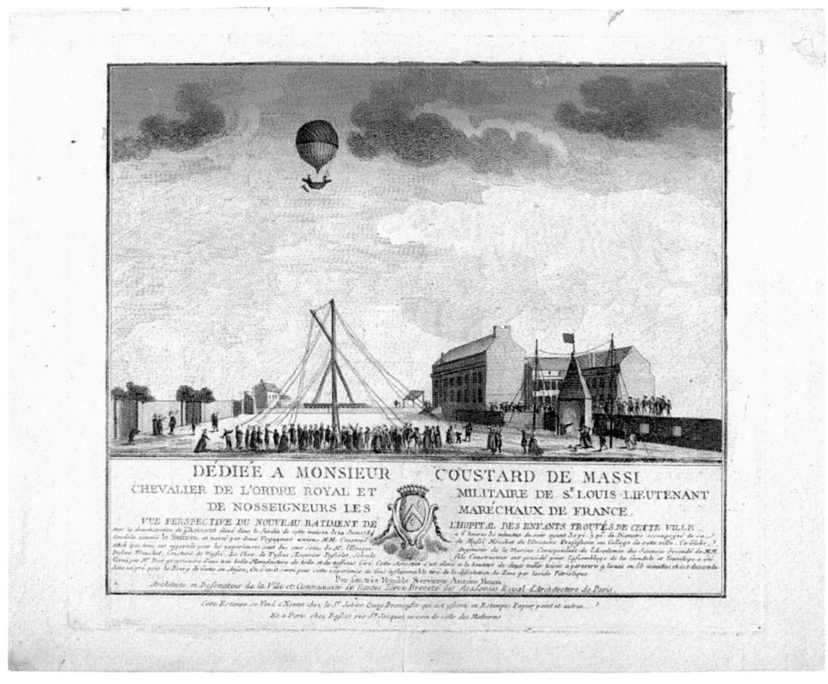

Fund-raising Aerial Show
[Dedicated to Mr. Coustard de Massi]
Coloured engraving by Fosseyeux
After Boissier
France, 1784
18.8 × 30.0 cm

In seventeenth-century France infant mortality was very high: more than 50 percent of infants died in the first year and almost 75 percent before the age of five. To try to improve this situation and to give protection to the wet nurses and in some cases to the parents, numerous edicts and regulations were issued during the seventeenth and eighteenth centuries. A copy of a law passed in 1667 governing the feeding of foundling children is in the Collection.[9] Following the revolution of 1789, very advanced infant welfare legislation was passed. A remarkable decree designed to cut the numbers of children abandoned by their parents begins: "Fathers and mothers who have as their only resources, the products of their labour, have a right to the nation's succour at all times that their earnings are not sufficient for the needs of their family."[10] Later concern for the lives of abandoned children is evident in a report of a plea to the Academy of Medicine of Paris, made by Theophile Roussel in 1891. He urged the Academy to do away with the tours, whose history revealed shockingly high death rates. In Rouen, for example, during the first half of the nineteenth century, a yearly average of 85 to 90 percent of infants left in tours died within a few days. Instead he recommended: (1) temporary assistance to mothers before and after delivery; (2) an open bureau without investigation and with professional secrecy, and (3) maternity homes with secrecy. Experience had shown that this resulted in more children being with their families, and the cost was less than the alternative wet nursing fees.[11] A certificate from the Commune of Nancy in 1798 exemplifies the keeping of statistics on abandoned children.

Indicative of the long-term follow-up in the supervision of the wards of hospices is a nineteenth-century Certificate of Origin (not shown) for foundlings and orphans, completed and signed by the Director of their institution and approved by the General Administration for public assistance. It states when the individual came to the hospital and that papers pertaining to his/her origin are in the hospital files. Such a document, in place of a birth certificate, was needed by minors who wished to marry. In this instance the director stated the circumstances of baptism; some might also vouch for the good life and morals of the person. The certificate is headed by a bust of St. Vincent de Paul.[12]

In England foundling hospitals were developed somewhat later than in France. During the Middle Ages responsibility for the care of the poor was assumed by religious institutions; these groups operated hospitals, asylums, and almshouses throughout England. Though most accommodated widows, orphans, and bedemen (church pensioners), some specified as well the care of exposed infants. Notable among these were St. Sepulchre, a daughter-house of St. Katharine's Asylum in London, and St. Leonard's in York.[13]

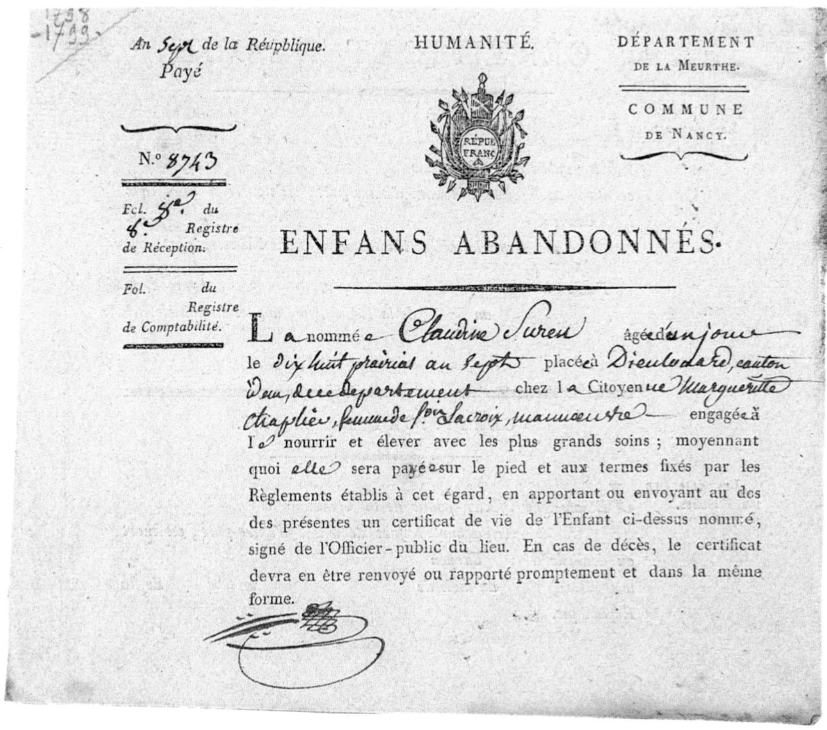

1798 -1799

An Sept de la République. HUMANITÉ. DÉPARTEMENT DE LA MEURTHE.

Payé

COMMUNE DE NANCY.

N.° 8743

Fol. 5e du 6e Registre de Réception.

Fol. du Registre de Comptabilité.

ENFANS ABANDONNÉS.

La nommée Claudine Suren âgée d'un jour le dix huit prairial an sept placée à Dieulouard, canton d'eau, de ce departement chez la Citoyenne Marguerite Chaplier, femme de Fois Lacroix, manoeuvre engagée à l'e nourrir et élever avec les plus grands soins ; moyennant quoi elle sera payée sur le pied et aux termes fixés par les Règlements établis à cet égard, en apportant ou envoyant au dos des présentes un certificat de vie de l'Enfant ci-dessus nommé, signé de l'Officier-public du lieu. En cas de décès, le certificat devra en être renvoyé ou rapporté promptement et dans la même forme.

Registration certificate of Claudine Suren, a one-day-old girl. It gives the district, the name of the woman who is to raise the child, guarantees her pay, and stipulates that, in case of death, the certificate must be returned promptly. The reverse side is a simple birth/death certificate to be signed by a secular authority.

As the population became more mobile and intimate ties with the parish church were weakened, many infants were simply abandoned. The impetus for reform came from the middle class. With deference to the prevailing belief "that a Multitude of Inhabitants is the greatest Strength and best Support for a Commonwealth," Dr. Cadogan[14] deplored Britain's lack of concern with the awful death rate among young children, as reflected in Graunt's *Bills of Mortality*.[15] He advocated improved nutrition and better care for children. His contemporary, the sea captain, Thomas Coram (1688–1751), went further. In his travels, Coram had seen the need for human labour in the expanding Empire, and he found abhorrent the spectacle common around London of infants deserted in the streets or murdered and flung on dunghills. Concerned, as was Cadogan, not with lost souls but with the waste of human life, Coram provided the initiative for starting a Foundling Hospital in London.

The Royal Charter granted in 1739 makes fascinating reading. The preamble describes on the one hand the helpless situation of countless infants born to be murdered, exposed, or trained in idleness, beggary, and theft, and on the other hand the existence of several legacies bequeathed to be paid to such an institution as Coram sought. The list of about 400 names of those anxious to lend their support as governors and guardians to such a hospital includes dukes, viscounts, lords, and others, among them William Hogarth,[16] whose Gin Lane series vividly depicts the depravity of the London poor.

The charter sets forth the officers of the corporation (John, Duke of Bedford to be the first president) and their administrative duties. A report of the General Committee (1740) outlines procedures for the "Reception, Maintenance and placing out of Children" as well as regulations for managing the hospital, all in great detail.

Portrait of Thomas Coram
Line engraving by J.W. Cook after Wm. Hogarth
England, mid 18 C
14.0 × 11.0 cm

Efforts of merchants during the reign of Queen Anne to start such a hospital had met with the same opposition previously expressed in France, on the basis that it "might seem to encourage Persons in Vice, by making too easy Provision for their illegitimate Children." But Coram's efforts received support from the beginning through legacies and private donations. A certificate was issued to identify authorized fund raisers, a print of which is in the Collection.[17] The cornerstone was laid in 1742, the building finished in 1752. Reference is made to admissions as early as 1741, in temporary quarters. By 1756 parliamentary support was needed, and with the use of public funds went the stipulation that no infants should be refused admission. Response was overwhelming: while admissions between 1741 and 1756 numbered 1384, admissions in the next year and a half were 5510, and in the succeeding year 4143. Many of the infants were diseased or starving, and the mortality rates were appalling (almost half). It is interesting to note that of the first 11,037 admitted, 44 returned to their parents.

Hospital token
Copper
OBV: FOUNDLING HOSPITAL
LAMBS CONDUIT FIELDS
COMPLETED 1741

REV: LONDON PENNY TOKEN
33 mm

Tokens struck in aid of the hospital building demonstrate the optimism of those who expected completion by 1741.

A Perspective View of the Foundling Hospital
[London] with Emblematic Figures
Coloured engraving by Grignion and Canot
after S. Vale
London, 14 April, 1749
34.0 × 42.3 cm

Myriads of Proselites sustain thy Cause,
Throng to thy Altars and obey thy Laws:
From hence, fair Venus, spring those sweet Supplys
To fill the Mansions which to thee arise.

These Mansions raised by Patrons kind & great,
Where Babes deserted find a safe Retreat.
Tho Frenchmen sneer; Their boasted first Design,
Brittish Benevolence shall far out shine.

To his grace John, Duke of Bedford, this photo is humbly inscribed.

By his grace's most grateful & obedient servant

Margrett Granville

An account of the hospital published in 1759 shows the tremendous concern and thought that went into both the spiritual and physical care of these children. Admission was carried out under strict security in compliance with the charter. Incredible care was taken to preserve the child's identity in secret, whether by means of a distinguishing mark or token, at the same time protecting his anonymity whilst a ward of the hospital.

Newcomers were registered, numbered, and baptized. Then, in accordance with Dr. Cadogan's preference, they could be sent to the country to a wet nurse. Inspectors were appointed to handle the arrangements, and money was provided for maintenance. A nurse was paid 1s 6d weekly in 1753, 2s if she provided clothing. Children were brought back to the hospital at age five for schooling.

It was in response to a request for help from the director of this hospital that Dr. Cadogan wrote his instructive essay on the management of children.[18] He was the physician for the hospital; while children were out with wet nurses they were to be fed and cared for according to Dr. Cadogan's directions. As for their care within the hospital this was described in detail in a report of the general committee.*

The strong emphasis placed on religion and spiritual matters as compared with physical and material well-being, is reflected in the allocation of pay: the Preacher, a guinea for each Sermon; the Reader, 40 pounds per annum (to read prayers in Chapel, baptize, bury, and teach the catechism); a nurse in the infirmary one pound yearly (more than a house nurse).[19]

The Account of 1759[20] bears the coat of arms accredited to Hogarth. When the hospital was completed Hogarth, a friend and supporter of Coram, organized his friends, among them Gainsborough and Reynolds, to decorate the walls with their art. "Moses Brought to Pharoah's Daughter" was painted by Hogarth, expressly for the hospital. An unexpected result of exhibiting art to raise funds for the institution was the founding of the Royal Academy in 1768.

Coat of Arms of London Foundling Hospital
(Attributed to Hogarth)
6.1 × 7.9 cm

*The report of the general committee included, among others, the following instructions for the care of children within the Foundling Hospital:
That such Children as have not had the Small Pox in the natural Way, be inoculated at Five Years old, in a proper Place out of the Hospital, Experience having fully evinced the Utility of this Practise by the Success which has attended the several Inoculations of the Children.

That at five Years old the Children be returned to the Hospital, and from that Time until they are six Years old, be taught to read, to learn the Catechism, Etc. and at proper Intervals exercised in the open Air, and employed in such a Manner as may contribute to their Health and induce a Habit of Activity, Hardiness and Labour.

That from six until they are apprenticed out, the Boys be employed in making Nets, spining of Packthred, Twine, and small Cordage, adapted to their several Ages and Strength; and that they mend their own Cloaths, Stockings, etc.

That the Boys be sent to Sea or Husbandry, except so many as may be necessary to be employed in the Garden belonging to the Hospital. It is intended to enlarge the Garden, in such a Manner as to supply the House and Parts adjacent with Vegetables, and to afford the means of instructing Boys in Gardening, to fit them for the service of such Persons, as may incline to take them for the Purpose.

That from six Years of Age the Girls be employed in common Needlework, Knitting and Spinning, in the Kitchen, Laundry, and Household work, in order to make them useful Servants, to such proper Persons as may apply for them, except so many as may be necessary to be employed in the Hospital. It is intended that all the Female Servants in the Hospital, shall be Persons brought up therein.

That the Boys be kept separate from the Girls, and never permitted to have intercourse together, either in their Employment, Diet, or Diversions.

That the Diet allowed to the Children be plain and simple, as small Broth, Porridge and Milk; Meat and Vegetables alternately, their Bread Coarse, and their Drink Water.

That their Diversions be innocent, active, and requiring Exercise; that all Games of Chance, Swearing, indecent Language or Behaviour, be strictly prohibited, and severely punished.

That the Children do constantly attend Divine Service in the Chapel on SUNDAYS, and that the Officers, etc. of the Hospital, do often remind them of their Duty.

An Account of the Hospital for the Maintenance and Education of Exposed and Deserted Young Children. London, 1759.

The chapel was erected in 1747 at a total cost of 6490 pounds, of which George II gave 2000 pounds; the balance was raised by public subscription. George F. Handel volunteered to give a concert in May, 1749, the funds to be used to finish the chapel, specifically to provide the windows and furnishings. This performance is described in ***Gentleman's Magazine*** of that month:

> The Prince and Princess of Wales, with a great number of persons of quality and distinction, were at the Chapel of the Foundling Hospital, to hear several pieces of vocal and instrumental music composed by George Frederick Handel, Esq., for the benefit of the foundation. 1st. The music of the late Fire Works, and the anthem on the Peace; 2nd. Select pieces from the oratorio of Solomon, relating to the dedication of the temple; and 3rd. Several pieces composed for the occasion, the words taken from Scripture, applicable to the charity and its benefactors. There was no collection, but the tickets were at half-a-guinea, and the audience above a thousand.

John Brownlow: *The Foundling Hospital*, 1847.

More than 100 performers took part, the majority being the foundlings themselves. The finale of the concert included "The Foundling's Hymn" (see p. 111). For his benevolence, Handel was enrolled as one of the Governors and Guardians of the Hospital.

Gold Medal
OBV: I KNOW THAT MY REDEEMER LIVETH
G.F. HANDEL around bust left
REV: FOR ITS DECAY'E WIDOWS AND ORPHANS
around BENEVOLENT CHORAL FUND
INSTITUTED 1791

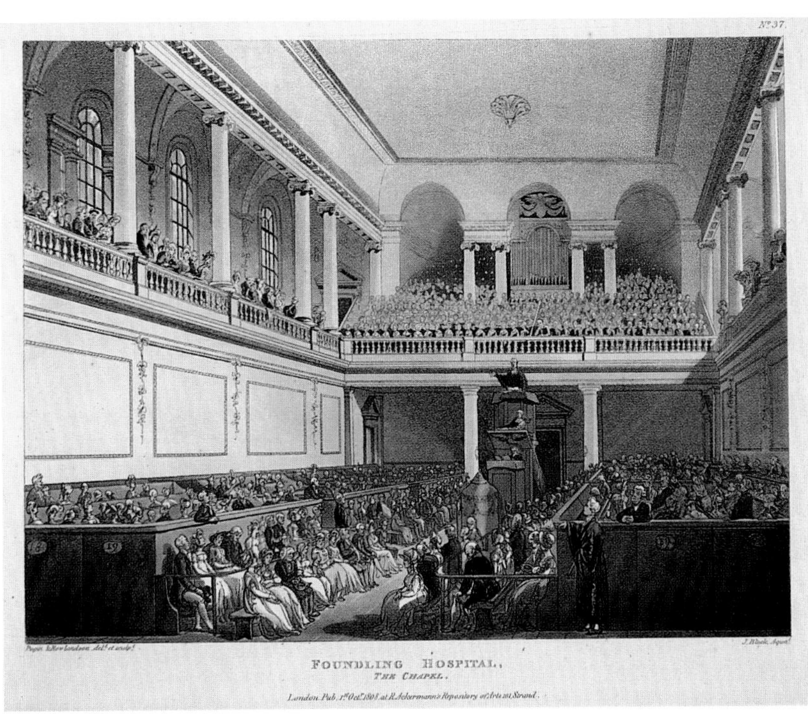

Foundling Hospital, the Chapel
Aquatint by J. Bluck after Pugin and Rowlandson, London 1808
19.4 × 25.5 cm

On May Day the following year Handel dedicated the organ that he had presented to the chapel, with a performance of his oratorio, "The Messiah." Subsequent yearly concerts netted the treasury of the charity 7000 pounds, an extraordinary amount for the time, and rewarded the composer/concert master with a popularity previously unknown to him. At the same time we must not overlook the benefits derived by the children raised there, from such a musical experience.* Handel left to the hospital in his will, a fair copy of the score of "The Messiah." A bust of him is on a gold medal struck for the benefit of the hospital.

L'institution des Jeunes Aveugles
[The Institution for Blind Youth]
By Hippolyte Lefebvre, 1909
Bronze
OBV: Blind girl knocking on door
REV: Four women and girl seated
80 × 69 mm

By 1758 the Foundling Hospital in London was so crowded that arrangements were made to establish county hospitals for at least 100 children each. Once the economics, administration, and admission policies of all these hospitals settled into a routine, few changes were made. Alterations were in accordance with modern progress: better accommodation, improvements in the health care of the children, and more attention to their future careers.

In the twentieth century, overcrowding at the London hospital brought another crisis and the institution was moved from Bloomsbury to Berkamsted (1935). Many items from the old hospital, including Handel's organ, were incorporated into the new building.[21]

The home at Berkamsted was neither happy nor successful, and the number of boarders by 1954 had fallen to 50. These children were dispersed to foster homes. In 1955 the Thomas Coram Foundation for Children was incorporated, which enabled the authorities to branch out into ventures more suited to the times. These include Coram's Children's Centre, and Adoption and Adolescent Projects.

Attention was also given to other needy groups in whose midst were possibly some foundlings. A proposal for an asylum for deaf and dumb children of the poor, to relieve "families and to render those useful who otherwise would be a burden to society," was outlined in 1792.[22] It was considered "an undertaking worthy of the British character." Christian religion was central to the plan that acknowledged the incorporation of the principles outlined in 1653 by Dr. Wallis for the instruction of such children. Similar asylums already existed in Paris and elsewhere.

A medal of a much later date provides evidence of assistance to the blind in France. It shows a girl led by a dog, knocking on the door of "L'Institution des Jeunes Aveugles"; the reverse shows the welcome within.

The practice of striking medals to raise funds for, and to commemorate, special projects was widespread. The Orphans Hospital founded by Catherine II of Russia (1763), the Royal Infirmary for Children in London (1820), the Jewish Orphanage at Amsterdam (1866) and the French Orphanage at St. Petersburg (1897) were among the many.

*A similar situation existed in Venice where Vivaldi (1669–1741) was concert master at L'hôpital de Pieta, the Foundling Hospital for girls. Being the instructor of the choir gave him the opportunity to work over his own compositions.

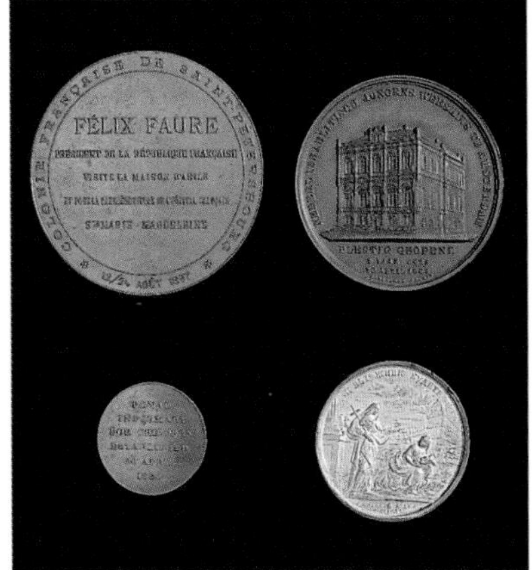

Medals struck for children's orphanages/hospitals

OBV:

Upper left: French Orphanage, St. Petersburg, Russia, 1897
Woman seated with three children, above shield bearing 1817–1897, hospital at right
Bronze, 79 mm

Upper right: Jewish Boys' Orphanage, Amsterdam, 1866,
Raising Orphans (in Hebrew) around seated woman with two children
Bronze, 70 mm

Lower left: Royal Infirmary, London, 1820
Hygeia with staff of Asclepios giving chalice to seated mother with three children
Bonze, 37 mm

Lower right: Orphans' Hospital, Russia, 1763
By the grace of God Catherine II Empress and autocrat of all Russia (in Russian) around bust right
White metal, 52 mm

REV:

Upper left: COLONIE FRANÇAISE DE SAINT-PETERSBOURG 12/24 AOÛT 1897 around FÉLIX FAURE PRÉSIDENT DE LA RÉPUBLIQUE FRANÇAISE VISITE LA MAISON D'ASILE ET POSE LA PREMIÈRE PIERRE DE L'HÔPITAL FRANÇAISE STE. MARIE-MAGDELEINE
[French colony of St. Petersburg 12/24 August 1897 around Felix Faure President of the French Republic visits the House of Refuge and lays the first stone of the French hospital Ste. Marie-Magdeleine]

Upper right: NEDERL. ISRAELISCH JONGENS WEESHUIS TE AMSTERDAM around hospital
PLEGTIG GEOPEND [Solemnly opened]
4 IJAR 5625
30 APRIL 1866

Lower left: ROYAL INFIRMARY FOR CHILDREN ESTABLISHED 26 APRIL, 1820

Lower right: and you will be alive the first day of September of the year 1763 (in Russian) around religious figure offering help to a mother and infant, hospital in background, right.

Toward the end of the nineteenth century a man emerged whose attitudes were similar to Thomas Coram's in the mid-eighteenth century. This was Thomas Barnardo. Deeply concerned about the numbers of destitute waifs in London, he established a home for them in 1870, the first of many. In 1882 he sent a group of children to Canada to begin a new life and by the 1890s more than 10,000 young "Barnardo" boys and girls were in Canada. Shelters were established for some; private homes were found for others. When supervision was poor or lacking, some children were grossly mistreated. Others were happy and did well. Such children continued to come to Canada into the twentieth century, and a few are alive to tell their stories. Barnardo homes still exist in Britain, Australia, and New Zealand.

LE RECONNAISSEZ-VOUS ?

Pour Elle
Paris, August 14, 1940

Wars are responsible for orphans in large numbers. A medal solicits help for orphans of personnel of the First World War. A 1940 copy of *Pour Elle* is a reminder of the thousands who lost trace of their families during the Second World War. It contains 38 pictures and descriptions accompanied by pleas for identification and location of family members. One moving article by a thankful mother, is entitled "J'ai retrouvé mon enfant" [I have found my child again].

Few children are abandoned nowadays in the manner of earlier times. But infants are born who are turned over to child welfare agencies: some are destined to be raised in a series of foster homes; some are adopted into families. Where children are known to be abused, they are removed from their parents, temporarily or permanently if the situation cannot be improved. The stigma attached to illegitimacy is much less than in the past[23] and many single mothers raise a child alone, by choice.

War orphan's medal
Bronze
OBV: L'OEUVRE DE PROTECTION DES ORPHELINS DE LA GUERRE DU PERSONNEL DES P.T.T. [The Society for the Protection of War Orphans]

REV: (not shown) 1914–1918 Tribute to war orphans of army personnel

65 × 52 mm

Notes

1. Aucoc [after 1811]
2. Spedale degli Innocente *[Hospital of the Innocents]* was one of the first classical structures of the Renaissance. Toward the end of a decade when malnutrition caused high mortality in the hospice, the spandrels of the arcade were decorated with enamelled terra cotta rondels by Andrea della Robbia (1487); children with outstretched arms appeal for support. (John Pope-Hennessy, The Healing Arts, *FMR America* no. 8, pp. 120-127, Franco Maria Ricci International Inc., New York).
3. Aucoc [after 1811].
4. Abregé Historique de l'établissement de l'Hôpital des Enfans-Trouvés, Paris, 1746 (960.1.1003).
5. Declaration du Roy, Feb. 25, 1708 (960.1.1277).
6. Aucoc [after 1811].
7. Declaration du Roy, Paris, 25 December, 1719 (960.1.1009)
8. Contrary to government policy today, wines and liquors were the only commodities exempted from this tax.
9. Arrest de la Cour de Parlement, touchant le nourriture des Enfants trouvés, Paris, 1667 (960.1.1274).
10. Décrit de la Convocation Nationale du 28 Juin 1793, l'an second de la Republique Française, Relatif à l'organisation des Secours à accorder annuellement aux Enfans, aux Vieillards et aux Indigens (960.1.1078).
11. Roussel, Théophile, Dépopulation de la France, *Le Tour*, Extrait du *Bulletin de l'Académie de Médecine*, Paris, April 14, 1891 (960.1.1361).
12. Enfants Trouvés et Orphelins Certificat d'Origine (960.1.1371).
13. Clay 1909.
14. Cadogan 1748:6.
15. Graunt 1676.
16. *Foundling Hospital, London*, 1739 Royal Charter Establishing an Hospital for the Maintenance and Education of Exposed and Deserted Young Children. London; Osborn, 1739 [Oct. 17]
17. Print TDPA 129.
18. Dr. Cadogan ended his treatise by telling the governors of the Foundling Hospital to publish it if they felt it would be of any use, adding: "I deliver it up as a *Foundling* to be disposed of as you think proper." (Cadogan 1748:34).
19. *Foundling Hospital, London*, 1759, An Account of the Hospital for the Maintenance and Education of Exposed and Deserted Young Children.
20. An account of the Hospital for the Maintenance and Education of Exposed and Deserted Young Children. London, 1759.
21. Nichols and Wray 1935.
22. *Plan of the Asylum for the Deaf and Dumb Children of the Poor,* [London], 1792, 4.
23. In Ontario the distinction between legitimate and illegitimate children has been removed (Children's Law Reform Act, R.S.O. 1980, ch 68).

Dr. Drake's own rattle
Includes whistle, teething ring and bells
Silver, heavily embossed and engraved
Birmingham, 1890
L:10.1 cm

Note the original use of bells was less to amuse the baby, more to frighten away the evil spirits.

AMULETS AND MAGIC MEDICINE

The folly and vanitie of Art Magicke I have oftentimes already taxed and confuted sufficiently...and still my purpose and intention is to discover and lay open the abuse thereof... And yet...the argument is such as deserveth a large and ample discourse, if there were but this only to enduce me, That notwithstanding it be of all arts fullest of fraud, deceit, and cousenage, yet never was there any throughout the whole world either with like credit professed, or so long time upheld & maintained.

C. Plinius Secundus [Pliny]. *The Historie of the World.* 1635: Vol 1, Book 30, p. 371.

If there be any suspition of sorcerie, witchcraft, or inchantment practised for to hurt young babes, the great horns of beetles, such specially as be knagged [gnarled] as it were with smal teeth, are as good as a countercharm and preservative, if they be hanged about their necks.

Ibid, p. 398

What makes the sun rise? the wind blow? rivers flow? fire burn? crops grow? The Ancients explained these and other natural phenomena by assigning a god or spirit to each. Later many concepts such as health and prosperity were aligned with various gods. Religion entered into all aspects of life; it coloured thinking and influenced every action. Magic, religion, and medicine merged in the primitive mind; spirits caused sickness. Amulets, as symbols of the gods, were the tangible link with the supernatural world. They were believed to be endowed with magic powers of protection and were worn by the living, buried with the dead, and placed strategically in buildings. Infants and small children, because they were particularly defenseless, were considered most in need of amulets.

In his *Historie of the World* written in the first century, Pliny discussed at some length the case for and against "Art Magicke." He deplored the frauds but was not averse to recommending amulets in many circumstances; this ambivalence is demonstrated in the quotes above. His work had a profound influence into the eighteenth century.

Francis Herring in the seventeenth century advised against amulets and other magic lest more effective remedies be neglected.[1] As the Age of Reason progressed, superstitions, although never dying out, played a smaller role in people's lives, particularly among the educated. Yet the "Vinegar of the Four Thieves," for use against the plague, was still listed in the *British Pharmacopoeia*, into the twentieth century.[2]

The largest single group of amulets in Dr. Drake's Collection (in excess of 300 pieces) is comprised of ancient Egyptian gods and their symbols. During the more than 3000 years that this great civilization flourished, there were many changes in beliefs, but two prime controlling influences of life, the sun and the Nile, remained constant. The Egyptians developed a complex hierarchy of gods and goddesses headed by the great sun god Ra, who had the body of a man and the head of a hawk, crowned by the disc of the sun circled by a serpent. In the beginning the Pharoah was believed to be the physical son and earthly embodiment of Ra; at death he joined him in the sky. Expectation of an afterlife gradually spread through society until by the eighteenth century BC, a time of general upheaval, such hopes were shared by all. According to belief, the spirit, freed from the body by death, sought some tangible form in which to dwell; hence developed the process of mummification and the use in tombs of paintings and sculptures depicting the deceased in the life he hoped to continue in the afterworld. A.W. Shorter claimed that the Egyptians recognized three classes in the universe: men, gods, and the dead.[3] Particular emphasis was placed on the last group.

Dr. Drake's favourite piece was the bronze figure of Isis with Horus in the classic mother and child pose. She usually wears a crown composed of a solar disc held between cow's horns, symbols of fertility and birth. As well as other bronze examples, there are in the Collection several of polished stone and faience, 1000–200 BC. Isis had many qualities as a healing and protective mother goddess; she was the consort of Osiris, a legendary king, who according to Plutarch was a religious teacher, framer of laws, and instructor in architecture. He was best known as Osiris, Lord of Eternity, and was depicted holding a flail and a crook in his arms, with the royal cobra, Uraeus, on his crown. His death and resurrection were symbolized by the Nile's cycle. According to legend Osiris was murdered by his evil brother, Seth, and brought back to life by Isis through her magic power. The crime was avenged by Horus, son of Osiris and Isis, in a fight with Seth in which Horus lost an eye. Thoth, the great Healer, restored the eye. This ibis-headed deity, the mind and tongue of Ra, was the god of wisdom and medicine. He was credited with inventing writing and producing magical and religious books that contained spells and incantations for exorcising evils that caused disease.

Bronze figures, Egypt
Left: Isis and Horus
500 BC
Ht: 19.0 cm

Centre: Uraeus
500 BC

Right: Osiris
1000 BC

Through the dynasties of Egypt texts were compiled to deal with ritual and magic, particularly as they affected death and burial. Pyramid texts of the Old Kingdom, augmented by coffin texts of the Middle Kingdom and the *Book of the Dead* in the New Kingdom, told how to minister to the dead to ensure an afterlife. Belief in the power of the written word was strong, and knowledge of the texts was thought to be essential to the soul's successful passage to the next world. Chapters of the texts were inscribed on the walls of tombs, later inside the coffins. With the advent of writing on papyrus, copies of the texts could be buried with the dead.

Osiris, Thoth, and Anubis, god of embalming, were the principal deities involved in the elaborate rites that were a part of the funerary cult. Small figures called "ushabtis" were placed in tombs to act as servants in the afterlife.

Thoth carving name of King Fuad
Egypt, 107
April, 1925

Ushabtis
Faience, ca. 500 BC
Ht: right, 3.8 cm

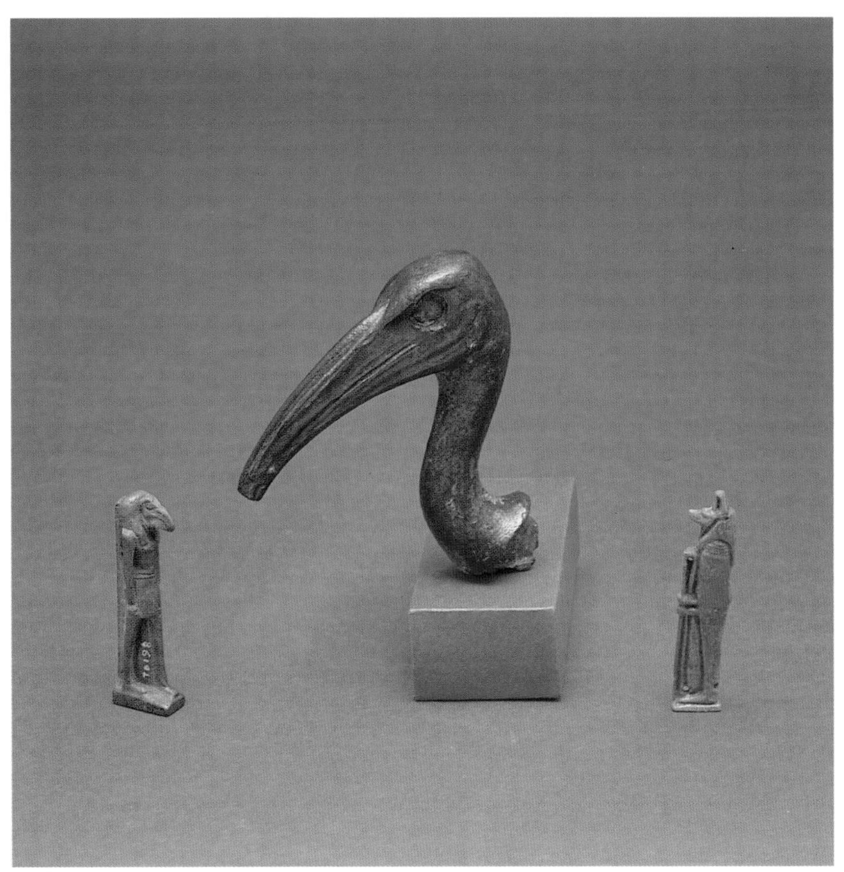

Egyptian gods
Left: Thoth, faience, 1000 BC

Centre: Ibis head, bronze, 1000 BC, Ht: 10.3 cm

Right: Anubis, faience, 500 BC

Preservation of the body from decay was supremely important because to the Egyptians this meant triumph over death and assurance of an afterlife. In the embalming procedure most vital organs were removed and stored in canopic jars; the heart, which was believed to be the centre of mind and emotion, was left in the thoracic cavity, and a scarab was placed on the breast of the mummy. The scarab beetle had particular significance. As perceived by the Egyptians, the dung beetle's struggle to roll its ball of dung along the earth was symbolic of the progress of the life-giving sun being rolled across the sky. This insect was reproduced in many materials and with various decorations to serve as both amulet and seal. Small examples were pierced for a wire ring and worn on the finger of the living or dead.

Eye of Horus
Egypt, 221
Dec. 8, 1937

Other amulets were placed on different parts of the body and wrapped in position or put beside the mummy in graves or tombs. The Eye of Horus was important to protect against the Evil Eye and to enable the deceased to see out of the coffin. A papyrus sceptre of faience, was believed to protect the mummy against crushing injuries; a headrest, to ensure that the head did not get severed from the body; a carnelian snakehead, to ward off snake bites and bleeding. *The Book of the Dead* directed that a Djed be placed on the neck of the mummy for stability and duration. The Sma representing the windpipe and lungs, was placed on the umbilicus to guarantee healthy breathing.

Eye of Horus
Faience, stone and carnelian, ca. 500 BC
Upper left: 4.6 cm

Amulets, Egypt
Clockwise from upper left:
1. Papyrus sceptre, faience ca. 500 BC
   Ht: 5.1 cm
2. Headrest, haematite, ca. 1000 BC
3. Djeds, feldspar and faience, 730–715 BC
4. Snake head, carnelian, ca. 1500 BC
5. Sma, obsidian

Scarabs, Egypt

Clockwise from centre left:

1. Pottery, girl holding ankh on reverse
2. Stone heart scarab, 500 BC
3. Child's scarab inscribed "Pa Sheri" [the child], 1300–1200 BC, very rare
4. Feldspar heart scarab with traces of gold, 400 BC, l: 5.7 cm
5. Mottled stone, 800–500 BC
6. Ivory, stone and faience scarabs/seals pierced for wearing
7. As above, blue faience

Except to watch an occasional procession, the peasants had little to do with the great gods and formalized religion. The latter was the domain of the priests. In their houses the common folk turned to Bes, a dwarf with feathered head-dress who was the god of children, dances, music, and games, and to Ta-Urt, a strange composite of the lion, crocodile, and hippopotamus, the goddess of childbirth and nursing mothers. There are more than 30 examples of each of these household amulets in the Collection.

Ptah-Sokar, an achondroplastic dwarf who was venerated as the creator of the universe, healer of the sick, and god of handicrafts, was the patron of workmen and artisans. According to *The Book of the Dead*, Ptah-Sokar had the power to reconstruct the decaying bodies of the dead—hence the presence in graves of many amulets like the earthenware examples shown, ca. 1000–100 BC. It is claimed that the first temple erected in Egypt was built in Memphis for Ptah to celebrate his miraculous cures. Remedies were revealed to supplicants in dreams during temple sleep or incubation, a practice also prevalent in Greek healing sanctuaries.

Ptah-Sokar,
Faience
Left: protected by Isis, 500 BC
Ht: 7.3 cm

Centre: 100 BC

Right: 1000 BC

Bes
Faience, 300–200 BC
Ht: centre, 3.7 cm

Ta-Urt
Left: Carnelian, 300 BC

Others: Faience, 500 BC

Note back view with wings of Isis for protection

Architect to King Zoser of the third dynasty (2780 BC) when the oldest pyramids were constructed, Imhotep was a sage, admired during his lifetime and revered as an equal of the gods after his death. His concern for sciences and the occult led to his becoming patron of doctors and ultimately demigod of medicine. He was celebrated for miraculous cures. He is shown here, a seated figure with a priest's shaved head and a scroll open on his lap.

Min, an Egyptian deity of fertility and abundant harvests, was worshipped from earliest times.

Just as important as encouraging virility and fertility was belief in the power of phallic symbols to ward off the Evil Eye and protect against sorcery. Whether the evil spirits were turned away by a sight so repellent or whether they were fascinated by the amulet, the result to the wearer would have been the same.

Imhotep
Bronze, ca. 300 BC
Ht: 5.1 cm

Phallic symbols, Egypt
Left: Clay

Right: Faience, 100 BC
L: 3.8 cm

Min
Bronze, 500 BC
Ht: 21.3 cm

A group of bronze fetishes includes an Etruscan stick-like man and three figures from Luristan: a grotesque horned manikin and possibly his mate, a female with the same horned head, and a small figure of indeterminate sex. Of particular interest is the bronze man of an earlier date, found in Italy, probably from Syracuse.

Roman phallic symbols of bronze, ca. AD 100 are shown with an Italian example of much later date. Also from Roman times are two fists, one from Egypt, and one from Palestine, each with the thumb placed between the index and the next finger. This sign is still used among prostitutes for soliciting. Roman lamps decorated with erotic scenes were no doubt aphrodisiacs of the time.

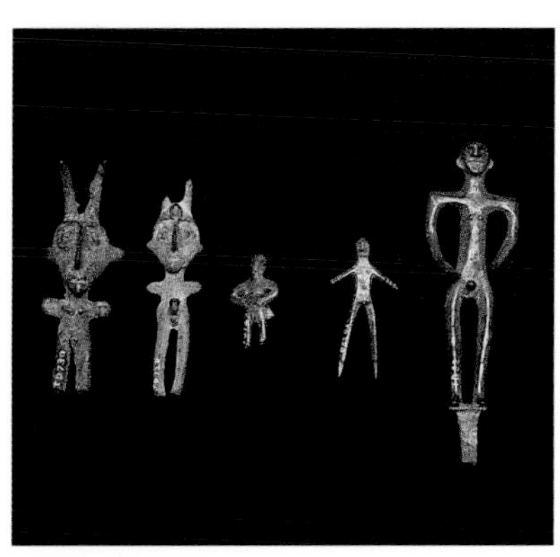

Bronze fetishes
From left to right:
1, 2, 3. Luristan, Persia
8–4 C BC
Ht: left, 8.4 cm
4. Perugia, Italy (Etruscan)
7–6 C BC
5. Syracuse, Sicily
6 C BC

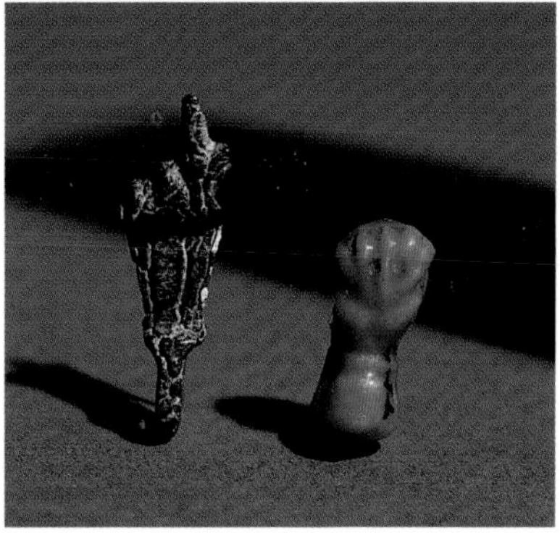

Phallic fists
Left: Bronze, Palestine AD 2 C
Right: Faience, Roman Egypt, AD 1 C
L: 2 cm

Pottery lamps
Roman, ca. AD 100
Diam: left, 7.6 cm
Right: a miniature/toy

Phallic symbols
Bronze
Upper: left and centre, Roman, ca. AD 100
Others: Italy, 17 C
L: centre, 4.7 cm

A group of Egyptian amulets pertains to female fertility and to birthing: the Aegis of Isis; the Crown of Isis; the Buckle of the Girdle of Isis, and the Triad of Nephthys, Isis, and Horus. Nephthys whose name means "mistress of the temple," was one of Horus' wet nurses. She was the goddess of death and, like her sister Isis, was a healing divinity endowed with magical skills and words of power.

Also from Egypt, small, bronze relic boxes, ca. 1000 BC, with a serpent, shrew-mouse, or lizard on top had small bones or ashes within and were probably votive gifts left at a temple to acquire merit. To facilitate childbirth a snakebox or a frog lamp was often placed in the delivery room; the frog or toad symbolized Heqt, the goddess of birth and fecundity. In Persia, representation of the convolutions of the intestines was also believed to ease the pain of childbirth.

Female fertility amulets
Aegis of Isis
Bronze, 1000 BC and 200 BC

Crown of Isis
Bronze, ca. 500 BC
Ht: right, 8.0 cm

Female fertility amulets
The Buckle of the Girdle of Isis
Jasper, ca. 400 BC
Carnelian, ca. 500 BC
Ht: 5.5 cm

Triad of Nephthys, Isis, and Horus
Faience, 500 BC
Ht: right, 4.5 cm

Relic boxes
Serpent
Lizard
Shrewmouse, l: 5.7 cm
Bronze, ca. 1000 BC

Childbirth amulets
Frog lamps, clay
Egypt, AD 200–400
L: 8.5 cm

Convoluted intestines, metal
Luristan, Persia, 500 BC
L: 6.7 cm

A most interesting obstetrical amulet is the eaglestone, supposedly obtained from the nest of the king of the birds. Traditionally it was thought that eagles took stones to their nests to facilitate egg-laying. An eaglestone worn at the waist during pregnancy kept the fetus from aborting, and strapped to the leg when the baby was due, facilitated delivery. It then had to be removed quickly lest it draw out other organs. Pliny wrote about it in the first century:

Eaglestone
Ireland, 17C
Diam. 4.5 cm

> The aegle stone called Aetites because it is found in an Aegle's nest preserveth and holdeth the infant still in the mothers womb to the ful time, against any indirect practise of sorcery or otherwise, to the contrary.[4]

Belief in its effectiveness lasted many centuries. The example here has a seventeenth-century silver mount with two loops and was found in Ireland. Writing at that time, Nicholas Culpeper explained:

> For its Use: This stone being hung about the Neck of a Woman with Child, so that it touch the Skin, preserves the Child in her Body, till the time of her Delivery come:...What makes the Birth easy...The Stone Aetites; held to the Privities instantly draws away both Child and After-burden; yea, draws out Womb and all, if you remove it not instantly after they are come away...[5]

It is said that John D. Rockefeller carried an eaglestone in his pocket for protection against shipwreck, disease, and other calamities.[6]

Amongst the rare books is a very old text, *La Vie de Madame Saincte Marguerite*, written about 1500. She was considered to be the patron saint of pregnant women, and merely placing this eight-page volume on the abdomen during labour was believed to produce a rapid, easy delivery.

Other cultures had mother goddesses who embodied the reproductive energies of nature and possessed characteristics similar to Isis. In Greece it was Demeter: according to legend the disappearance of her daughter to the underworld, and her return, accounted for the changing seasons. This gave rise to the elaborate festivals that climaxed in the Eleusinian Mysteries, the greatest celebration in the Greek calendar.

> In Greek mythology, Demeter and Persephone were mother and daughter. Persephone was carried off by Pluto to the underworld, and Demeter forbade the corn to grow until her child was returned; she went to Eleusis to await her arrival. Zeus, king of the gods, ruled that Persephone should spend two-thirds of her time above ground with her mother, and one-third in the netherworld. Thus, each September when crops were harvested, the rites and mysteries as first revealed by Demeter at Eleusis were celebrated. Faith in the recurring cycle of growth and harvest gave hope of an afterlife. Part of the festival's great appeal lay in the promise of happiness beyond the grave for those initiated into the sacred Mysteries.[7]

Shown with Demeter is Artemis of Ephesus (Diana to the Romans), characterized by multiple breasts. In her capacity as moon goddess she also presided over childbirth. Ishtar was the Assyro-Babylonian goddess of love and voluptuousness. As a member of her cult, every woman had a religious duty to prostitute herself to a stranger at the sacred sanctuary, and the wages thus earned were dedicated to the goddess. The late Isis/Ishtar figure shows crosscultural influences.

Terra cotta figures of goddesses
Artemis/Diana
Syracuse, Sicily, ca. 500 BC

Ishtar
Asia, 1000 BC

Isis/Ishtar
Egypt, AD 1 C – 2 C

Demeter
Boeotia, Greece, 500 BC
Ht: 23.5 cm

In ancient societies children, if considered at all, were depicted as small adults. However, the Greeks in their rare portrayals showed them plump and carefree, playing with games, toys, and pets, and wearing minimal clothing with a cord, which hung from one shoulder across to the opposite hip. To this cord amulets were attached, a favourite being a bell for protection against the Evil Eye. The custom was followed in many lands.

A painting by Velázquez shows an early seventeenth-century child with amulets, including a bell, hanging from one chain across the breast and another around the waist (see cover).

Some of the most delightful objects from the Ancient World are pieces of children's jewellery. Necklaces, rings, and bracelets had a more important function than adornment: magic power was attributed to the material and design. Gold and precious stones were much prized, and those that were unusual in markings, shape, or texture, were deemed more effective than plain ones. "Evil spirits were pleased with the sight of the rare and the beautiful and mitigated their attack accordingly."[8]

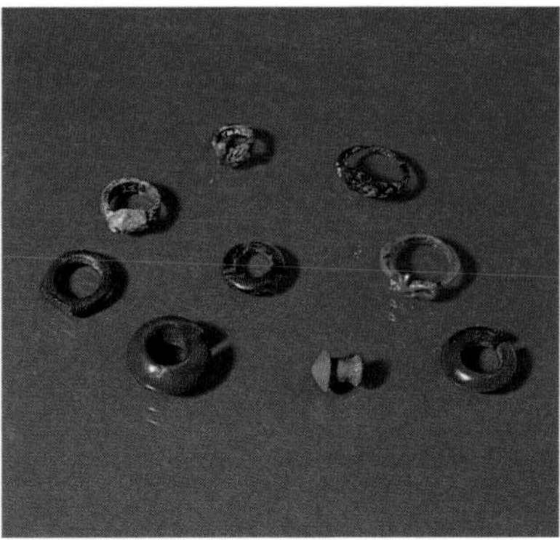

Ancient Egyptian and Roman jewellery
Clockwise from left:
1: Carnelian ring, Egypt, 300 BC
2: Faience ring, frog bezel, Egypt, 300 BC
3: Faience ring, Ta-Urt bezel, Egypt, 300 BC
4: Bronze ring, Roman Palestine
5: Faience ring, Eye of Horus bezel, Egypt, 1580–1380 BC
6: Carnelian earrings, Egypt, ca. 1000 BC
7: Faience ear stud, Egypt, 500 BC
8: Carnelian earrings, Egypt, ca. 1000 BC
9: Centre: Carnelian earring, Egypt, ca. 1000 BC

Bell amulets
Clockwise from upper left:
Clay, Greek, found in Italy, 200 BC
Ht: 7.0 cm
Bronze, Italy, 200 BC
Bronze, Pompeii, AD 1 C
Bronze, Palestine, AD 100–200
Bronze, Palestine, AD 100–200

The finely crafted gold earrings and delicate chain bracelets from ancient Cyprus, must have been prized possessions. Glass bracelets from Roman Palestine are now encrusted with a lovely iridescence, the result of being buried in sand for 16 centuries. A later iron bracelet, also from Egypt, is quite different; an earlier bronze armlet is from Luristan, Persia. Bronze fibulae (brooches) were useful, rather than amuletic, pieces. The equivalent of modern safety pins, they have changed little in design over the centuries.

Bronze fibulae
Left: Athens, 800–700 BC
L: 3.6 cm

Right: Italy, 150 BC

Metal jewellery
Left: Iron bracelet
Egypt, AD 400
Diam: 5.1 cm

Right: Bronze armlet
Luristan, Persia, 500 BC

Bracelets
Glass, Roman Palestine,
AD 250–300
Diam: 5.3 cm

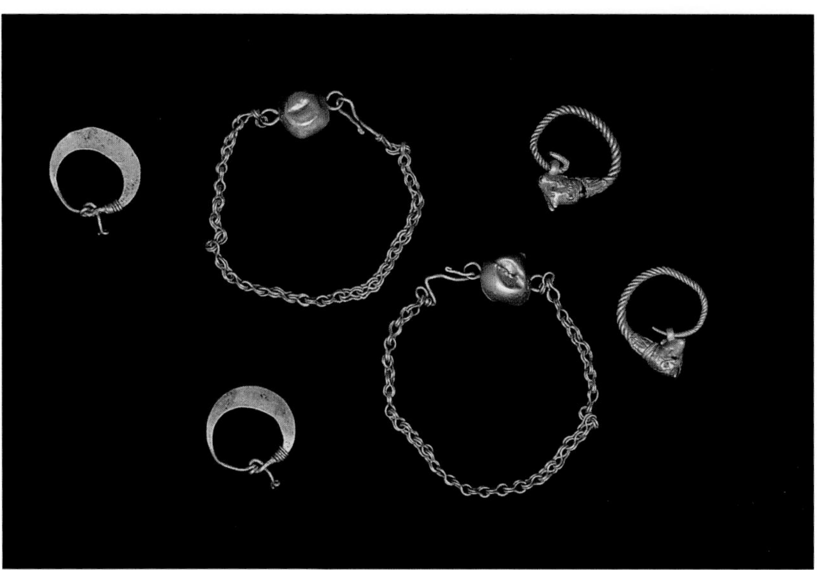

Gold earrings and bracelets
Cyprus, 500–300 BC
Diam: left earring, 1.6 cm

The first necklaces were made of shells and pierced stones. Cowrie shells, because of their resemblance to female pudenda, had a mystic quality believed effective against the Evil Eye; they were, and still are, much valued by many cultures. Some shown here are from Egypt; others quite similar, were found in tombs on Mt. Carmel, Palestine. Present-day Sicilians make a necklace of cowrie shells for a teething baby. This is considered a protection against the Evil Eye and is good to bite (see p. 216).

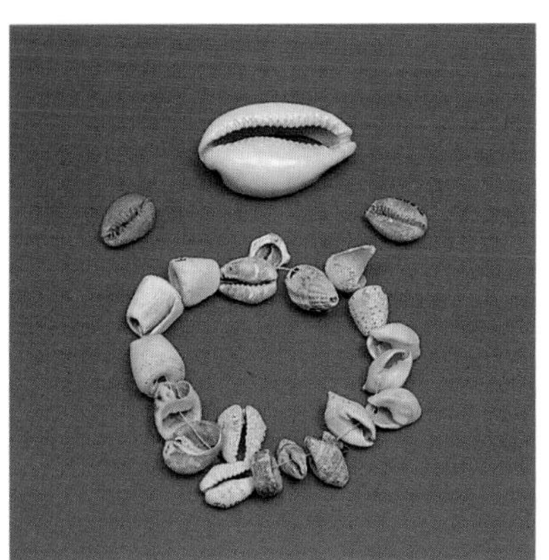

Shells, mostly cowrie
Upper three: Egypt, ca. 3000 BC
L. of largest: 4.5 cm

Others: Palestine, 2000 BC

Different stones were credited with special properties: white chalcedony, alabaster, and white coral increased the supply of breast milk; haematite and carnelian worked against bleeding; red agate, against scorpions and spiders; green agate, against eye disease; brown or tawny agate brought health, happiness, and riches. Budge lists over 50 stones and their professed prophylactic and therapeutic qualities.[9] More than half of these include protection against the Evil Eye, often in conjunction with other values. Beads found in Roman Palestine were undoubtedly regarded as amuletic: lapis lazuli, carnelian, banded agate. Those of stone from Italy show the geometric banding and the "good eyes," like the mosaic beads which were made in Egypt from 1500 BC onward and were worn to protect against the Evil Eye. The Egyptian coptic rosary exemplifies the use of beads in the Christian religion.

Belief in the magic of a word or a combination of letters is illustrated by a large Gnostic Christian bone ring inscribed with partial abracadabra legend. According to Thomas Pettigrew, Serenus Sammonicus, a Roman physician, second to third century AD, recommended this magical word as a charm or amulet to cure ague or other diseases. Written or spoken it would be equally efficacious. It frequently appeared written in a triangular pattern:[10]

ABRACADABRA
BRACADABR
RACADAB
ACADA
CAD
A

Amulets
Bone ring,
Byzantine, AD 4 C – 6 C

Ivory heart
Egypt, ca. AD 600
L: 5.1 cm

The ivory heart pendant from Egypt, ca. AD 600, is decorated with dots surrounded by concentric rings, symbols still used in Africa to represent "good eyes" capable of averting the Evil Eye.

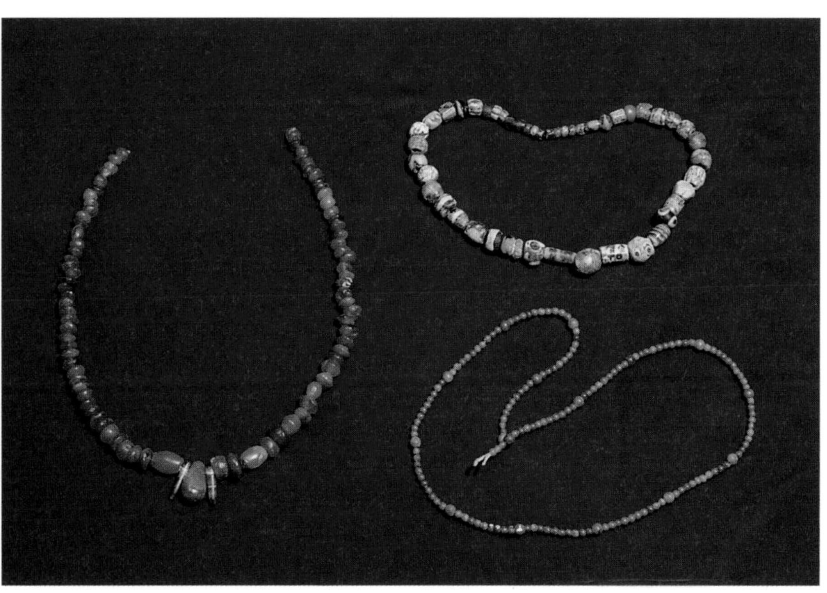

Beads from around the Mediterranean
Left: Carnelian and banded agate, Mount Carmel, Roman Palestine
Central axe pendant and a few others biconically drilled, early 3rd millenium BC
Other beads, later date

Upper right: Stone and glass beads, Italy, 100 BC
L: 29.2 cm

Lower right: Wooden rosary, Egypt, mediaeval
L: 43.2 cm

A number of pieces are Arabic: a dark red glass rectangle with linear decoration, and several pendants of coloured stone with seventeenth-century silver mounts. A chalcedony heart is from Ireland.

Because of the nature of the Jewish religion, Hebrew amulets are rare. The authority on Hebrew amulets is the Kabbalah, a very ancient work that deals with Jewish mysticism in theory and practice.[11] The pentagram, the seal of Solomon, was a medical symbol in the Ancient World. It continued to be used as a magical talisman against the Evil Eye in Europe and beyond from the Middle Ages. It was impressed on children's cradles and elsewhere in their environment. The crenellated disc of slate shown is incised with a hexagram, sometimes substituted for the pentagram and commonly called the Star of David, surrounded by symbols protecting against fire.

Pendants
Carnelian
Arabia, 17 C

Jadeite
Europe, 17 C

Chalcedony
Ireland, 17 C

Glass
Arabia, AD 700–715

Carnelian
Arabia, 17 C
L: 3 cm

Faith in the power of spells and incantations was great: a bulla, a flat round capsule containing magic substances or incantations, was sometimes worn by children and adolescents in Roman Egypt. The practice seems to have spread and persisted, because William Beckett in eighteenth-century England described, somewhat scornfully, the carrying of some texts of scripture as protection against casualties and disease.[12] The polygonal die, ca. 300 BC, referred to in "Play and Education" (see p. 280) could just as easily be a magic talisman used for incantations.

It was thought that liquid took on the attributes of objects it touched. A cippus of Horus standing on two crocodiles, from pre-Christian Egypt, was used in this way. Water poured over it, believed to be endowed with healing powers, was drunk as a tonic.

Liquid placed in the terra cotta bowl inscribed inside and out in Early Arabic characters, perhaps a deliberately mysterious script, was assumed to take on the magic of the inscription; the bowl was found at Thebes. Similar terra cotta bowls described by E.A.T.W. Budge are called devil traps.

Cippus of Horus
Stone, Egypt, ca. 200 BC
Ht: 6.4 cm

Amulets
Left: Shield of Solomon
Stone, diam: 5.1 cm

Right: Bulla, Roman Egypt,
Metal, AD 100

Magic bowl
Terra cotta, Egypt, AD 400–500
Capacity: 2475 cc

The Scrafiato christening bowl or tyg has a whistle in the rim and the inscription: IF U LOVE ME LEND ME NOT IF I HAM FOR I SHALL B FORGOT 1711. Whistles, like bells, had two purposes: the one, to entertain or amuse, the other, to frighten away witches and evil spirits.

From Naples, 1748, a silver rattle, known as a siren, portrays Diana of Ephesus riding the tails of two sea horses. This would have been worn by a mother, attached to a baby's cradle, or hung about the house, especially in a window, to ward off the Evil Eye.[13]

Scrafiato christening bowl
England, 1711
Capacity: 3000 cc

Coral has a long amuletic history. According to legend recounted in Ovid's *Metamorphosis*, Perseus laid Medusa's severed head on some twigs, which instantly turned to stone; nymphs then scattered the twigs in the sea and they became coral.

> Lest the hard sand injure the Gorgon's head,
> He makes it soft with leaves, and over them
> Strews sea-weed for a cover, and puts down
> Medusa's head. And the twigs, all fresh and pliant,
> Absorb another force, harden and stiffen
> In branch and leaves. The sea-nymphs test the wonder
> With other boughs, and the same wonder happens
> To their delight, and they use the twigs as seedlings,
> Strewing them over the water, and even now
> Such is the nature of coral, that it hardens,
> Exposed to air, a vine below the surface.[14]

Pliny wrote, "The branches of coral hanged about the neckes of infants and young children are thought to be a sufficient preservative against all witchcraft and socerie."[15] In modern times the British royal children can be seen in photographs wearing coral necklaces. Being smooth, hard, and cool, in addition to having magic qualities, coral was an ideal material for teething sticks. Seventeenth-, eighteenth- and nineteenth-century gum sticks with silver bells and sometimes a whistle are described on page 284, and a coral necklace is shown on page 216. Pettigrew in 1844 suggested that coral would protect against fits, sorcery, poison, and bad dreams, and claimed that the ringing and rattling of the bells has been esteemed inimical to witches and sorcerers.[16] In this they served the same purpose as the fourth-century pig rattles , seen on page 277.

Fear of yet another onslaught of bubonic plague was a constant and widespread concern of the peoples of Europe for centuries. The highly lethal epidemics that ebbed and flowed in the fourteenth century were known as the Black Death; one outbreak that caused catastrophic loss of life in the seventeenth century was the Great Plague of London.

Mention is made on pages 192 and 193 of the "Vinegar of the Four Thieves" used for protection by those who mingled in disease-infected areas. Faith was also placed in specific amulets of gold, silver, or other metal to give immunity against plague. These highly valued treasures could be worn or carried. They display Christian, pagan, and classical symbolism.

Rattles

Left: Silver mount in form of jester, moveable head with whistle in back, bells in hands, coral teething stick at feet
England, 19 C

Centre: Silver, Naples, 1748
11.4 × 7.9 cm

Right: Silver gilt mount with bells, whistle, coral teether
London, 1798

16 C Plague amulets
OBV. and REV.
Descriptions of plague amulets are provided in Appendix at end of this chapter.

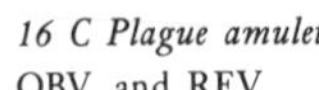

16 C Plague amulets
OBV. and REV.

17 C Plague amulets
OBV. and REV.

The same intellect that merged magic, religion, and medicine spawned the custom of using votive objects to acknowledge the help of the gods in time of need. These replicas of afflicted parts of the body were placed in sanctuaries in hope of a cure or in gratitude for a healing. This practice was particularly associated with the cult of Aesculapius, god of health, whose principal sanctuary was at Epidaurus and dates from the sixth century BC. The magnificent open-air theatre is in use today, and walking toward it through the sacred grove still gives a feeling of entering a serene and spiritual place.

Votive objects
Left: Terra cotta woman in labour
Egypt, 300 BC
Ht: 7.6 cm

Right: Terra cotta uterus septus (two openings)
Greece, ca. 250 BC

The healing process entailed cleansing and regeneration. After ablutions and offerings at the alter came sleep in the abaton sanctuary or in a special dormitory where the "cure" took place. A votive object and a tablet were usually left and became a clinical record; many survive.

Two pottery votives relate to child bearing and delivery: one is from Egypt, a figure of a woman in labour; the other, a uterus septus with fallopian tube or bladder, is Greek. Twins were thought to come from such a uterus.

Terra cotta feet from Syracuse, and an ear and an eye from Italy, all date from the first century. A hollow bronze sandalled foot was sent to Dr. Drake by a dealer in the belief that it was a votive. It is now apparent that this item is typical of the terminal ornamentation then used for the leg of a small table or stool.[17] Such are the pitfalls of collecting!

At the entrance to the sanctuaries there were shops that sold all manner of objects to appeal to gods and men. In addition to anatomical parts, there were oil lamps, small dishes, jugs, feeders, and many surgical instruments. Gifts to honour the gods, reward the priests and attendants, and perhaps a souvenir to take home, were all part of the expedition to an Aescularium, an experience which engaged spirit, mind, and body.

Amulets today are not uncommon: the rabbit's foot to bring good luck, the horseshoe above the door to preserve good fortune within, a St. Christopher's medal carried to ensure a safe journey, or a copper bracelet worn to alleviate arthritic pain. In some regions, such as Southern Italy, the power of the Evil Eye is still greatly feared. Eye contact is thought to cast a spell and hit the victim with a curse. As seen in the following modern advertisement, the Inca sun god may be entreated to guarantee anything you wish from life.

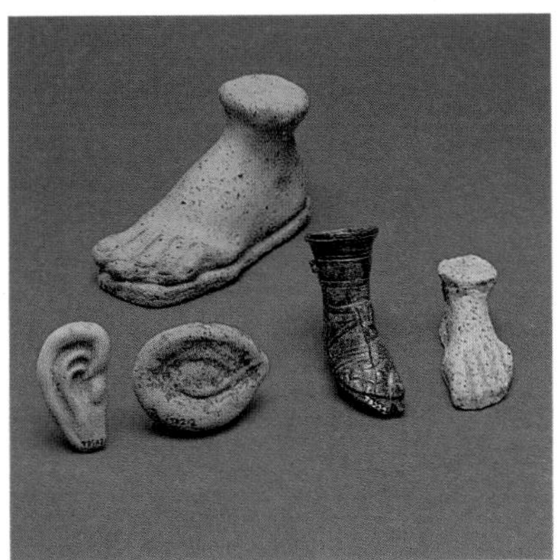

Votive objects AD 1 C
Bronze sandalled foot, Pompeii, mistaken for a votive
Ht: 5.1 cm
Pottery feet, Syracuse
Pottery ear and eye, Italy

Small pieces of Greek pottery
Upper: Cyprus, Graeco-Phoenecian 800–750 BC
Left: Corinth, 550 BC

Right: Syracuse, 400–200 BC

Lower: Corinth, 550–500 BC
Diam: 6.2 cm

When you get your amulet, look into the Sun God's face until you can picture him with your eyes closed. Then press the amulet against your temple or forehead and make your wish. Wish for wealth, success, health, power, love, anything. And watch your dreams begin to come true right away. You have 365 days in which to prove it works. Or it costs you absolutely nothing!

Advertisement
An excerpt from "How to Get the Inca Sun God to bring you Miracles of Wealth and Happiness," *National Enquirer*, Lantana (Florida), 26 December, 1976.

Appendix

Page 168 16 C *Plague amulets*
Clockwise from upper left: 1-5

1. WER. DISE. SCHIANG: AN. SIET. DER. SOL. NIT. STERBEN around 1528 and NVM.RI.ZI. in field
   Rev. WER. AN. MICH. GELAVBETHAIDAS. EWICH. IEBEN around IOANNES. 3. in field
   Silver, traces of gilt, crude wire loop for suspension, 40 mm
2. WIE. DI. SLANG: SO. MOSE. ERHOHET: SO. MVS. DES. MENSCHEN. SON. ERHOHET. WERDEN. AVF. DAS. ALL. DIAN. IN. GLAVBN. HABDAS, EWIG, LEBE, IOHA. 3 in seven lines in exergue.
   Rev. DER. HER. SPRACH. ZV. MOSE: MACHE. DIR. EIN. ERNE. SLANGE: VN. RICHT. SI. ZVM. ZAICHEN. AVF: WER. GEBISSEIST. VND. SICHT. SI. ANDER. SOL. LEBEN. NVMERI. ZI. 1530 in eight lines in exergue
   Silver, 42 mm
3. ACTVT. PER INOBEDIENCIA: VNIVS: HOMIS: MVLTI: PECATORES: CONSTITVTI: ILLIVS. PZ₃: DELICT. MORS: REGNAVIT. GEN: Z₃: ET. FAR. in two lines around K B in field.
   Rev. ITA. PER. VNI: OBEDIENTIA: IVSTICONSTITVEN: MVLTI. ET. ABVNDANCIA. GRA: D. NACIOPIS ET VSTICI. ACCIPIETES INVITA. REGNABVT. VNV. IESVM P.R. Z₃. in two lines around crucifixion scene
   Silver plugged, 43 mm
4. MVLTA. SVNT. MALA. IMPIORVM. in exergue 1587
   Rev. QVI. DNO. FIDIT. BONITATE. EIVS. CIRCVM. in exergue DABITUR
   Silver, 30 mm
5. SIC VI. FREXIT. MOSES. SERPENTE. IN. DESERTO. SIC. EXALTETVR. FILIVS.. HOMINIS. IN. SALVTE. CREDE NCIV. 10. 3 in six lines in exergue.
   1531 in field
   Rev. DIXIT. DOMINVS. MOSE. FAC. SERPENTE. ENEV. ET. ERIGE. EV. IN. SIGNV. VT. QVI. LESVS. ASPICIAT. SALVET. NV ZI in six lines in exergue. Crude loop for suspension.
   Silver, 35 mm

Page 168 16 C *Plague amulets*
Clockwise from upper left: 1-5

1. DES. HERREN. CHRISTI. BLVTT. IST. ALLEIN, GEREONTT. VND GVTT. 1557
   Rev. DIE. AEHRINSCHLAN. So. MOSES. AVFFRICHTFT. ANSAHEN. WVRDEN. WIDER. GESVNT. around N.XXI in field. Loop for suspension.
   Silver gilt, 53 mm
2. ITA. PER. IESVM. CHRISTVM. GRAITIA. PROPAGATVR. IN. OMNES. ROMA. 5
   Rev. VT. MOSES. SERPENTEM. ITA. CHRISTVS. EXAITATVS. 10. Crude loop for suspension. Medal framed with ornate wire rope.
   Silver gilt, 44 mm
3. ET. EGO. SI. EXALTATVS. EVERO. A. TERRA. OMNIA. TRAIIAM. AD. ME. 10. IZ
   Rev. FAC. SERPENTEM. EREVM. ET. PONE. PRO. SIGNO. PCVSSVS. EVM. ASDEXERIT. VIVET around NV ZI in field.
   Silver, traces of gilt, 60 mm
4. ECCATANOSTRA. IPSE PERTVLIT IN CORPORE SVO SVPER LIONVM. VT. PECCATIS MORI-VI IVSTICIE VIVAM
   Rev. AC SERPENTEM EREUM. ET. PONE. PRO. SIGNO. PERCVSSVS. EVM. ASPEXEIT VIVETNVM. ZI.
   Silver, 71 mm
5. GLEIC. WI. DI. SLANG. SO. MVS. DESS. MENSN. SON. ERHOT. WERON. AVE. DZ. ALDI. AN. IN. GLAVBEN. HABN. DZ. EBIC. LERN. in two lines around IOANNES. Z. in field
   Rev. DER. HER. SPRAC. ZW. MOSE, MAC. DIR. EIN. ERNE. SLANG. VND. RICT, SI. ZVM. ZEGN. AVF. WER. GEPISN. IST. VND. SICT. SI. AN. SOL. LE. in two lines around NVM RI.ZI in field
   Twelve solder marks on edge where medal has been mounted.
   Silver, 47 mm

Page 169 17 C *Plague amulets*

Upper Left: B: M: V: ALTEN: OETTINGENSIS around Madonna standing inscribed shield
IHS.V.R.S.N.S.M.V.S.M.Q.L.I.V.B. around shield in field
C C S M L and N D M D on cross of shield
C S P B in field of shield
Rev. Z.D.I.A.B.I.Z. S.A. B. Z. H.G.F. B.F.R.S. around MONACHIUM in exergue
Oval shape with loop for suspension
Brass, 47 x 43 mm

Upper right: IMAGOS: XV STIPAP: MART: PATRONI CATHEDR: ECCL: CHIEMENSIS. around MAXILLA DIVI XVSTI in exergue
Rev. IMAGOS: SEBASTIANI PATRONI CATHEDR: ECCLIAE CHIEMENSIS, oval shape
Brass, 45 x 42 mm

Lower Left: CRVX. S: P: BENEDICTI. above, S: GER: to left, Z. DIA. BIZ. SAB. Z. HG. BFRS. IHS. MAR in shield
Rev. Inscribed shield as in obverse of lower right below battle scene
Loop for suspension
Silver cross, 49 × 47.5 mm

Lower right: S. VOALRICVS to left CRVX. S.T. BENEDICTI in centre
S. AVTA.X. to right. Inscribed shield like shield on obverse of upper left
Rev. CRVX. S. VDALRICI. below battle scene
Loop for suspension
Brass cross, 52 × 46 mm

Notes

1. Herring 1636.
2. Squire 1916.
3. Shorter 1937.
4. Plinius Secundus [Pliny] 1635: Bk 36, 590.
5. Culpeper 1737:100, 108, 110.
6. Budge 1930: preface XXXV.
7. Pentreath 1964:54–58.
8. Budge 1930:327.
9. Budge 1930:306–325.
10. Pettigrew 1844:53–4.
11. Budge 1930:Ch 8
12. Beckett 1722.
13. Elworthy 1895 (reprinted 1970).
14. Ovid 1955:BK4, *ll.* 743–53.
15. Plinius Secundus [Pliny] 1635: Bk 32, 430.
16. Pettigrew 1844:59.
17. Hayes 1983.

The Royal Gift of Healing
Frontispiece from John Browne's
Adenochoiradelogia, London, 1684
Engraving by Robert White
England, late 17 C

TOUCHING FOR THE KING'S EVIL

> This is to give notice, That His Majesty [Charles II] hath declared his positive resolution not to heal any more after this present April until Michaelmass next. And this is published to the End that all Persons concerned may take notice thereof, and not receive a disappointment.
>
> *The Intelligencer.* April 17th, 1665.[1]

Sarah Johnson, mother of the eighteenth-century scholar immortalized by James Boswell, was persuaded by the eminent medical scientist Sir John Floyer, formerly physician to Charles II, to take her ailing two-and-a-half-year-old son Sam to Queen Anne's first touching ceremony of Lent, March 19, 1712. The journey from Lichfield took three days by stagecoach, and she had to be in London the day before to obtain a ticket of admission. It was a trying and expensive venture under any circumstances, and Sarah was pregnant at the time. Her husband, Michael, was convinced it was worthwhile to undertake the pilgrimage.[2]

What was this important ceremony? It was an opportunity for people suffering from the King's Evil, to present themselves to be touched by the reigning monarch, in the belief that a cure would be effected.

The disease commonly referred to as "the King's Evil," scrofula, or struma, is tuberculosis of the lymph glands of the neck. The usual onset is in early childhood, and it affected many, many children in Europe in past centuries. It may manifest itself intermittently for many years, sometimes with open, suppurating sores, or it may run its course and disappear. The remissions between bouts were often accepted as cures.

John Browne, surgeon to Charles II, described the ceremony in great detail as it was practised in the reign of his sovereign. In a solemn religious service from the Book of Common Prayer, the King, sitting in his royal chair, was assisted by the chief officer to the Yeoman of the Guard, two chaplains, and several surgeons in the presence of a number of nobles and spectators. At the point in the service when the chaplain read, "They shall lay their hands on them, and they shall recover," an ailing person knelt before the King and was touched by him. The statement was repeated and the royal hands were laid on each individual. After further Bible readings and prayers, the sick each knelt again before the King. As a chaplain repeated, "That Light was the true Light, which lighteth every man which cometh into the World," the King put a gold piece hanging from a "white Silk Ribbond" about the neck of each sufferer. All present knelt before the King for prayers. Then the King washed his hands and departed and the service was over.[3]

The origin of such belief is uncertain. Many attribute its beginning to Edward the Confessor who reigned from 1042 to 1066. A young, married, scrofulous girl, unsuccessful in becoming pregnant, was commanded in a dream to be washed by the king. Her pleas were answered and she was kept at Edward's court until well — about a week. In a year's time she gave birth to twins. About 80 years later the story was recorded by William of Malmesbury as a miraculous cure.[4] Chroniclers through the years focused on this event as proof of the divine healing power of royalty. In hot weather and during epidemics of plague and other infectious diseases, English monarchs avoided holding ceremonies; such abstinence is announced in the quote at the beginning of this section. Otherwise they apparently continued touching for scrofula. Henry VII, who reigned from 1485 to 1509 was responsible for establishing a particular order for the procedure to be followed at the healings, and it was soon published in the Book of Common Prayer.

The Rev. Dr. William Tooker, chaplain to Queen Elizabeth and later Dean of Lichfield, wrote a treatise concerning the healing powers of kings and queens, particularly that of Elizabeth I.[5] Ability to cure the King's Evil was evidence of the inherited power of English monarchs. Tooker flattered Her Majesty regarding her extraordinary abilities in touching or healing and attributed the power to all English Christian sovereigns. Though the well-regarded sixteenth-century French surgeon, Ambrose Parey, discussed the "King's evill" and its cures, he made no mention of the Royal Touch.[6]

Francis Herring, in a book first published in 1603, warned against placing too much faith in amulets and other magic, including touching for the King's Evil, indicating that it might or might not do any good but it could also do harm by eliminating any other, perhaps more effective, treatment.[7] At about the same time as Herring was cautioning against such blind faith, Shakespeare, in *Macbeth*, reflected the general public acceptance of the king's healing powers (see facing page).

Nonetheless, confidence in the cure persisted. *A Miracle of Miracles*,[8] is a eulogy of Charles I in which the writer includes among the many virtues of the king, his willingness to use his God-given powers of healing to cure those afflicted with the King's Evil, by touching their sores at times appointed for their visits. He extolls the magnitude of this King's power, giving as proof the effectiveness of "a piece of Handkircher dipped in the King's Blood" at his execution, in restoring the sight to a blind "Mayd...who by the violence of the Disease called the Kings Evill was blinde one whole Yeare."

Samuel Pepys, in his diary entry of June 23, 1660, makes reference to the poor people standing all morning in the rain in the garden waiting for the king to touch. It was not until the following year, April 13, 1661, that Pepys himself witnessed the ceremony: "...I went to the Banquet-house, and there saw the King heale, the first time that ever I saw him do it; which he did with great gravity, and it seemed to me to be an ugly office and a simple one."[9] The ceremony in Pepys' time would have been the same as that described by Dr. Browne. Charles II during two decades touched more than 92,000 people, sometimes as many as 600 at one ceremony.

Malcolm: ... Comes the king forth,
I pray you?

Doctor: Ay, sir; there are a crew of wretched souls
That stay his cure; their malady convinces
The great assay of art; but, at his touch,
Such sanctity hath heaven given his hand,
They presently amend.

Macduff: What's the disease he means?
Malcolm: 'Tis call'd the evil:
A most miraculous work in this good king,
Which often, since my here-remain in England,
I have seen him do. How he solicits heaven,
Himself best knows; but strangely-visited people,
All swoln and ulcerous, pitiful to the eye,
The mere despair of surgery, he cures;
Hanging a golden stamp about their necks,
Put on with holy prayers; and 'tis spoken
To the succeeding royalty he leaves
The healing benediction...

William Shakespeare. *Macbeth* Act IV, Scene 3

It seems that, in spite of attempts to dispel the trust of people in the power of the Royal Touch, many continued to believe in its healing qualities throughout the seventeenth century. Richard Wiseman believed the extraordinary power possessed by kings was given by God; French kings had it too. He had no difficulty attesting to the miracles, for they "should need no other proof than the great concourse of Strumous persons to White-hall, and the success that they find in it. I myself have been a frequent Eye-Witness of many hundreds of Cures performed by his Majesties Touch alone." He recalled also "What Miracles of this nature were performed by the very Blood of his late Majesty of Blessed memory [Charles I]" and reviewed claims of cures made by writers back to Edward the Confessor. "This we are sure, the Miracle is not ceased." Observing that skeptics of the time attributed cures to the journey to Whitehall and change of air, imagination, or the wearing of gold, Wiseman refuted these, indicating that Londoners had no change of air, infants had no imagination, and Charles I in his extremity had no gold, yet he effected cures.[10]

John Browne's treatise, published in 1684, is totally supportive of the efficacy of the Royal Touch, performed by "Kings of England" for "above 640 years," again dating its origin to Edward the Confessor. He gives many examples of cures by the kings' "Sacred Touch."[11]

However, the recurrence of remedies for the King's Evil in recipe books of the seventeenth and eighteenth centuries (then a common source of guidance in most households) reflects the fact that not all who were afflicted with the disease relied on the ceremonies for their treatment. During the reign of William III (1689-1702) the ceremony was allowed to lapse, chiefly because the king felt the rite a silly superstition. Persuaded only once to perform the ceremony, William remarked to those brought before him, "God give you better health and more sense."[12]

Queen Anne, who reigned from 1702 to 1714, was pressured to restore the custom as proof to the people that she was the rightful monarch. As had been the custom, announcements of her intent were read in parish churches and published in newspapers throughout the country. Such a notice from the *Gazette* of Feb. 28, 1712, was reprinted by C.J.S. Thompson, thus:

> It being her Majesty's royal intention to touch for the Evil on Wednesday the 19th of March next and so to continue weekly during Lent, it is Her Majesty's command that tickets be delivered the day before at the office in Whitehall and that all persons shall bring a certificate signed by the Minister and Churchwardens of their respective parishes, that they have never received the Royal touch.[13]

This would have been seen by inhabitants of Lichfield where the Johnson family lived.

Not everyone had the same confidence in the touching as did Samuel Johnson's noted doctor, for by the eighteenth century doubts about the cure were more broadly publicized. A chapter entitled "Of the Royal Touch" in a book published by J. Handley in 1721 expresses his complete lack of faith in the healing ceremony:

> ...fewer Children have been cured, by the Royal Touch, than Adult Persons, their Immaginations being not so capable of being struck with this sort of Royal Hocus Pocus, as the others; but why the Original Royal Saint [Edward the Confessor], who it is pretended had this Gift bestow'd on him; shou'd have it for the Cure of a Scrophula, rather than

> Gout, Stone, or Leprosy, (much more afflictive Distempers) or rather, why not for the Cure of all of them, ... , is a Riddle, that none but a Priest, or Popish Bigot can unfold..."[14]

One of the most skeptical surgeons was William Beckett, a contemporary of Handley, whose letters to two physicians[15] appeared in a publication now very rare (London, 1722).[16] He revealed that writings such as Tooker's *Charisma*, 1597, and stories like *A Miracle of Miracles*, 1649, readily believed by all classes in their time, did not fare well under close scrutiny. Historical documentation of the Royal Touch was unreliable: if the supernatural gift really existed, why did it frequently fail, and why was it sometimes possessed by people not of royal blood? Indeed he felt cures had nothing to do with inherited supernatural power, the ceremony, or the gold coin. In fact "more People have died of this Disease in those Reigns when our Kings did touch, than when they did not," and, like Francis Herring, he was convinced that "when our Kings did not touch, the people sought out for early Help for their Maladies, whereby great Numbers were cured; whereas when our Kings did touch, they depended so much upon its Efficacy, that they neglected all other Means till their Cases became...incurable."

Some of the other remedies for the King's Evil still recommended in the eighteenth century were recorded long ago by Pliny. Among a multitude of treatments suggested by him are the following: herbs, such as plaintain applied to the affected part or worn about the neck (such herbs to be kept with the patient after healing to prevent return of the disease); ointments, such as the ashes of a weasel in hog's grease, ashes of a serpent in bull's tallow, ground snails' shells, or simply the blood of a weasel applied to the wens; the meat of the middle part of a snake, eaten, or its ashes dissolved in liquid and drunk.[17]

Beckett thought cures were due to the great excitement incurred by a visit to London and to the King; "it must procure a fresh Turn to the Blood and Spirits, give the effete and languid Nerves a fresh Vigour, excite the intestine Agitation of the Particle of the Blood, and produce an agreeable Alteration in the Whole Constitution."

It is interesting to note that Beckett pointed out the habit of using the words "touching," "curing," and "healing" interchangeably. Therefore one touched was assumed healed. For example, he observed that when Dr. Fuller reported "I have seen the King solemnly Heal in the Choir of the Cathedral of Salisbury," Fuller must have *seen* no more than touching. Similarly when Dr. Carr claimed King Charles II in a certain time "healed 92,107," the registry showed that exact number to have been "touched." "No Body can suppose," said Beckett, "that he gave himself the Trouble of going so many miles and so many different Ways...to enquire into the event." In other words, there was no assessment of the results. However, at a later date, during the reign of Louis XVI (1774–1792) in Paris, 2400 patients touched were formally investigated. Only five assured cures were reported.[18]

Opinions about the royal cure remained controversial, but the age of scientific enlightenment was approaching. As printed matter became more available, critical views were publicized, and fewer believed in the rite. Although Queen Anne revived the practice, it was performed on a smaller scale and ceased toward the end of her reign (1714). The ceremony last appeared in the Prayer Book of 1719.

Toward the end of the eighteenth century Underwood observed that the onset of scrofula was generally between ages 2 and 12. Children whose health was frail as a result of poor diet, or who were weakened by some other childhood disease, seemed more apt to contract scrofula. He noted that it frequently disappeared at puberty. Making no reference to the earlier faith in the Royal Touch as a cure, he stated, "I have little to recommend for the cure of it."[19]

Although reigning English monarchs no longer touched, exiled Stuarts continued to do so. James the Pretender (James III of England, James VIII of Scotland) had touched in Scotland and in France during the reign of Queen Anne, and he continued to do so in Italy until his death in 1755. His son, Prince Charlie, held healings in Scotland and, as late as the 1770s, in Italy. Cardinal York, brother of Prince Charles, who would have been Henry IX, did likewise in France until the revolution, and then in Italy until his death in 1807.

Through the centuries some eminent men who were not of royal blood purported to be healers, with considerable success. Most notable among these was Valentine Greatraks, an Irish priest, who during the reign of Charles II rivalled the popularity of the King.

Contrary to the conviction of the previously mentioned Rev. Dr. Tooker (1597), who believed that Christian kings and queens of England had always had power to heal while those in France had never possessed it, other writers discussed the practice of touching in France. Wiseman referred to it a century after Tooker, and Browne about the same time claimed French kings received "a sprig of right" from the primitive power of the English Kings! Farquhar referred to documentation of early healings in France, where the ceremonies continued later than in England. In 1824 it is recorded that 121 persons were sent by accredited surgeons to be touched by Charles X.[20]

The beginnings of the practice are not so easy to establish. Touching as a means of healing was known in ancient times: such rites were practised in Egypt and Babylon, and the Bible repeatedly refers to healing by the laying on of hands or by touching. Because of the lack of specificity of disease in earlier times, Farquhar was content to begin the story of the King's Evil with Edward the Confessor, at least in England. In France it undoubtedly began sooner; some claimed the origin as far back as Clovis in the fifth century. Other writers were not so lenient as Farquhar regarding the role of Edward the Confessor. Pettigrew, in an analytical history of the Royal Touch up to and including the time of Queen Anne, like Beckett and Handley earlier, doubted the credibility of the historical documentation of the origin of the rite. He emphasized the ease with which faith in the ceremony developed during the Middle Ages, when belief in superstitions was general among the ignorant and the humble, the educated and the rich.[21] Beckett (1722) had been more emphatic, claiming it would have been heresy to doubt in those times.[22]

Mention has been made in the description of a typical ceremony of a coin being hung on a ribbon around the neck of the scrofulous individual. This custom was never established in France; coins given there were in the nature of charity to defray expenses and carried no amuletic intent. Succeeding pages follow the use of coins for the ceremonies in England, with particular emphasis on those in Dr. Drake's Collection. (Unless otherwise inferred, the general body of numismatic knowledge is based on the reports of Farquhar, published in the *British Numismatic Journal* of 1918—1919, volumes 12, 13, 14, and 15.)

In England, no regular gold coinage deserving the name of currency was issued before the age of Edward III (reigned 1327–1377). Records of the Tower of London at the time of Edward I (reigned 1272–1307) show that the sum given to each patient at every touching was one penny; household accounts during his reign include the expenses of healing.

Edward II (1307–1327) continued the practice; he habitually had his coins blessed at the altar before distribution. On a journey to Scotland in 1316 he found time to heal at each stopping place. During the reign of Edward III it was not uncommon to carry a gold noble (a gold coin first minted during the reign of Edward III) as an amulet when going into battle, but only the silver pennies such as those used by his two predecessors were given for the King's Evil.

Silver pennies of Edward I, II and III
OBV:
Edward I: EDW R' ANGL' DNS hYB
19.5 mm.
Edward II: EDWAR R ANGL DNS hYB
19.0 mm.
Edward III: EDWARD: ANGL:R:DNS:hYB
17.0 mm.

REV. of above:
CIVITAS LONDON

Edward IV, in 1465, was the first to order the gold angel. Its design, with St. Michael slaying a dragon on the obverse side and a sailing vessel on the reverse, would suggest he bestowed it in touching, but no record has confirmed this. The existence of the angel pictured, apparently pierced for use in the touching ceremony, is a strong indication of such use. It is a very rare specimen.

Gold angels continued as coin of the realm. Possibly Henry VI, in his brief restoration, healed and bestowed such a coin, but the first monarch recorded as having given the gold angel at healing ceremonies was Henry VII, who instituted the formal ceremony. An angel was the standard doctor's fee, the equivalent of three days' sustenance. Henry VII's angel bore the same legend as that of Edward IV, and so did that of Henry VIII (1509–1547).

Mary I (1553–1558) a Roman Catholic, introduced a new legend: A DOMINO FACTUM EST ISTUD ET EST MIRABILE IN OCCULIS NOTRIS [It is the Lord's doing, and it is miraculous in our sight]. Later modifications are seen in the examples illustrated. James I left no trace of the miraculous in his legend.

One reads of the probability of other current coinage being used for touching. Farquhar did not think so, especially in the reign of Elizabeth, but the presence of the two pattern half groats among Dr. Drake's coins related to touching, reinforces this possibility. The clipping of one and the piercing of the other, would encourage such belief.

Except for the depiction of the reigning monarch, the same pattern continued in use on the angels. James II issued both silver and gold touchpieces of similar patterns. The sailing vessels go in opposite directions and the legends differ slightly.

By 1633 angels were coined exclusively for presentation and ceased to be struck altogether in 1642. In 1664, after the restoration of Charles II, a replica of the gold angel was struck to be used exclusively as a touchpiece or healing piece. It is noteworthy that St. Michael (the angel) was relegated to the reverse of the coin and the ship appeared on the obverse. In 1684 a new smaller gold touchpiece was produced with half the previous value.

Gold angels and silver pattern half groats
OBV:
Upper left: Edward IV (1461–1483) 28 mm
EDWARD DEI GRA REX ANGL. Z FR(A)NC.

Upper right: Elizabeth I (1558–1603) 29 mm
ELIZABETH D. G. ANG. FR: ET HI REGINA

Lower: Elizabeth I half groats of 1601
26 mm.
VNVM. A. DEO. DVOBVS. SVSTINEO.

REV. of above:
Upper left: PER CRUCEM TUAM SALVA NOS XPC REDEMPT.
[By your cross, save us, Christ our Redeemer]

Upper right: A. DNO. FACTUM: EST. ISTUD: ET: EST. MIRABI(LE)
[It is the Lord's doing and it is miraculous]

Lower: AFFLICTORUM CONSERVATRIX

Coins used for touching
OBV:
Upper left: Gold angel of James I (1603–1625) 26 mm
JACOBUS D: G: MAG: BRI: FRA: ET HIB: REX

Upper right: Gold angel of Charles I (1625–1649) 26 mm
CAROLUS D. G. MAG. BRI: FR: ET HIB. REX.

Lower left: Gold Touchpiece of Charles II (1660–1685) 22 mm
CAR. II. D. G. M. B. FR. ET. HI. REX.

Centre: Silver touchpiece of James II (1685–1688) 19.5 mm
JAC. II. D. G. M. FR. ET. H. REX.

Lower right: Gold touchpiece of James II 18.5 mm
JACO. II. D. G. M. B. FR. ET. HI. REX

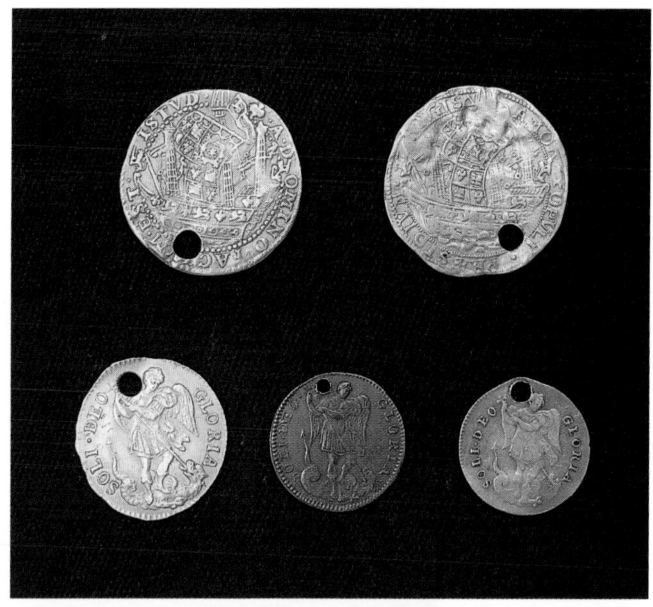

REV. of above:
Upper left: A.D. DOMINO FACTUM EST ISTUD. [It is the Lord's doing]

Upper right: AMOR POPULI PRAESIDIUM REGIS [The love of his people is the King's safeguard]

Lower left: SOLI. DEO. GLORIA [Glory only to God]

Centre: SOLI. DEO. GLORIA.

Lower right: SOLI. DEO. GLORIA.

Gold, silver and brass touchpieces
OBV:
Upper left: Gold, Queen Anne (1702–1714) 21.5 mm
ANNA D. G. M. BR. F. ET. H. REG.

Upper right: Silver, James III (the Pretender) 20.5 mm
JAC III. D. G. M. B. F. ET. H. R.

Lower left: Brass, James III (the Pretender) 21.0 mm
IAC. III D.G.M.B.F.ET. H.R.

Lower right: Silver, Henry IX 21.5 mm
H. IX. D. G. M. B. F. H. R. C. EP. TUSC

REV. of above:
Upper left: SOLI. DEO. GLORIA (early piece before Queen Anne's legend appeared)

Other three: SOLI. DEO GLORIA

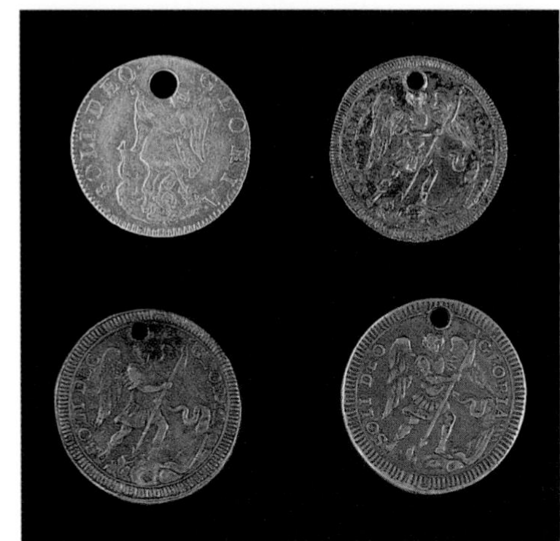

Because of his lack of belief in the healing powers of royalty, William III had no touchpieces made during his and Mary II's reign, but when Anne was persuaded to touch, it was not long before her own piece was struck bearing the legend: "I touch, God heals," in keeping with her own conviction. This would have been the same as that received by the young Samuel Johnson on his big trip to London.

As has been mentioned, James the Pretender touched in France and in Scotland during the reign of Queen Anne. His silver touchpiece shown here was struck in Italy and bears the title to which he aspired: James III. A duplicate of this in copper or brass was probably also used for healing.

Even while James still lived, and continuing after his death, Prince Charles touched in Scotland and in Italy using touchpieces bearing Charles III, which are extremely rare. Toward the end of the eighteenth century, his brother Cardinal York touched in Italy and gave touchpieces designated Henry IX, a title to which he had aspired.

Though the exiled Stuarts were touching abroad, no ceremonies were available to the sick in England after the reign of Queen Anne.[23] Faith in the touchpiece itself as a cure survived; the pieces were often lent to friends and relatives, or even shared for extended periods.

From the time of Henry VII there was a need to control the numbers of people appearing to be touched: to keep the ceremonies manageable, to prevent repeated visits by the same person to obtain more gold, and to minimize exposure of the court to infectious disease. Hence the introduction of admission passes, tickets, or tokens.

No tangible evidence of such a pass has been found to indicate its existence before the days of Charles I. Brass and/or copper tokens of the mid-seventeenth century were felt for some time to be base metal touchpieces used by Charles I because of his financial distress. But Farquhar eliminated all doubts in 1914 when she found a letter of 1635 indicating that, because previous admission tokens made by freemasons had been counterfeited, new copper and brass tickets were ordered from the mint.

These were collected at the healing ceremonies and returned to the warden of the mint as a check on the number of angels given out at the healings. Their scarcity, in spite of their low monetary value of twopence, can be attributed to the fact that they were returned to the mint: when no longer in use they would have been melted down for other purposes. Such coins were never touchpieces. Some tokens, probably from the period of Charles I, had a blessing hand touching one of several heads and on the reverse a crowned rose and thistle.

Another coin considered by some to be an admission token had doubts cast upon its use by Farquhar. Such tokens were counterfeited, and more people were admitted to be touched than had been arranged for: many who genuinely wished for the cure and some who were merely seeking the gold coin. This resulted in the gold pieces being short in number, causing unseemly wrangling, even in the presence of the king. Charles II then ordered from the mint larger tokens the size of the gold angels.

As well as the tokens shown (brass, copper, and brass ringed with copper), copper ringed with brass tokens were made, but the most rare are those of brass ringed with copper (copper with brass plug).

Tokens for admission to touching ceremonies
OBV:
Upper left: Copper, Charles I (1625–1649) 21.0 mm
HE TOUCHED THEM

Upper right: Copper coin of 17 C 21.5 mm questioned as a token by Farquhar
PRAY FOR THE KING

Lower left: Brass, Charles II (1660–1685) 28.0 mm
CAR.II.D.G.M.B.FR.ET.HI.REX

Lower centre: Copper, Charles II 29.5 mm
CAR.II.D.G.M.B.FR.ET.HI.REX

Lower right: Copper with brass plug, Charles II 28.0 mm
CAR.II.D.G.M.B.FR.ET.HI.REX

REV. of above:
Upper left: AND THEY WEARE HEALED

Upper right: LORD GIVE THY BLESSING

Lower three: SOLI DEO GLORIA

Note the small nick in the specimen in the centre above 'DEO' is indicative that it had been returned to the mint and re-issued.

Among interesting items in the files of the Drake Collection are two documents relating to admission tokens. One is a report in *The Anthenaeum* of a meeting of May 27, 1914 at which Helen Farquhar identified four specimens of "the medalet or pass" of 1635; the other is the original letter written two days later by W.J. Andrew, an eminent coin consultant, to "Manton," explaining to the latter the identity of his "very rare" coin, a seventeenth-century admission token. These tokens or tickets are not so rare as they were then thought to be.

Further precautions taken by Charles II included issuing application forms for touching. These were distributed to the parishes. When the doctor diagnosed scrofula the applicant was registered by the priest, and his application was signed and taken to the appropriate centre to obtain an admission token.

These practices continued through the reign of Queen Anne and were in force when Samuel Johnson appeared at one of the last touching ceremonies. His mother, on the recommendation of Dr. Floyer, would have filled out an application for the Royal Touch, had it signed by her parish priest to assure that Samuel had not been touched before, then journeyed to Whitehall to obtain an admission token, and appeared next day with young Sam to have him touched. In his *Life of Samuel Johnson*, Boswell states that Johnson claimed to have received no benefit from the touching. He did, however, treasure his gold touchpiece for the rest of his life, and it is now in the British Museum.

Of the 987 coins, tokens, and medals in the Drake Collection, 31 relate to the Royal Touch: eight admission tokens, ten touchpieces, four gold angels, and nine early coins of the realm, possibly given by the king when touching.

Notes

1. The Intelligencer 1665. "Touching for the King's Evil", a clipping pasted on the inside cover of *A Free and Impartial Enquiry into the Antiquity and Efficacy of Touching for the Cure of the King's Evil*, William Beckett, London, 1722.
2. Clifford 1955.
3. Browne 1684; Bk 3: 95–101.
4. Beckett 1722:8–9.
5. Tooker 1597. This book was described by Pettigrew in 1844 as a "great rarity."
6. Parey 1649.
7. Herring 1936.
8. [n.a.] *A Miracle of Miracles* ... 1649.
9. Braybrooke, ed. 1825.
10. Wiseman 1676.
11. Browne 1684; Bk 3: 73.
12. Farquhar 1918:118.
13. Thompson 1946:49.
14. Handley 1721:419.
15. One of these physicians addressed by Beckett was Sir Hans Sloane, then President of the College of Physicians, also Founder of the British Museum.
16. Beckett 1722:25,30,33.
17. Plinius Secundus 1635; Bk 30: 378–379.
18. Farquhar 1918: 183.
19. Underwood 1784:141–143.
20. Farquhar 1918: 182.
21. Pettigrew 1844.
22. Beckett 1722:30.
23. Woolf 1979; Vol. XLIX: 99.

Porcelain cottage incense burner
England, Staffordshire, 19 C
Ht: 14.0 cm

AGAINST THE YLL AYRES

If any man be bound by Religion, consanguinitie, office, or any such respect to visite the sicke parties; let him first provide, that the chamber bee well perfumed with odoriferous trochiskes, or such like, the windowes layd with the herbes aforenamed, the floore cleane swept, and sprinkled with rose-water and vineger: that there be a fire of sweet wood burning in the chimney, the windowes being shut for an houre, then open the casements towardes the North. Then let him wash his face and hands with rose-water and rose-vineger, and enter into the chamber with a waxe candle in the one hand, and a sponge with rose-vineger and wormwood, or some other Pomander, to smell unto. Let him hold in his mouth a peece of Mastic, Cinamon, Zodoarie, or Citron pill, or a Clove. Let him desire his sicke friend to speake with his face turned from him.

When he goeth forth, let him wash his hands and face with rose-vineger and water as before, especially if he have taken his friend by the hand as the manner is and going presently to his owne house, let him change his garments, and lay those wherein he visited his friend, apart for a good time before he resume them againe.

Francis Herring. *Certaine Rules, Directions, or Advertisements for this time of Pestilentiall contagion.* 1636, B2 recto.

Long before perfumes were used simply to make one's person more appealing, scents were regarded as being a necessary part of one's environment. Their healthful qualities were held in high esteem, and faith in their protective powers against disease prompted the extension of their use to the persons, cradles, and nurseries of infants and children. Scents were kept in solid form and later in vinegars long before techniques for producing essences were developed.

It is recorded that Henry VII (England), regarded as a thrifty monarch, paid 10 shillings for one pomander.[1,2] At that time, (1492), the average labourer took six months to earn such a sum, and the wage was sufficient to cause him to pay an annual income tax.[3] Francis Herring in his early seventeenth-century book of directions against the plague, quoted above, reflects the general willingness of people to pay for aids to better health: "A little health is worth a great deal of gold."[4]

Mary Queen of Scots, in her meticulous care to appear dignified before her onlookers at her execution in 1587, wore a pomander chain about her neck.[5] Queen Elizabeth I, in a portrait painted about the same time, had a pomander suspended from the girdle.[6] Scene III of Hogarth's mid-eighteenth-century *Marriage à la Mode*

A Consultation of Doctors on the Case of Sir Toby Bumper
Coloured etching by George Woodward
After Thomas Rowlandson
London, 1809
21.0 × 33.0 cm

shows the Countess wearing a pomander, again hanging from the waist.[7] Portraits of royal children showed them similarly adorned (compare with cover).

Such was the importance placed upon these scent balls in past centuries. Air in homes, in public places — indeed wherever people gathered — was foul beyond present-day conception. Great houses employed a man whose sole duty it was to perfume the rooms daily! Is it any wonder that individuals felt a need to carry some source of pleasant fragrance on their persons? Alexander Pope in *Thoughts on Various Subjects* said, "Praise is like ambergrease; a little whiff of it, and by snatches, is very agreeable..." In malodorous surroundings, "a little whiff," would indeed be welcome.

A pomander [pomme d'ambre] usually contained ambergris, a fragrant wax-like substance secreted by the sperm whale, mixed with pleasant smelling spices. In the thirteenth century the ball was carried in the hand or in a bag and gave off a pleasant fragrance when warm. Convenience encouraged the use of a container to hold the waxy ball, and the term pomander came to be applied interchangeably to the case or to the contents.

It was natural to add a loop for suspension so that the ball might be carried more easily, hanging on a chain from the waist or around the neck. Pure practicality gave way to adornment, and jewellers began making cases of increasing elegance and intricacy.

As belief in the preventive qualities of aromatic vinegars spread, the pomander was supplanted by a vinaigrette, a case usually gilt-lined, containing a sponge soaked in vinegar, held in place by a grille. But with the ladies the pomander did not lose its popularity; they much preferred the pleasant aroma of the scent ball to the harsh vinegars. As more exotic spices became available in dry form, containers were divided into compartments or loculi, each of which held a scented powder. Some even contained a vinaigrette in the selection. Table pomanders were also used: larger devices of elaborate design serving the same purpose. Canes carried by doctors and clergymen, particularly when visiting the sick, frequently were topped by pouncet[8,9] boxes; staves borne by royalty and other notables on ceremonial occasions were similarly equipped. These were brandished, often ostentatiously.

A Visit to the Doctor
Coloured etching by George Woodward.
After George Cruikshank
London, ca. 1809
20.8 × 32.0 cm

During the plague of 1665, faith in the preventive powers of aromatic vinegars popularized their use. The preparations of aromatic vinegars and scent balls were elaborate and varied. A favourite was the Marseilles vinegar recorded by a physician in 1721, following the plague in that city in 1720.[10] Hannah Glasse, known to be the author of *The Art of Cookery* written "by a Lady," refers to "four Malefactors (who had robbed the infested Houses, and murdered the People during the Course of the Plague)" who "owned, when they came to the Gallows, that they had preserved themselves from the Contagion, by using the above Medicine [Marseilles vinegar] only; and that they went the whole Time from House to House, without any Fear of the Distemper."[11]

Pomanders
England
Left: The top of the shaft terminates in gold fruit with a loop for suspension, the bottom ends in a scalloped circle of gold marked in 6 sectors. This sweet ball still emits a pleasant fragrance when warmed in the hand. Unknown date, but 15 C style
Diam: 3.0 cm

Right: This carved hollow nut shell with ivory lid was a controversial artifact until recently. Personal belongings of sailors raised with the Mary Rose, flagship of Henry VIII, included many early 16 C pomanders, some examples almost identical to this specimen. Amuletic power was attributed to the nut shell per se.

The formula for "Vinaigre des quatre voleurs," as it became known, persisted through centuries in popular cook books. Study of these recipes in a number of old household guide books reveals the vinegar of the four thieves to be basically consistent, the variations being few and minor: the essential ingredient was known by 1811 to be acetic acid.[12] Instructions are found as recently as this century.[13] A sample is reprinted in *Dick's Encyclopedia* in 1975:[14]

> Dried tops of large and small wormwood, rosemary, sage, mint, rue, lavender-flowers, of each 2 ounces; calamus root, cinnamon, cloves, nutmeg, garlic of each ¼ ounce; camphor ½ ounce; concentrated acetic acid, 2 ounces; strong vinegar, 8 pounds. Macerate the herbs etc. in the vinegar for 2 weeks, strain, press, and add the camphor dissolved in the acetic acid.

Thomas Muffett, writing in 1655, tells how Hippocrates rid Athens of the plague by lighting fires in every street "to purifie the aire, for verily, as running water, like a broome, cleanseth this earth, so fire like a Lion, eateth up the pollutions of the aire...cleanliness and good fires, cannot but either extinguish or lessen any infection." Dr. Muffett goes on to advise as well, the use of other outward correctors and perfumes "to ensure that the infection be wholly amended." For plague in winter he recommends elaborate herb-burning fires and a wine-based perfume; for plague in summer he lists a different set of herbs for burning and a vinegar-based perfume.[15]

So, for centuries foul odours were thought to cause disease, and pleasant fragrances were believed to counteract bad smells and their effects. Much faith was placed in the efficacy of both pomanders and vinaigrettes as preventives, sometimes as curatives.

Artifacts in the Drake Collection exemplify the devices mentioned to combat the "yll ayres" and reflect the variety of materials and craftsmanship from the sixteenth to the nineteenth century.

Two very early pomanders were undoubtedly produced for different classes of English society: the black, waxy ball moulded around a gold shaft, for the wealthy; the carved nut shell, for a lower class.

Silver pomanders of the sixteenth to eighteenth century, and their contemporary vinaigrettes, are difficult to date. Because of their small size and intricate design, they were "legally exempted from liability to be assayed, and from payment of duty (when it was imposed)."[16] Many therefore bear no hallmarks. Vinaigrettes of the late eighteenth and nineteenth centuries were a Birmingham specialty and many of these were hallmarked.

Simple spherical pomanders were common. Two European examples are shown: one plain silver gilt, the other beautifully engraved[17] and pierced.

Pomanders
Left: ? Europe, 18–19 C
Silver gilt, undecorated, hinged in the middle with a separate silver grille
Diam: 3.5 cm

Right: Northern Europe, ca. 1798
Silver, intricately engraved and pierced in a floral pattern, unscrews to form two hemispheres. Origin and date of chain not known.

More elaborate pomanders were also popular in the sixteenth and seventeenth centuries, often divided into compartments to offer a selection of individual spices.

Seventeenth- and eighteenth-century silver pomanders were made in many shapes and designs, still with the same basic construction of several loculi for different scented powders, and sometimes a compartment closed by a grille to hold an aromatic sponge. A death's head locket was a common shape even earlier in northern Europe. Other forms include urns, eggs, pears, acorns, apples, and whimsical "Punch hats".

Silver gilt pomander,
? Germany
The outer surface of the footed sphere is covered with a chased,[18] foliate motif. Only traces of the original gilt are evident. The looped finial unscrews to release six loculi, each with a sliding lid. Four are inscribed B.[19] Muscaten (nutmeg), B. Negelen (cloves), B. Lavendel (lavender), and B. Schlag (schlag tree).[20] Though probably German, its domed base incorporates an Elizabethan sixpence dated 1568.
Ht: 5.8 cm

Brass table pomander
? Burma, 17 C
A peacock standing in the centre is surrounded by five heart-shaped compartments, with lids engraved in peacock motifs.
Diam: 7.6 cm

Silver pouncet box
19 C
The top has a circular grille. The upper half is elaborately chased in a fine floral pattern over an etched[21] background. The lower half is scrolled filigree.[22] The inside centre holds a brass plate dividing 2 compartments, with holes which may be opened or closed by a revolving disc. The collar is engraved with "Jimmy" and the Greek letters for Eureka.
Diam: 3.8 cm

Novelty silver vinaigrettes
Left: Ram's horn
Birmingham, Jan. 29, 1871, silver repoussé[23] mount topped with coloured glass to represent cairngorm.
L: 8.0 cm.

Centre: Chased silver Punch hat, India, ca. 1800, mango-shaped jingles. Of seven such Punch-hat containers in the Collection, three are vinaigrettes, one of which contains an urn-shaped container with hinged lid.

Right: Ram's horn
Birmingham, 1878–1879, silver repoussé mount topped with topaz

Of several horn-shaped vinaigrettes, some are made of horn or cut-glass with silver mounts, some are all silver. Many are decorated with semi-precious stones. All are attached by short chains to a ring.

By far the most common vinaigrettes are box-shaped: rectangular, square, oval, round, hexagonal, and a popular variant shaped like a purse — frequently produced in Birmingham. There are 35 of these in the Drake Collection.

Vinaigrettes, Birmingham
Left: Gold, engraved in acanthus leaf pattern over finely chased background, 1843
L: 5.0 cm
Right: Silver, engraved in classical style with gilt interior, 1849–50

Silver pomanders and vinaigrettes
Clockwise from upper left:

1. Pomander, Europe, ? Spain, 18 C, pear shape, three compartments
   L: 4.1 cm
2. Vinaigrette, Birmingham, ca. 1811, apple shape, hinged vertically, grille pierced in floral pattern
3. Pomander, Naples, 17 C, three compartments One of 10 urn shapes of 17 C Italian craftsmanship
4. Pomander, France or Germany, 15–16 C, skull shape, hinged vertically, posterior portion having six loculi, closed by a screw, the inner end of which is a tiny spoon suggesting the use of snuff
5. Vinaigrette, Germany, early 18 C, acorn shape, two compartments plus additional in small fruit
6. Pomander, Germany, early 18 C, egg shape, three compartments

Vinaigrettes

Left to right:

1. Gold, England 1817–1818, resembling a pocket watch, flat surfaces chased and edges heavily embossed[24]
   Diam: 2.8 cm
2. and 6. Pinchbeck,[25] England, ca. 1830, resembling pocket watches, faced with patterned mother-of-pearl
3. Silver, Birmingham, 1847, purse shape, overall acanthus leaf engraving including gilt grille
4. Silver, ? Europe, 19 C, oval with scrolled cherub pattern in repoussé around vacant cartouche edged in beading, intact sponge held in gilt interior
5. Silver, 19 C, hexagon, deeply engraved in acanthus leaf pattern, turquoise set in lid, reeded[26] sides, gilt interior with grille

Semi-precious stones were used to enhance the beauty of the boxes, and frequently the decorative stones were more prominent than the box itself. Of 16 such pieces most unusual perhaps, is a silver pair with agate lids, fine examples of Birmingham workmanship.

It was not uncommon to include some gimmick in a vinaigrette: one has a compass, another a whistle. A child's reticule has a vinaigrette and a mirror in the lid of the metal frame.

As sanitation and personal cleanliness improved, as the spread of infection became better understood and other means were employed to ward off disease, the devices described gave way to scent bottles and smelling salts bottles. Popular in the nineteenth century, these latter bottles are familiar to many. One variant still in use during the influenza epidemic of 1919 was the camphor locket: some older people today associate the smell of camphor with the public school classroom of their childhood. A few camphor lockets, silver, gold, and pink tin enamel, resemble pocket watches.

Vinaigrettes featuring semi-precious stones
19 C
Left and lower: Identical oval boxes
Birmingham, 1858–1859, lids of agate set in chased silver framework, F.G. in cartouches in bases of silver repoussée, sponges remain.

Upper centre: Black helmut shell cameo portraying a classical scene set in a light gilt frame engraved with overall floral pattern, projections set with garnets between blue enamel leaves
L: 3.6 cm

Right: Silesia, ca. 1830, mottled amethyst top and bottom in a gold frame engraved in latticework pattern

Silver camphor locket
Birmingham, 1902–1903
A cake of camphor can be held between the two circles, each pierced in a stylized pattern and suspended from the swivel of a loop.
Diam: 4.0 cm

Vinaigrettes with gimmicks
Child's knitted reticule, England, 19 C
Vinaigrette in lid
L: 10.0 cm

Horn-shaped vinaigrette, England, red glass cut in honeycomb pattern, engraved silver lid, metal whistle on other end

Silver sphere, London, 1872–1873, engraved in wavy pattern with vacant cartouche top and bottom, hinged to open. One lid contains a compass, the other covers the finely pierced grille enclosing the sponge of a vinaigrette in a gilt interior.

The use of scented fumes in religious ceremonies gave rise to the word "perfume" from the Latin, *per fumum* [through smoke]. In Biblical times, perfume was a luxury of the affluent. The wise men paying respects to the baby Jesus became known as kings because bringing gifts of such great value as gold, frankincense, and myrrh implied the wealth of royalty. The Collection has many perfume or scent containers and smelling bottles, including a number from the ancient world: from Egypt where glass was first made about 3000 BC and from scattered parts of the Roman Empire. In Hebron, Palestine, glass making was, and still is, a flourishing art.

Perfume bottles
Moulded glass
Egypt, AD 600–700
L: 2.5 cm

Moulded and cut glass
Egypt, ca. AD 500

Blown glass
Tyre, ca. 800 BC

Moulded and cut glass
Egypt, ca. AD 500

Blown glass
Egypt, AD 600–700

Blown glass
Egypt, AD 600–700

Blown glass perfume bottles
Upper: from Palestine:
Nazareth, AD 1 C–8 C
L: 3.6 cm

Hebron, AD 1 C–8 C

Hebron, AD 8 C–9 C or later

Lower: Roman:
Palestine, AD 100

Hebron, AD 200

Egypt, AD 200

Syria, AD 100

Perfume bottles, Peking
Glass: 1776–1820
Silver: Netherlands after 1820
Ht: left, 13.3 cm

Clear cut-glass, stained[27] and flashed[28] on outside, painted with chinoiserie pattern within, both with Dutch silver mounts embossed and etched, one with a pierced, etched, scalloped silver collar

Mediaeval monasteries in France and Italy manufactured perfume and guarded their secret formulas. By the twelfth century, French glove makers were given the privilege of making perfume to disguise the unpleasant smell inherent in leather. When clothing was voluminous, elaborate, unwashable, and expensive to replace, and when baths were infrequent, perfume became a necessity. Such was the situation in the French courts of Louis XIV and XV. Napoleon used incredible amounts of scent, even on the battlefield.

Perfume bottles of the Orient are well known and two fine examples from late eighteenth-century Peking are worth noting.

The need for scent was just as necessary in England, although the Puritans damned its use and its popularity rose and fell with the times. Small children shared in its benefits. Most perfumes, then as now, were imported, but old English recipe books abound with directions for scented waters. Interesting samples are *King Edward's Perfume,* and *Queen Elizabeths Perfume*, published in *The Queen's Closet Opened* and included in the recipes at the end of the chapter.[29]

The removal of an oppressive duty on flint glass in England in 1845 gave tremendous impetus to the manufacture of objects that could compete with Bohemian glass at home and abroad. Improvements in colour and the techniques of casing,[30] flashing, and staining glass greatly broadened the scope of its use. About the same time new artificial essences became available, and beautiful examples of overlaid[30] glass bottles appeared at the Great Exhibition of 1851; immense popularity of scent bottles resulted.

Most examples in the Collection date from the eighteenth and nineteenth centuries. Some are simple bottles; others are combinations for scent and smelling salts, scent and aromatic vinegar, or scent, smelling salts, and pomander; a few include an extra such as a patch box, a tape measure, or a pin holder.

Nineteenth-century scent bottles, mostly Victorian, were made in a great variety of shapes and sizes. Glass was the basic material, although ceramics were also used. Some bottles were fitted into cases of tortoise shell or silver filigree; others were completely encased in leather or shagreen.[31]

Among various glass bottles, plain, cut, and painted, unique shapes are plentiful, including that resembling a pocket watch. Novelty items were produced as scent bottles, some of them in silver. Two in the Collection combine thimbles, measuring tapes, and perfume bottles. A pocket-watch-shaped bottle has a vinaigrette on one flat surface.

Perfume bottles
Left: Ceramic, Europe, mid-18C
Ht: 6.9 cm

Right: Enamel, England, 19 C, hand-painted with embossed floral decoration, silver gilt finial on stopper

Cases with perfume bottles
Left: Shagreen case, England, 19 C, containing one glass bottle with stopper, silver cartouche on lid
Ht: 6.2 cm

Right: Octagonal tortoise shell case, 1796, with two compartments for bottles, one shown separately

Cut-glass perfume bottles
England, 2nd half 19 C
Left: Clear glass cased in blue and deeply cut, foliate pattern embossed on silver cap
L: 8.2 cm

Right: Silver patch box, Birmingham, on one side of bottle, engraved with pattern similar to delicate glass cutting, mirror on lid

Perfume bottles
Clockwise from upper left:
1. Hyalith[32] glass with gold decoration, Bohemia
   Gilt cap, France, 1740
2. Hyalith cut glass, Bohemia, purply black, traces of gold decoration
   Embossed silver cap, France, ca. 1838
3. Glass, drop-shaped clear glass layered over red, white and blue vertical stripes, 19 C
4. Moulded glass perfume bottle or snuff mull,[33] purple, in the shape of a sea horse
   Silver mount, England, 19 C.
5. Glass, small drop shape, purple with engraved geometric markings, silver mount
   L: 4.4 cm

Although many believed in the antiseptic qualities of perfumes, of greater medical interest are the smelling salts bottles and gemels.[34] Introduced in the late eighteenth century and popular through the nineteenth century, when it was fashionable for ladies to swoon now and then and their tight corsets encouraged them to do so, bottles were carried filled with ammonia-based salts, some derived from hartshorn. The stimulating effect of sniffing these volatile salts was enjoyed by both sexes.

Divided bottles, with two compartments, were commonly for smelling salts and scent/aromatic vinegar. Of this type, the Collection embraces five cranberry- to ruby-coloured, two Bristol green, one Bristol blue, and eight clear glass. Also included are three cranberry red, one Bristol blue, and two clear glass gemels, all with gilt mounts.

One unusually large bottle is of particular interest, as it accommodates a vinaigrette, common pins, and space for a picture as well as smelling salts or perfume.

Perfume bottles, England
Silver filigree: thimble containing glass bottle, screws on to tape measure case, ca. 1840

Silver with vinaigrette, London, 1872, S. Morden & Co.
Edge of container, perimeter of lid of vinaigrette and lid of container decorated with card-cut[35] silver bands, gilt grille of vinaigrette pierced in foliate design
Diam: 4.7 cm

Cut-glass smelling salts bottles, England
Clockwise from upper left:

1. Cranberry gemel, London, 1860, S. Morden & Co., multi-faceted,[36] 10 panelled, plain silver gilt mounts, aromatic vinegar end has glass liner under spring tension against lid, silver gilt vinaigrette in middle has grille pierced in scrolled leaf pattern, other end for smelling salts has cork lining inside lid
2. Ruby red smelling bottle, June 29, 1872, panel-cut,[37] silver gilt mounts with repoussé decoration and engraved base, top lid spring-mounted to enclose smelling salts, perfume, or aromatic vinegar. Bottom has two compartments: a vinaigrette with hinged grille and sponge; a hinged lid containing a glass covered section, for a picture, and 15 straight, gilt-headed pins, positioned like the spokes of a wheel, to fit between the two compartments
   L: 14.2 cm
3. Clear smelling bottle, 19 C, panel-cut, 2 chambers, one for salts, one with sponge for aromatic vinegar, lids with engraved floral design
4. Bristol green smelling bottle, late 18 C, multi-faceted, 10 panels, silver mounts in foliate repoussé, one cap hinged over glass stopper for aromatic vinegar, the other, with cork lining, screwed for smelling salts

It is often difficult to distinguish between vinaigrettes and snuff boxes. The latter tend to have larger holes in the grille. The cylindrical container with three sections, was possibly used for snuff, aromatic vinegar, and game counters.

Pomanders, vinaigrettes or camphor lockets were worn by children, particularly royal or noble children, as seen in paintings of the past few centuries, like that on the cover. Sometimes they were hung from the hood of the cradle. Children of poorer families used scent balls (later camphor) tied in a rag, or simply a ball of rag dipped in aromatic vinegar, as did their elders.[38] Some fortunate ones enjoyed fragrance in the nursery, where pastilles smoldered in attractive pottery or porcelain burners (see photograph introducing this section). Whether jewelled or unadorned the scents were widespread in their use and highly treasured by all ranks of society.

Combination silver gilt container
London, 1864
Two compartments have push-on grilles with pierced shamrock pattern, the third has a screw lid with monogram *MP* and stylized leaves.
L: 11.4 cm

APPENDIX

Recipes to Protect Against the Yll Ayres

Doctor Reads Perfume to smell against the Plague

First take half a pint of red Rose-water and put thereto the quantity of a hazel nut of Venice-Treacle or Nithridate, stirring them together till they be well infused, then put thereto a quarter of an ounce of Cinnamon broken into small pieces, and bruised in a Mortar, twelve Cloves bruised, the quantity of an hazel nut of Angelica root sliced very thin, as much of set wall roots sliced, three or four spoonfuls of white-wine Vinegar; so put them all together in a glass, and stop it very close, and shake it two or three times a day together, so keep it to your use; when you wet the spunge, shake the glass: in the Winter you may put to it three or four spoonfuls of Cinnamon Water or Sack.

Printed for Obadiah Blagrave.
The Queen's Closet Opened. London, 1683.

King Edward's Perfume

Take twelve spoonfuls of right red Rose water, the weight of sixpence in fine powder of Sugar, and boyl it on hot Embers and Coals softly, and the house will smell as though it were full of Roses; but you must burn the sweet Cypress wood before, to take away the gross air.

ibid.

Queen Elizabeths Perfume

Take eight spoonfuls of Compound water, the weight of two-pence in fine Sugar, and boyl it on hot Embers and Coles softly, and half an ounce of sweet Marjoram dried in the Sun, the weight of two-pence of the powder of Benjamin. This perfume is very sweet, and good for the time.

ibid.

Sweet Balls to carry in ones Hand, for the Prevention of ill Airs or Scents

Make Paste of Almonds, four ounces; mingle with it a little Bean-Flower, then knead it, being made wet with Orange, or Jessamin-water, and drop two or three drops of the Oyl of Cloves, Nutmeg, Cinnamon, or any other Scents, as you will please to have it Scented with, and make them up into Balls, or hollow Boxes.

Written by a lady *The Whole Duty of a Woman.*
London, 1701.

Pomander, Pine.

Take two ounces of Labdanum of Benjamin and Storax one ounce, Musk six grains, as much of Civet, as much of Ambergrise, of Calamus Aromaticus, and Lignum Aloes, of each a scruple; beat all these in a Mortar, and with a hot Pestle, till it come to a perfect Paste, then take a little Gun Tragacanth, steeped in Rose-water, and rub your hand withal, and make it up with speed, make them into what shapes you please, print them and dry them.

Wm. Salmon, M.D. *Salmon's Family Dictionary or Household Companion.*
London, 1710.

Balsamic and Anti-putrid Vinegar

Acetic acid may be mixed with aromatics, as in Henry's thieves vinegar, in a quantity sufficient for a small smelling-bottle, at no great expense. But it is the acetic acid which is useful, and not the aromatics which are added for the pleasure of the perfume. Acetous acid or common vinegar, with or without aromatics, has little or no anti-putrid quality.

Printed for John Murray. *The New Family Receipts Book.* London, 1811

Smelling Bottle

Reduce to powder an equal quantity of sal-ammoniac and quick lime separately, put two or three drops of the essence of burgamot into a small bottle, then add the other ingredients, and cork it close. A drop or two of ether will improve it.

Published by the editor. *The Housekeeper's Receipt Book or the Repository of Domestic Knowledge.* London, 1816

Advertisement of R. Hayward, Chymist

Also may be had, Mr. Greenbough's celebrated Volatile Salt of Vinegar which is the best Smelling Bottle for reviving the Spirits, and recovering Persons immediately from Fainting or Hysteric Fits: it is a certain preservative from all Putrid Disorders; it relieves the Head-Ach almost instantaneously, and is so great a Purifier of Air, that no Person should go into Playhouses or any crowded rooms without it. Price 2s. 9d. the small, and 5s. the large bottle.

Quoted by Dr. T.G.H. Drake in the *Journal of History of Medicine and Allied Sciences,* 1960 Vol. XV, No. 1; Morning Chronicle, London, 15 Sept. 1801.

Notes

1. Hughes 1949.
2. pomander: (1) A mixture of aromatic substances usually made into a ball and carried in a small box or bag in the hand or pocket, or suspended by a chain from the neck or waist, especially as a preservative against infection. (2) The case in which this perfume was carried, usually a hollow ball of gold, silver, ivory, etc. often in the shape of an apple or orange (*The Complete Oxford English Dictionary*).
3. Rogers 1894.
4. Herring 1636:C2, verso.
5. Quennell M and CHB 1931:Part II, 8.
6. Portrait of Elizabeth: The "Portland" Queen Elizabeth at Welbeck Abbey, signed with initials of Marcus Gheeraeds, probably about 1578.
7. Scene III from Hogarth's *Marriage à la Mode*, entitled "The Countess's Dressing Room", National Gallery, painted in 1744, reproduced in *English Furniture Illustrated* by Oliver Brackett, revised and edited by H. Clifford Smith, 1950, Ernest Benn Limited, London, p 167.
8. See sample recipes in the Appendix p. 207.
9. pouncet: originally pounced meaning perforated. Hence pouncet-box, a perforated box for scents.
10. Drake, TGH Notes left with the Collection.
11. [Glasse] 1755:329.
12. [Rundle] 1811:170.
13. Squire 1908. (Dr. Drake's notes mention that this also appeared in the 19th edition of *Companion to the British Pharmacopoeia.*)
14. Dick 1975:463.
15. Muffett 1655:24–25.
16. Jackson 1921:73.
17. engraved: incised, metal cut away in a linear pattern with a sharp pointed tool or graver.
18. chased: decorated gold or silver done with a hammer and punch so as to produce a pattern by pushing but not cutting the metal. Done from the front, it is flat chasing.
19. B. probably stands for Botanik, indicating botanical or plant material.
20. *Pharmacopoeia*, Vienna, 1860. Schlag is listed as the berry or bark of the schlag tree.
21. etched: engraved with acids rather than a sharp instrument.
22. filigree: delicate, thread-like gold or silver wire, formed into patterns.
23. repoussé: chasing done from behind, pushing the metal into bulges.
24. embossed: pressed or beaten from the back producing a raised design.
25. pinchbeck: an alloy of copper and zinc used in imitation of gold. The metal was invented by Christopher Pinchbeck, an English watch maker who died in 1732. Hence pinchbeck indicates sham, counterfeit or cheap (*Random House Dictionary*).
26. reeded: relief fluting where the surface is raised in thin ridges.
27. staining: a thin film of metallic oxide covering the surface inside or outside, is fixed by a light firing.
28. flashing: a very thin film of coloured over clear glass produced by brief dipping into molten coloured glass.
29. (n.a.) *The Queen's Closet Opened* 1683:78.
30. casing: layer of glass completely covering another colour or colours. Patterns can be cut or ground away to reveal colour(s) beneath. If patterns are eaten away with hydrofluoric acid, it produces cameo glass. Casing is also called *overlaying*.
31. shagreen: shark skin.
32. hyalith: opaque black glass, invented about 1817.
33. mull: snuff container. First literary reference TG Smollet 1771 (*Oxford English Dictionary* 2nd Ed. Vol X).
34. gemel: a divided bottle, hinged in the middle to form two identical sections for scent and for smelling salts.
35. card-cut: applied flat relief decoration.
36. faceted: cut with flat surfaces as in gems.
37. panel-cut: cut in a series of identical facets or panels, such as around a bottle.
38. Early settlers in America, especially the ladies, carried dried flowers and herbs tied into a rag ball. Along the shores of Chesapeake Bay, in Maryland, one of these little treasures was called a "Tussy Mussy."

Tin-glazed earthenware pill tile
England, ca. 1700
Arms of the Society of Apothecaries.
At its centre is Apollo with bow and arrow in hand, over a slain dragon. He is flanked by a pair of unicorns. At top centre, a rhinoceros stands on a knight's helmet. Motto: Opiferque per orbem dicor [I am called helper throughout the world].
Ht: 30 cm

Note there are identical examples in the Fitzwilliam Museum, Cambridge, and in the Wellcome Museum, the Science Museum, London.

'POTHECARIES, POTIONS, PURGES AND PALLIATIVE CARE

Whenever any of their children appear indisposed, or do not seem to thrive, ..., away the mothers run to the apothecary.

William Buchan. *Advice to Mothers*.
1804, pp. 153–154.

The above practice is reflected in the traditional skipping jingle:

O, dear mother what a pain I've got!
Take me this minute to the 'pothecary shop.
How many pills did they give her?
One, two, three ...

Pages of Buchan's book are devoted to berating mothers for their reliance on medicines. A century later, during an address in which he condemned the public for delighting in patent medicines and being in the hands of advertising quacks, William Osler stated that "... the desire to take medicine is perhaps the greatest feature which distinguishes man from animals."[1]

A concerned mother of an ailing child nowadays uses home remedies such as bedrest, hot or cold baths, hot tea or broth, ginger ale, or others, according to the complaints or disorders of the child. If her concern grows sufficiently, she calls a doctor. Until recent times it was not so simple.

Historically in England, as in France, traders in spicery dealt in medicines. By the thirteenth century they had divided into two classes: grocers and apothecaries, and in the fourteenth century both groups belonged to the Fraternity of St. Anthony. Through the Middle Ages apothecaries were trained in a seven-year apprenticeship; their practice was regulated first by the Grocers Company and in the seventeenth century by the Society of Apothecaries in London. Inspection of shops was carried out by the Master Apothecaries in cooperation with the Royal College of Physicians of London. The society held jurisdiction over the city and seven miles beyond, but left many rural areas unguarded against unqualified usurpers. It was responsible not only for the Chelsea Physic Garden, established in 1673, but also for the manufacture of medicines from it. In France practice was regulated by the Corporation of Spicer-Apothecaries in Montpellier, and supervision was carried out by the Medical School of the University of that city.

During the eighteenth century the apothecaries in London polarized toward medicine, becoming general practitioners; their former assistants, the chemists and druggists (and a few apothecaries), veered toward pharmacy and eventually formed the Pharmaceutical Society (1841). In France progress toward establishment of a School of Pharmacy was rapid, and textbooks and research on the continent were beneficial to apothecaries. But internal strife between factions — chemists, druggists, surgeons, and apothecaries — slowed progress in England. Medical education centred around Gresham College (London), the Royal Society, and the Royal College of Physicians, but these institutions and the universities of Oxford and Cambridge paid little attention to pharmaceutical education. It was much later before university schools of pharmacy were established in England.

Before the nineteenth century, physicians treated royalty, nobility, and the wealthy, but seldom visited the sick of other classes. Physicians charged for their services, whereas apothecaries charged for their medicines. Apothecaries were known to meet with physicians in the pubs to discuss problem cases, and they, with their apprentices, would visit the sick. In times of crises (the Great Fire, the Plague) when the wealthy fled the city, apothecaries stayed behind and treated those in need. Apothecaries too offered their treatments to royalty and nobility. The royal family had at least one court physician and one court apothecary, often more.

In the Middle Ages and during the Renaissance, a mother with a sick child would try a number of home remedies; then, if she lived in the country, she might seek out the lady of the manor or her priest; if near town she would consult the local apothecary.

Herbs headed the list of treatments. Rhubarb enjoyed a popularity that spanned many centuries in many countries. One of the earliest and most famous guides was the *Greek Herbal of Dioscorides* written in the first century. Dioscorides was a Roman army surgeon. His book became the standard reference for 15 centuries; though many Herbals were written, little new knowledge was added. Some of the earliest physicians tried, for the benefit of the herb diggers, to supplement with illustrations the information about plants, but Pliny, whose first-century *Historie of the World* contains voluminous information about herbs, supported others who criticised the poor quality of the plant illustrations and the fact that a drawing made at any one season could not be considered typical for the whole year. Pliny's discussions about the use of herbs convey the incredible extent to which they were employed. In one book he dealt individually with dozens of herbs cultivated in the garden; in another he elaborated similarly on those growing in the wild. In many instances he expressed his own doubt as to their efficacy, but admitted to the faith held by others. Supplementary treatments through the centuries included warm baths in which a variety of herbs played a major role.

The writers of herbals gave detailed instruction for identifying and selecting herbs of good quality, indicated the use to which they should be put, the most efficient methods of storing them, and the best containers to preserve their quality. As to their gathering, much superstition surrounded the whole process. Some should be dug at midnight, some in the morning dew, some only at full moon; precautions must be taken such as standing to the windward or avoiding the presence of buzzards to evade a personal curse — a few examples of an extensive folklore.

Quacks, of whom there were many, were able to gather from the Herbals such as the widely-used and highly-regarded *Gerard's Herball*, by 1633 in its second edition, enough information to make their nostrums sound appealing to a gullible public. By then illustrations were of a useful quality.

Concurrent remedies of animal origin were plentiful, most of them quite repulsive to us today: ox bile, pig brains, millipedes, mice, hare's brain, earthworms, hartshorn, viper's brain, and more. Specific examples and their sources are given (p. 214).

Many of these remedies had a purging or costive effect. Other treatments included enemas, bleeding, blistering, and poulticing.

Primarily to relieve pain, reduce fevers, and cure other common ailments such as diarrhoea, these practices were an attempt to draw out excess humours, particularly from the brain, or to absorb acids from the blood, preparing them for elimination, and finally to excrete the products to rid the body of its plethora. Hence many of the medicines, herbal and other, were emetic and more were for purging.

The Greek humoural theory, taught by the school of Hippocrates and widely disseminated by Galen, was still influencing many physicians to varying degrees, even into the eighteenth century. The four humours — blood, phlegm, yellow bile, and black bile — embodied characteristics (hot, cold, dry, moist) that must be kept in balance for good health. Proportions could be altered by drug treatment: *simple* drugs affecting one quality, *composite* drugs affecting more. Drugs not fitting one of the regular categories, such as emetics and purgatives, were called *entities*.[2]

From the days of Hippocrates bleeding, especially for fevers, was popular and became so common in nineteenth-century England and France that few patients escaped it. Flaubert's 1857 story of provincial life in France, *Madame Bovary*, describes vividly the bleeding of a villager and the fainting of both the patient and an observer.

For bleeding and lancing most likely a surgeon would be called upon. Unlike physicians, surgeons were not always professionals. In the days of Ambrose Parey and before, surgeons were of the tradesmen's class, and known as barber-surgeons, for it was the barber who first did the surgery. The eighteenth century saw the surgeons establish themselves professionally.

By the eighteenth century, apothecaries, pharmacists, and physicians were gaining a better understanding of their medicines, and drugs with specific action on the body were being isolated. The popular herbals were gradually superseded by more scientific books on botany and pharmacology, and some of the herbal mixtures were replaced by more specific doses in liquid or in pill form.

Mice

Nineteen centuries ago Pliny advised feeding sodden mice to children to cure bed-wetting (Pliny, Bk. 30, p. 398). Remains of mice have been found in the alimentary canals of Egyptian mummified children, unquestionably given as medicine. For bed-wetting in Southern Italy today, mice are still fed to children (Walton Brooks McDaniel, *Conception, Birth, and Infancy in Ancient Rome and Modern Italy*, 1948, p. 52).

Hartshorn

Hartshorn appears to be one of the remedies that retained popularity for centuries. As were the horns of other beasts such as rhinoceros and unicorn, (note their presence on the apothecary coat of arms), the deer's horn was endowed with amuletic properties in ancient times. Later it came to be used medicinally: Phaer in the sixteenth century gave harsthorn for "flux of the belly," powdered with goats' or swines' claws and mixed in red wine (Tho. Phaer, *Boke of Chyldren*, 1550 edition, Y1 and Y5 plus 3 leaves); Harris in 1689 included burned "harts-horn" or spirits of "hart's horn" among antacids listed for the relief of gripes, regarding hartshorn as safe for infants and children (W. Harris, *Diseases of Infants*, London, 1694, pp. 51–3); Theobald recommended it in 1764 for difficult teething (J. Theobald, *The Young Wife's Guide*, London, 1764); Buchan about the same time used spirits of hartshorn in inflammatory diseases including teething, and listed hartshorn in his later book in 1793 as one of about 200 remedies to be kept in a physician's dispensary (Wm. Buchan, *Domestic Medicine*, Boston, 1793, pp. 441–2), and Moss claimed in 1781, that "to dispel the wind" nothing gives such relief to infants as "spirit of harsthorn...It is endowed with a property which makes it a desirable medicine for children; which is it corrects and removes acidity or sourness, a principle cause of griping with children, ... it may be given ... with ease and safety" (Wm. Moss, *An Essay on the Management and Nursing of Children* ... London, 1781, pp. 173–4). The powdered horn and the extractions from it, contain the active ingredient ammonium carbonate, itself referred to as hartshorn (Block, J.H., Roche, E.B., Sorne, T.D., Wilson, C.D., *Inorganic Medicinal and Pharmaceutical Chemistry,* Philadelphia, Lea and Febiger, 1974, p. 428).

The Anglo-Saxons before the Norman conquest used buckthorn berries as a laxative under the name of hartshorn, and Welsh physicians in the thirteenth century prescribed the juice of the berries boiled with honey as an aperient drink. The title "Syrup of Buckthorn" still prevailed in 1921 (Flückiger, F.A. and Hanbury, Daniel, *Pharmacographia*, 2nd ed., London, MacMillan, 1879, p.157, and Lloyd, John Uri, *Origin and History of all the Pharmacopeial Vegetable Drugs, Chemicals and Preparations*, Cincinnati, The Caxton Press, Vol. 1, 1921, p. 264).

It is not always possible to judge which preparation was intended when hartshorn was prescribed, but when Phaer specified "the pouder of a hartes horn in a powder mix for canker in the mouth of children," he meant the horn of a deer (p. 41, 1955 edition).

Vipers

Pliny recommended vipers in the second century. "The braines of a viper if they be put in a little fine skin, and worn by a yong child, helpeth it to breed teeth without any great pain; for the same purpose serve also the teeth of serpents, so they be chosen the biggest that are in their heads: ..." (Pliny, *Historie of the World*, p. 398). Powdered vipers were prescribed by Astruc in 1746 as treatment for convulsions in children (Astruc, John, *Treatise on all the Diseases Incident to Children*, London, 1746). Vipers in some form were still used medicinally in England toward the end of the eighteenth century, for an apothecary's order was: "Mr. Sole to William Jones 28 Nov. 1781. Please send by very first coach one or two dozen but not more of live vipers which we are very much in want of" (G.M. Watson, "Some Eighteenth Century Trading Accounts," *Evolution of Pharmacy in Britain*, Poynter, ed.).

Examples to illustrate the persistent recommendation for the use of animal-derived substances through many centuries

From the days of antiquity the pill has been a practised means of administering medicines. During the ninteenth century the hand-made pills from the pharmacist's dispensary gave way to compressed tablets and capsules of laboratory manufacture in more accurate dosage. But the isolation of active ingredients was not always easy, and the extraction of some was elusive. Until the middle of the present century, for example, the active ingredient in foxglove was still prescribed in such manner as "1½ grains digitalis leaf."

Children were not exempt from any of these treatments; when one approach failed, another would be tried — and another, often simultaneously. Infants of teething age received more than their share. Harris exemplified the many who regarded teething as a disease and thereby deemed treatment essential.

> Among the many Diseases that do threaten for the life of Infants, there is none that produceth so many grievous Symptoms as their laborious and difficult breeding of Teeth. The Sickness of nine months ... doth not expose Mothers to greater hazard, than Breeding-teeth, doth their Offspring.
>
> Walter Harris. *An Exact Enquiry into, and Cure of the Acute Diseases of Infants.* 1694.

There were very few who regarded teething with little apprehension. Cadogan firmly believed that healthy children with balanced humours had no problems; Struve simply stated that teething is no disease; and Huxham in France regarded the process as normal though painful.

Parents today are aware that many infants become fretful, even immensely upset, while teething. Some babies are irritable, feverish, have worrisome diarrhoea or constipation, get rashes, and are truly miserable. But present-day parents do not worry that teething will cause convulsions and death. In earlier times when infant mortality was high, many children died before the age of two. For many, infancy was a time of delicate balance between life and death, and the extra stress of teething, sometimes combined with the risks of weaning, could tip the scales against survival. It is understandable then that as early as the days of Hippocrates teething was often regarded as a dreaded disease, and some of this attitude persisted for centuries. Not surprisingly, parents, nurses, and physicians sought preventive and curative measures to help children through this dangerous period.

Practices commonly adopted can be roughly divided into three broad categories: (1) those based on superstition; (2) those aimed at minimizing the associated symptoms, and (3) those directly hastening the process of eruption. The three approaches were used singly or in combination. Unclassifiable suggestions arouse one's curiosity, for example: treating the baby's nurse for baby's fever.[3]

Among the first suggestions to ease teething are those by Pliny previously mentioned: brains of a viper or teeth of a serpent worn about the neck, and another, the gritty substance from the little horns of shell-snails hanged about a young infant.[4] Phaer recommended "the first tooth of a colt set in silver and borne or red corrale set in silver and hanged about the neck," adding a special note to emphasize the amuletic qualities of coral.[5]

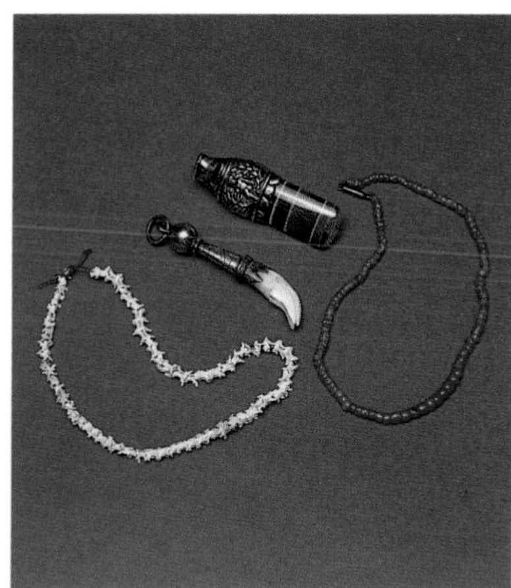

Teething sticks and necklaces
Banded agate teething stick (rare), embossed silver mount with whistle, 19 C
L: 6.3 cm

Wolf's tooth, silver mount
Germany, 17 C

Snakes' vertebrae necklace
Germany, 19 C

Coral necklace

The same writers, and many later, advised lenitive measures of the second category. These included rubbing the gums with fingers dipped in oil or grease containing palliative substances, and giving the baby firm, cool substances on which to chew. Most of the approaches to soothing did not overlook the amuletic, however. For example, to the rubbing grease, already flavoured or sweetened with honey or mixed with soothing herbs, Paulus Aegineta reported that the Greeks of the late sixth and early seventh centuries added the brains of a hare, the custom based on faith in the amuletic effect.[6] He added that the flesh of an old pickle relieves pruritis of the gums!

Usually it was the mother or nurse who rubbed the baby's gums, but Sainte-Marthe (1535–1623) suggested that annointing the baby's own fingers with appealing flavours, would encourage the child to chew on *them*.[7] Though iris root, a liquorice stick, bone, or ivory were commonly offered for chewing, a coral stick, polished banded agate, or a mounted wolf's tooth were strongly recommended — all with amuletic connotations — throughout the sixteenth and seventeenth centuries. Coral and colourful semiprecious stones were believed to ward off the Evil Eye, the wolf's tooth, to encourage the growth of strong teeth like those of the beast. Substances assumed to have amuletic characteristics, were also made, from ancient times, into necklaces worn for protection but also to be chewed upon.

Although hard substances on which teething babies could bite remained popular, Mauriceau, in mid-seventeenth-century France, introduced a clean wax candle as an alternate soother. It was he who suggested adding bells to the hard sticks, not to avert danger as many thought, but to divert the child from the pain, for he had no faith in any of the popular lenitive or amuletic cures, founded as they were on superstition, not reason.

Teething Sticks
Clockwise from bottom left:
Coral on silver mount with whistle and bells, ? London, 1787
Coral on silver gilt mount with whistle, London, 1786–1787, 13.9 cm
Mother-of-pearl on silver Beatrix Potter cat, Birmingham, 1914–1915
Ivory on silver repoussé shell with bells, France, ca. 1838
Coral on gold mount, England, 19 C

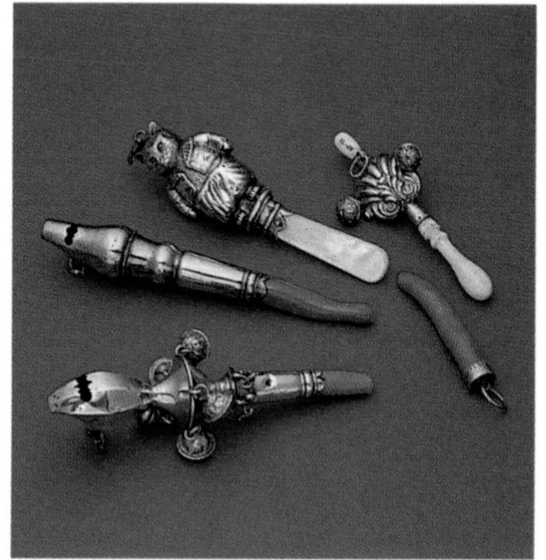

During the eighteenth century, writers in Britain also began to doubt the use of very hard teethers, on the ground that they toughened the gums so that the teeth had more difficulty erupting. At the same time many were censoring the use of amuletics, claiming that brains of a hare or a wolf's tooth had no advantage over other similar agents. In 1742 Joseph Hurlock, who wrote the first treatise in England devoted entirely to dentition, chose the wearing of particular necklaces — snakes' vertebrae, coral, cowrie shells (see p. 162), henbane or peony — as the target for his strongest criticism. He felt that people were free to wear whatever necklace they wished, but that innocent children were being deprived of more rational treatment by credulous parents. His contemporary, Cadogan, agreed with him, as did most nineteenth-century British authorities who followed. Yet the use of hard-substance teething sticks and necklaces remained widespread.

Portraits of French royal children of 1682–1683 showing coral teething sticks.
Engravings by de L'Armessin
France, ca. 1682–1700

[The Duke of Burgundy etc., son of Louis, Dauphin of France and Marie Anne Christine Victoire of Bauierre, grandson of Louis the Great, King of France, and Marie Therèse of Austria. Born at the castle of Versailles, 6 Aug., 1682. The King gave him at the same time the title of Duke of Burgundy. He was baptized by the Cardinal of Bouillon, Grand Almoner of France in the presence of their majesties.]
23.5 × 16.3 cm

[The Duke of Anjou, second son of Louis Dauphin of France and Mme Marie Anne Christine Victoire of Bauierre, born at the Royal Palace of Versailles 20 Dec., 1683.]
24.1 × 17.1 cm

A London apothecary of the eighteenth century, Basil Burchell, developed anodyne necklaces for teething which became extraordinarily popular and remained so for decades. The composition is uncertain, but they were probably henbane or peony root. Henbane is in the same family as belladonna. The benefit might have been amuletic, but chewing on the necklace would have been soothing. Some of the hyoscyamine might have been absorbed to relieve the gripes that frequently accompany teething. Many of Burchell's tokens advertising his necklace — and his sugar plums for worms — survive (see addendum to this chapter "Apothecary and Related Tokens"). According to a letter to Dr. Drake, two eminent physicians, Drs. Tanner and Chamberlain, strongly recommended the teething necklace in 1767. It also disclosed that in 1814 the necklace sold for nine shillings.[8]

J. Theobald, in condoning the use of coral, urged nurses to tie it with a ribbon around the waist. In France, Brouzet recommended tying toys to the neck, body, or hand so as not to lose the toy or thrust it down the throat.

The approach in France was generally more gentle. Raulin, Icart, Protat, and Léger, in the late eighteenth and early nineteenth centuries were opposed to hard substances and favoured a piece of soft bread, marshmallow, or liquorice root. By this time Rousseau's writings were popular, particularly *Emile*, in which he declaimed the use of hard teethers as hurtful.

Teething sticks and teething rings are presently used; rings of rubber or firm plastic, some hollow and filled with water intended to be refrigerated, are readily available. Bread sticks or dried crusts are commonly offered to fretting babies. In more painful teething mild pain killers are prescribed, sometimes rubbed over the gums.

Dr. Samuel X. Radbill in 1964 read a lengthy paper before the American Folklore Society, devoted entirely to "The Folklore of Teething." The modern child still leaves a lost tooth under the pillow, under a rug, or in a glass of water, to await the reward of the "tooth fairy." Dr. Drake himself wrote in 1932: "In my own childhood care was taken to burn my primary teeth after they had been extracted by the string attached to the door knob method; since, if they were thrown away and consumed by a dog, the secondary teeth would be similar in form to those of a hound."[9]

Many treatments commonly used for illnesses in adults were adapted for children's disorders, including the symptoms of teething. Used for almost all ailments of children, they are discussed later.

A Royal Nurse
Engraving by Bonnart, probably Henri
Paris, 1690–1695
26.5×18.5 cm

Note similar rattle p. 285

The third and final approach to treating troublesome teething involved the surgeons, who focused on cutting the gums in an effort to hasten the second stage of eruption. The first stage was considered to be the breaking out of the jawbone; the second, the eruption through the gum. Lancing was usually recommended only at stage two. In the mid-eighteenth century, Hurlock assessed the pros and cons of lancing: he referred to Parey's recommendation of the procedure (1635) using a lancet or a knife, *not* the nurse's fingernail, but noted that cutting had not been common since then. It was, however, advised as a last resort by Mauriceau in 1668, using a lancet or a thin groat, and again by Harris in 1694, using a penknife or a razor, not a lancet, to keep the wound from healing too quickly. Hurlock concluded that lancing the gums was helpful. Brouzet[10] in 1755 still condoned cutting with the nurse's fingernail, but added that if a lancet became necessary, one should employ a surgeon. John Hunter and George Armstrong both preferred a fleam as the ideal instrument. Most authorities held lancing in reserve until other treatments had been tried.

Leech jar
Tin-glazed earthenware
England, ca. 1800
Ht: 33.4 cm

Adult treatments adapted for children's disorders, even for teething, included: poulticing, blistering, and bleeding, aimed at drawing out humours or acids; enemas, emetics, laxatives, purges, and costives, to control the process of elimination.

Poultices were applied to the stomach or the back; blisters were raised behind the ears or at the nape of the neck. Most bleeding in infants was done with leeches applied to the feet, the arms, behind the ears, and sometimes to the stomach. Leech jars were a common sight in the apothecary shops. We are inclined to think this treatment is a little primitive, but in the mid-1950s, a doctor at the Toronto General Hospital stepped into an elevator on a Monday morning and was confronted by the enormous black eye of an orderly. The doctor inquired as to the man's well-being and the orderly asked, "Doctor, do you think I should use these?" Wherewith he pulled a box from his pocket containing a number of leeches. With that particular problem leeches were probably quite beneficial.

Babies were not entirely spared the opening of a vein. Walter Harris recommended bleeding the baby before purging for even the youngest infants, in a limited number of disorders.[11] This bleeding was from a vein and required the use of a lancet.

So frequently were lancets employed that various sized blades folding into handles, usually of tortoise shell, were carried in special cases that held up to six lancets. Of the many lancet cases in the Collection made of silver, ivory, tortoise shell, leather, and other materials, a few are shown.

Instruments for cutting gums
One fleam, three steel blades folding into brass handle
England, ca. 1840
L: 17.7 cm extended

Two lancets, steel blades folding into tortoise shell handles
England, 19 C

Lancet cases
England, 19 C
Upper left to right:

1. Silver case with four lancets, London, cartouche: Dr. Burns to Dr. Middleton
2. Mother-of-pearl with four lancets, ht: 7.0 cm
3. Green snakeskin with lancets folding into mother-of-pearl handles
4. Tortoise shell case carved in chinoiserie design, containing one lancet
5. Shagreen case for five lancets with blades folding into tortoise shell handles
6. Silver case with six lancets, Dr. Bartley engraved on one side, W.B. on other

Centre: Tortoise shell, with three lancets folding into tortoise shell handles

Lower: Red morocco leather case for one lancet

Lancets: One blade folding into mother-of-pearl handles
One blade folding into tortoise shell handles

Relating to vaccination
Wooden lancet case
England, 19 C
Dr. Jenner's portrait

Tortoise shell lancet for vaccination
England, 1854
L: 5.7 cm closed, with 2 cm blade
(The vaccination is intracutaneous, the vaccine being dripped into a scratch.)

In the nineteenth century, treatment of the gums by lancing flourished. Hugh Ley in 1836, in agreement with Hunter earlier, believed that cutting was necessary and that it could be repeated as often as needed. A friend in her 90s today, whose father was an Ontario doctor, recalls parents bringing children to his office when she was a child, to have their gums cut. The procedure persisted into the twentieth century, but is no longer practised today.

Of particular note are the case and lancet shown. The case portrays Dr. Jenner who discovered smallpox vaccine, and the lancet is one of a specialized type for vaccination, with a grooved blade down which a drop of the vaccine can flow. Edward Jenner, a friend of the famous surgeon John Hunter, lived in Berkley in southwest England, and there developed the vaccine in the 1790s. He vaccinated a number of children of whom his nephew was among the first. His results were published in 1798. Within a few years there was a vaccination institute which gave courses to teach vaccination, and the method soon was used in America. The first was performed in 1801 by the Reverend John Clinch[12] in Trinity Bay, Newfoundland. Jenner believed that universal vaccination would eliminate smallpox. Through the efforts of the World Health Organization all contacts of smallpox victims were vaccinated, and almost two centuries after Jenner's discovery the disease is considered to be wiped out.

For centuries, in addition to lancets and scalpels, physicians, apothecaries, and in some instances barber-surgeons used a great variety of small instruments: needles, knives, saws, spatulas, curettes, scoops, probes, and tweezers. A 1720 case contains a few. Early instruments were made of iron, bronze, or bone; later gilt, even gold was used. Many were found in London, dating from Roman times.

Belief in the need to control elimination from the body grew to the extent that lavements and purges, often with counterbalancing costives, were used even before untoward symptoms appeared, and purging in various forms and strengths became the common way to deal with many illnesses in the late seventeenth and eighteenth centuries. Prior to that, suggestions were made of cathartic mixtures including honey, of gentle clysters or suppositories at birth[13] or when otherwise needed; laxatives were more likely to be recommended for the baby's nurse.

Shagreen instrument case
Silver cartouche, engraved
England, ca. 1720
Contents, not necessarily the original
England
Silver earspud at one end, steel file with hooked terminal at other
Silver probe at one end, needle eye at other
Silver probe
Silver spatula at one end, steel forceps opening at other
Scalpel, silver handle, steel blade
L: 10.7 cm

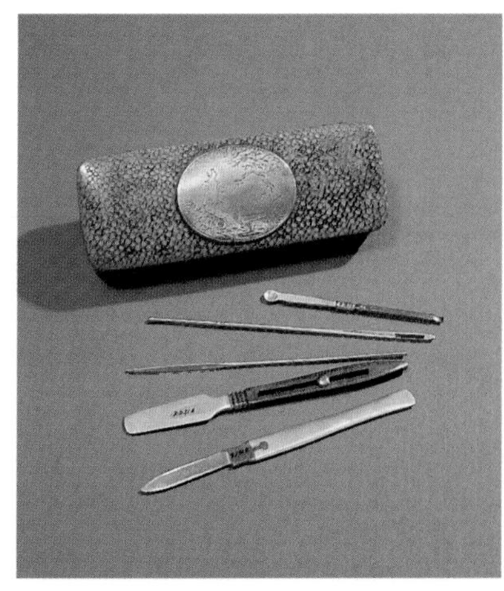

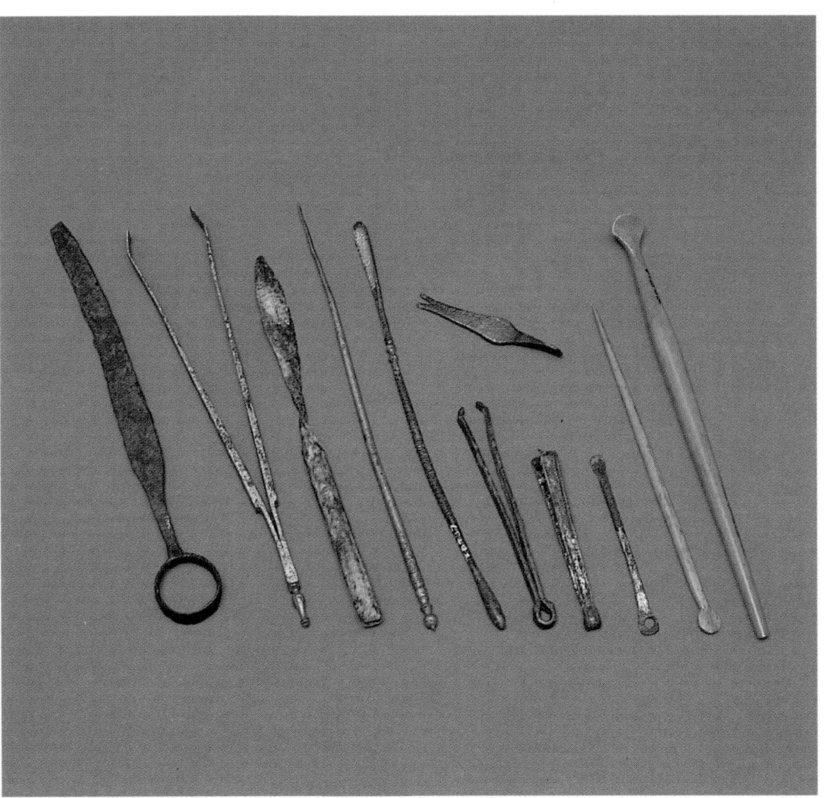

Roman London instruments, ca. AD 100
Most found in River Walbrook
Left to right:
1. Saw, bronze, l: 15.0 cm
2. Tweezers, bronze with traces of gilt
3. Scalpel, bronze
4. Needle, gilt
5. Probe, gilt
6. Tweezers, gilded bronze
7. Tweezers, gilded bronze
8. Earspud, bronze with traces of gilt
9. Probe, bone
10. Probe, bone

Above:

11. Bronze implement with bifurcated tip

In England the beliefs of eighteenth-century authorities differed regarding treatments: some advised purging, then bleeding, then blistering; others claimed one should never purge before bloodletting. Convictions varied as to how to purge — with clysters, more gentle lavements, or medicines with sufficient strength to accomplish the objective. Similar divergence of opinion reigned over the use of emetic medicines. George Armstrong, who established the Dispensary for the Infant Poor in Soho, London, in 1769 preferred an antimonial wine or antimonial puke (tartar emetic in water), which acted both as an emetic and a purge, to be followed by a chalk julep or other antacids. This was favoured by many contemporaries.

Purging became so widespread as to become a common subject portrayed by caricaturists. A visit from the apothecary, perhaps trailed by his apprentice carrying an enema syringe of huge proportions, was undoubtedly dreaded by many a patient.

One enema syringe is so large that Dr. Drake initially felt it was meant for a cow. Then he acquired a caricature, now unfortunately missing from the Collection, of an apothecary rushing off to see a patient, as the apprentice kept pace behind carrying the enema syringe. Relative proportions revealed its immense size. Confirmation is apparent in the porcelain figure seen here and in various other caricatures. Artists of the seventeenth and eighteenth centuries, when bawdy humour was so prevalent, frequently highlighted the commonly used or misused enema syringe and undoubtedly exaggerated its size. After all Dr Drake's first impression may have been correct.

Enema syringes
Pewter
England, ca. 1800
L: 91.4 cm extended

Porcelain figure with pewter syringe
Paris, Edm. Samson 1873–1876,
Ht: 17.1 cm

Leather with bone tip
Guiana or Brazil, 18 C
L: 20.3 cm

Brisk Cathartic
Coloured etching by James Gillray
London, Jan. 26, 1804
25.5 × 21.1 cm

Gentle Emetic
Coloured etching by James Gillray
London, Jan. 28, 1804
38.0 × 28.0 cm

Brisk Cathartic and *Gentle Emetic* are two of a series. See also *Breathing a Vein* p. 240

Le Remède [The Remedy]
Coloured lithograph by Delpech after Aubry
France, 1830–1850
20.0 × 15.0 cm
Children were well acquainted with the popular treatments of their day

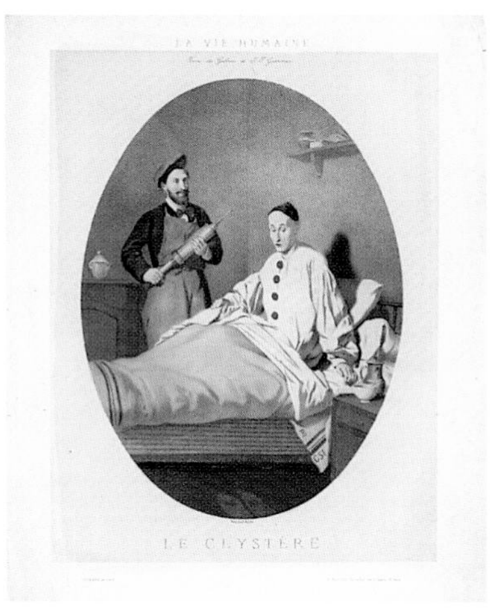

Le Clystère [The Clyster]
La Vie Humaine [Human Life Series]
Coloured lithograph by Carot after J. Pezous
Paris 1840–1870
46.3 × 36.3 cm

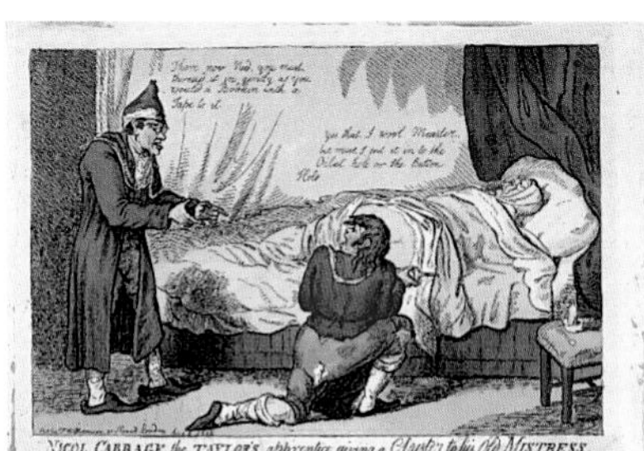

Nicol Cabbage the Taylor's Apprentice giving a clyster to his old mistress
Coloured etching
London, 8 Aug. 1804
21.3 × 33 cm

La Curiosité punie
[Curiosity punished]
Aventure hydrauli, comique et vraie
[A comic and true water experience]
Coloured etching by G. de Cou
Paris, early 19 C
16.8 × 23.3 cm

Nelson's philosophical book of 1753 on educating children devotes pages to teaching children to take medicine — a symptom of the widespread acceptance in England of the need for medicines.

John Locke at the turn of the eighteenth century advocated not giving children any physic for prevention. Eminent physicians, William Buchan and Michael Underwood,[14] by the end of the century had tempered their approach and agreed that if a person is healthy, natural habits should not be counteracted.

Jack, bove down — with a Grog Blossom Fever
Coloured etching by Elmer William
London, 12 Aug. 1811
21.8 × 30.4 cm

'hold — I must stop your Grog Jack — It excites those impulses, and concussions of the Thorax, which acompany Hernutations by which means you are in a sort of a kind of a situation — that your head must be — Shaved — I shall take from you only 20 oz. of blood — then swallow this Draught and Box of Pills, and I shall administer to you a Clyster.
Stop my Grog — Belay there Doctor — Shiver my timbers but your lingo bothers me — You may batter my Hull as long as you like, but I'll be d—'nd if ever you board me with your Glyster pipe.

Around 1760, when Buchan took charge of the Ackworth branch of the Foundling Hospital in Yorkshire, he found "Every cupboard and every shelf in the house was filled with phials and gallipots"[15] and half the children died annually. With the approval of the governors of the home, Buchan forbade the nurses to give any medicine without his personal sanction. The annual mortality rate fell to 1:50 and the cost of drugs to one percent of the previous expense.

The majority of physicians were not so prohibitive. S.H. Jackson, in 1798, claimed that as long as nurses continued to cram children with food, purging would be necessary; it was the cramming that must cease. In 1802 Struve simply stated that clysters were good for children.

Even Underwood (1784) declared opiates safe for children though the child be very young and the medicine often repeated. They were prescribed by many, if not routinely, then in desperation. Armstrong, opposed to the use of opiates, prescribed calomel (mercurous chloride) for costiveness.

The most outspoken writers against all these abuses of children, were John Herdman (1807), a strong supporter of the theories of Buchan, and John Roberton (1827) who urged that the bowels be regulated with regimen and gentle lavements if necessary, with the aim of achieving looseness rather than a purge. If all else failed, he approved the use of calomel, but he made scathing remarks about the use of laudanum and other opium preparations. He claimed that opium was poisonous to infants, except in minute doses, and that even tiny amounts were very dangerous. Yet Roberton had observed that infants, particularly those connected with public charities where it was convenient to have them sleep a great deal, were given opium-based medicines such as: "laudanum, syrup of poppies, Godfrey's cordial, Dalby's carminative, and similar potions."[16] Many thus handled just faded away. It was probable, according to Roberton, that almost all infant deaths reported as smothering from being overlaid, were in fact caused by laudanum overdose.

> It is doubtful whether treatises on domestic medicine are ever of use. Their most obvious effect is to create a fondness for administering physic, and a whimsical and often pernicious anxiety under trifling ailments. The readers of such books are generally the best friends of the apothecary, and the most troublesome patients to the physician.
>
> John Roberton. *Observations on the Mortality and Physical Management of Children.* 1827, p. 269.

The same ubiquitous use of medicines prevailed in France. An edict of the king in 1777 ordered free remedies for nurslings of the poor from Paris who were being raised in the provinces, and 2258 boxes of medicines were to be sent annually to their wet nurses.[17]

The Nurse for Rocking the Duke of Berry*
22.3 × 16.7 cm
Without opium and without fuss, this royal baby whom I rock finds his rest in the back and forth movement.
* See p. 64

The royal nurse rocking the Duke of Berry is obviously proud of putting her nursling to sleep without administering opium. Her comment infers the common use of the drug for infants.

By the early nineteenth century the prevalent use of medicines gave rise to the development of special spoons for administering the doses. One designed by C. Gibson was demonstrated to the Royal Society in 1828. The earliest known are dated 1827. The Gibson spoon, or castor oil spoon, was a covered bowl with a hinged trap-door, a small hole in the tip, and a hollow, flanged handle. Medicine put in through the trap-door flowed into the patient's mouth through the tip of the bowl, the flow being controlled with the finger tip over the end of the hollow handle. A desperate parent could blow through the handle, a desperate child could blow back. At what point would medicine get into the lungs?

The early medicine spoons made of silver and pewter were soon augmented by simple ones of pottery and porcelain, usually supported by feet.

Medicine spoons
Clockwise from top:
Silver, simple style, supported on three feet
London, 1836
Capacity: 23 cc

Gibson spoon, silver, 1827, Maker: W.B. (Wm. Bateman)
Inscribed on guard "C. Gibson, inventor 71 Bishopsgate St. Within"
Capacity: 12 cc

Porcelain, probably Germany, 1850, with feet
Capacity: 20 cc

Porcelain, England, 19C, with feet
Capacity: 4 cc

Pewter, Gibson style, England, 19 C.
Maker: Maw-Aldersgate St., London
Capacity: 40 cc

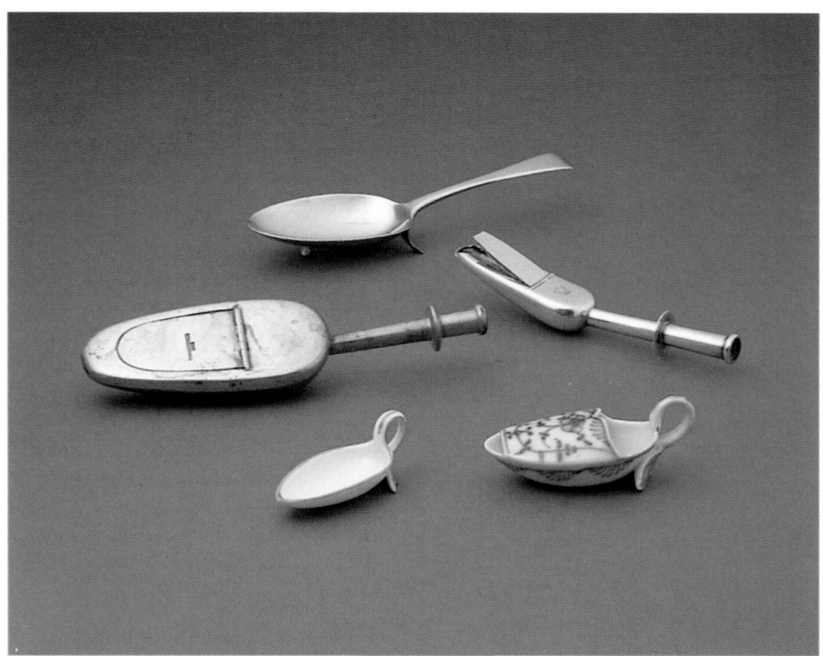

Writers did not miss the opportunity to bring malpractice to public attention. Charles Dickens (1812–1870), following his custom of attacking social injustices to children, depicted in his novels the regular dosing of youngsters with medicines they fought against taking. As with other established habits shown to be unwise, the reliance on physic was slow to decline. Sir William Osler, as quoted earlier, was concerned with man's urge to take medicines.

Dependence on medicines is not dying out: it is simply changing from one set of remedies to another, and the set today includes vitamins, tranquilizers, antidepressants, and antibiotics.

Some of the medicines mentioned, particularly herbal concoctions, were blended in the home, but many were purchased from the apothecary or pharmacist. Vessels for storage in the shop and for transport to the home have survived through centuries. These include bottles, storage jars for liquids, powders, and ointments, and dispensing pots of varying sizes.

Medicine bottles
England
Clockwise from left:
Mid 17 C (Plague period)
Capacity: 50 cc

Ca. 1700

Early 17 C

Mid 17 C (Plague period)

Ca. 1700

The glass has become iridescent as a result of chemical reactions in the outer layers when exposed to moisture and temperature fluctuations where it was buried.

Spouted tin-glazed earthenware drug jars
England, 17 C – 18 C

Marked: ACETOS ST.
Recipe found in jar, dating ca. 1675:
Syrup of vinegar: a simple acid syrup prepared by dissolving sugar in vinegar by heat, regarded as soothing and antiseptic
1660–1672
Ht: 18.4 cm

Marked: S: DE: FUMARIA-SIM.
Syrup of fumitory, possibly anthelmintic
Dated 1666

Marked: S. SIMPLEX
Simple syrup: sugar and water

Marked: MEL ROSAR
Honey and roses: gently heat rose petals in honey — demulcent properties
1672–1690

Spouted tin-glazed earthenware drug jar
Marked: O. TEREBIN:
Oleum terebinthae: oil of turpentine used as a stimulant, diuretic, anthelmintic and rubefacient
Late 17 C - early 18 C
Ht: 20.0 cm

Note everted necks on most drug containers facilitated tying covers, usually parchment, over the top.

Probably the oldest artifact in the Collection is an ointment pot from predynastic Egypt, 3500–3000 BC. It is still half-filled with a greasy substance. Other Egyptian ointment pots are pleasingly bulbous, smooth, black stone and anhydrous gypsum dating from about 2300 BC, and alabaster produced another thousand years later.

More than a millennium after the dates of the alabaster pots, Pliny wrote: "Now as touching the keeping of Ointments, they are best preserved in pots or vessels of Alabastre:. . ."[18] His book gives many recipes for ointments — basically ground herbs in grease. Phaer lauds the value of a new herb in the sixteenth century, namely water betony, and gives the recipe for an ointment for itch effective in young children.

> Against suche unkynde ytche, he may make an oyntment thus. Take water of betony, two good hādfulles, daysye leaves, & alehofe, otherwise called tūnour or ground yuye, of eche one handfull, the red docke rotes, two or thre, stampe them altogether, and grynde them wel, then mingle thē with freshe grease, and again stampe them. Let them so stande. viii. daies to putrify till it be hoare, then frye them out and strayne them and kepe it for the same entent.
>
> This oyntment hath a great effect, both in yong and olde, and that without repercussion or driving backe of the matter, whiche should be a peryllouse thynge for a young chylde.
>
> Tho Phaer. *The Boke of Chyldren.* 1550, [p. 35].

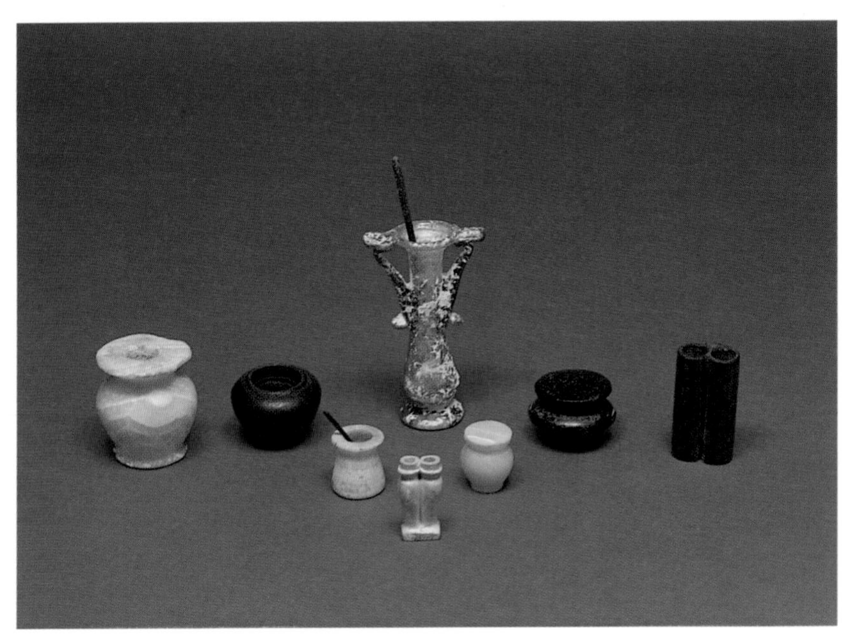

Ancient ointment and/or kohl pots
Clockwise from left:
1. Alabaster, Egypt, 1200–1000 BC
2. and 4. Black serpentine with lids, Egypt, 2340–2260 BC
3. Glass kohl pot, heavily encrusted Palestine or Syria, AD 4 C
   Ht: 11 cm
   Metal rod for extracting kohl
5. Wooden kohl pot
   Egypt, 2000 BC to birth of Christ
6. Alabaster with lid, Egypt, 1200–1000 BC, filled with kohl
7. Faience kohl pot, Egypt, 300 BC
8. Anhydrous gypsum, Egypt, ca. 2000 BC, with rod

Pottery ointment pot
Egypt, Thebes, 3500–3000 BC
Ht: 11.4 cm

Tin-glazed earthenware pots,
England, 17 C
Centre: drug storage jar, ca. 1700
Ht: 17.2 cm

Left and right: Striped dispensing pots
Late 17 C

Lower left: Lambeth dispensing pot, ca. 1660, contains original ointment from plague period

Lower right: Black dispensing pot, ca. 1660

Lower centre: Lambeth dispensing pot, ca. 1700

Sir Edward Tertils Salve, called the "Chief of all Salves," described in 1683, contains resins, waxes, mastick, camphor, and the ubiquitous "harts fuet."[19] In the years when cleanliness was not a personal goal, rashes and itching must have been continual sources of discomfort. Infants undoubtedly suffered almost constantly from diaper rash. The prevalence of ointment pots is therefore quite understandable.

Tin-glazed earthenware drug dispensing pots,
England, 18 C
Clockwise from left:
Blue stripes, 18 C

Lambeth, ca. 1700
Ht: 5.7 cm

Pearlware, ca. 1800
Marked: Delescot
No. 19 Duke Street St. James's

Last half 18 C

2nd half 18 C

1730s

Early 18 C

Tin-glazed earthenware Albarello drug jars
Italy or Spain, 17 C

Marked: O. CITONEOR
Ointment of quince: Syrup prepared by boiling quince with sugar and water, used as an astringent
St. Roch* with his dog
Ht: 19.6 cm

* St. Roch was the 13 C saint thought to protect from plague.

? Spain, 2nd half 17 C
Marked: TO VNG. D'ARAGON
A dozen herbs with gum resins in a base of bear's grease used as wound salve
Ht: 18.4 cm

Tin-glazed earthenware drug jars, 18 C
Netherlands, 3rd quarter 18 C
Marked: C: COCHLEAR
Cochlearia hortensis or lemon scurvy gross; an antiscorbutic
Ht: 13.5 cm

Netherlands, Duijn 1763-1777
Marked: BALS LUCATELL
Ointment of red sandalwood, olive oil, pine resin and other ingredients used to treat ulcers

England, 18 C
Marked: P: RUFI [Rufus pills]
Pills of aloes and myrrh, anti-pestilential
Straight neck for lid

Netherlands, 18 C
Unmarked

Pill containers
Three compartme s
Ivory, England, 1[illegible] C
Ht: 3.8 cm

Silver, Dublin, 1863

Such containers had miscellaneous uses: pills, counters, patches, etc.

Similar dispensing pots and storage jars were used for pills. A few of the latter, like the Rufus pill jar illustrated, are so labelled.

People carried pills with them in small boxes similar in design and artistry to the vinaigrettes discussed earlier. They are indistinguishable until opened: the absence of a grille and gilt in boxes made of silver, usually marks the pill box. Simple pill containers were frequently compartmented cylinders.

The Japanese developed exclusive containers for carrying pills, spices and other small items on their person. A beautifully carved wooden or ivory compartmented box, called an *inro* hangs on a cord, usually at the waist, held in place by a *netsuke* or toggle at the end of the cord. Sometimes an additional sliding toggle or *ojime* secures the closing.

Inroes with netsukes and ojimes
Japan, 19 C
Upper left: Carved wooden inro, red lacquered five compartments,
Ht: 7.6 cm
Carved wooden ojime, red lacquered
Carved ivory netsuke

Upper right: Carved ivory inro, orange lacquered, five compartments
Carved ivory netsuke, lacquered
Carved wooden ojime, lacquered

Lower: Carved wooden inro, lacquered, five compartments
Gourd netsuke

Mortars
Upper: Bell Metal, Netherlands, 1593 (dated)
Marked: GODT HEBBE DANCK-VOR SINE GNADE 1593, wt: 3.64 kg.

Lower left: Bell metal, ? Spain, 1497 (dated)
Wt: 1.25 kg.

Lower right: Bell metal, France, 18 C
Wt: 2.04 kg.

Significant in apothecary shops were the pill tiles which provided a clean smooth surface on which to form the pill pipe and cut, before shaping pills. Many were works of art, commonly of tin-glazed pottery. They were hung to mark the location of the dispensary, and to verify the credentials of the apothecary. A rare example introduces this chapter.

To make the various preparations in the apothecary shop or at home, the grinding, bruising, or stamping to pulverize the herbs and chemicals was accomplished with mortars and pestles. Frequently called "bell mortars" because they were made of the same quality brass as is used for resonant bells, they ring when the rim is struck.

Mortars and pestle
Left to right:
Brass, England, 18 C, wt: 1.59 kg
Pestle: brass England, 18 C, l: 19.6 cm

Bell metal, England, 16 C, wt: 1.48 kg

Iron, England, 17 C, wt: 7.55 kg.

Bell metal, England, 14 C, wt: 2.39 kg

Brass, England, 14 C, wt: 1.31 kg.

So essential were mortars and pestles that smaller glass ones were accommodated in medicine chests. Not all people had easy access to apothecaries or physicians, especially in the country. Large manors might have had their own physician/apothecary, but smaller ones could not. Often it was the lady of the manor who kept the medicine chest, supervised its use, and dispensed aid to the tenants. Some were known to enjoy this responsibility immensely. The home medicine chest became prevalent and was used by physicians, surgeons, and apothecaries as well. Specially constructed kits were made for military surgeons. Most were beautifully crafted wooden cases with compartments for bottles which fitted snugly, drawers for small instruments and ointments, with divisions to fit a glass mortar and pestle, weigh scales, a graduate for measuring, and so on. Some had a hidden compartment, which opened only by a device triggered from inside the lockable cabinet. The small chest shown simply holds six medicine bottles. There are 10 chests in the Collection.

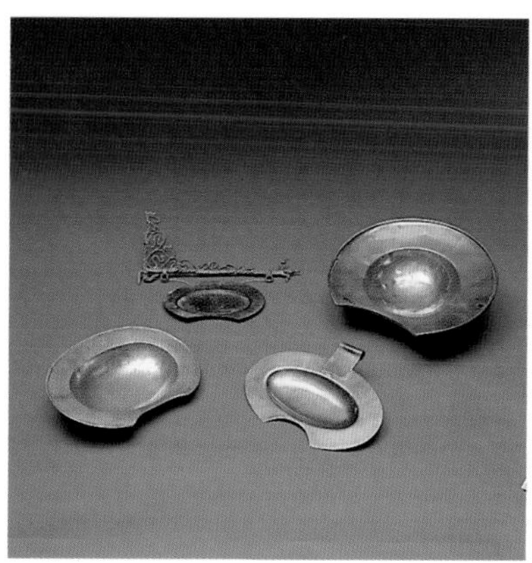

Metal barber-surgeon bowls
Clockwise from upper left:
Brass, Denmark, early 20 C, l: 15.6 cm
Brass, Continental Europe, 19 C
Brass, Denmark, 20 C
Pewter, Germany, 18 C

Just as a pill tile marked the location of the dispensary in many apothecary shops, so, by the late eighteenth century, a metal barber-surgeon's bowl hung outside to mark the shop itself. Such bowls were similar to the ceramic bowls used within. According to Pliny,[20] barbers first established themselves in Rome and the first man to cut his hair [shave] daily was Scipio Africanus. After him, Emperor Augustus regularly used a razor. Originally, the barber and the surgeon being the same man, their bowls were used for both trades. For shaving, the barber's bowl was placed with the arc of the rim at the neck of the client; soap was put in the depression in the rim and water in the bowl. For bleeding, the arc of the rim could be placed on the forearm of the patient with the elbow flexed, an incision made with a scalpel in a vein of the upper arm and the blood collected in the bowl. These bowls were pewter, brass, pottery, and porcelain. Though in England barbers and surgeons split company in the eighteenth century, the term "barber-surgeon bowl" continued in use.

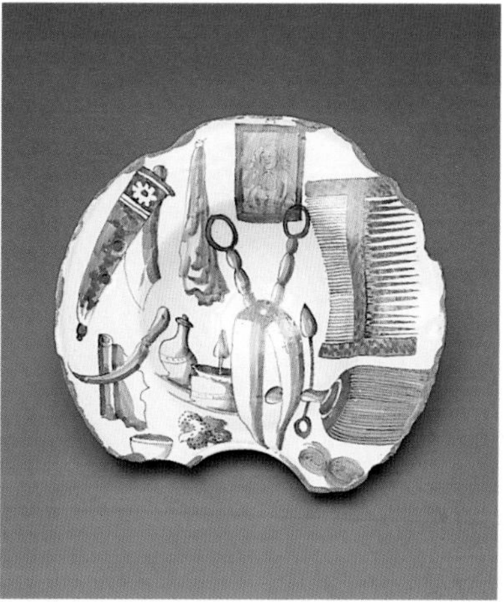

Tin-glazed barber-surgeon bowl
England, ca. 1700
Diam: 30.5 cm

Medicine chests
Left: Brass-trimmed wooden medicine chest
England, ca. 1850
Containing medicine bottles, hand balance with weights, glass mortar and pestle, graduate and syringe, hidden compartment in the back, sliding door is released by pulling forward a small, well-concealed rod inside.
Ht: 22.8 cm
Right: Fishskin over wood
2nd half 18 C
Brass lockplate and feet

Earthenware barber-surgeon bowls, 18 C
Left: Lead-glazed, Continental Europe, probably France, mid-18 C
L: 35.6 cm

Centre: Tin-glazed, England, possibly Bristol, ca. 1770

Right: Creamware, England, Leeds pottery impressed, late 18 C – early 19 C

Hard paste porcelain barber-surgeon bowls
The Orient, 18 C
Left: Chinese export, ca. 1750, l: 32.9 cm

Centre: Chinese export, 18 C

Right: Japanese export, ca. 1700–1750

Tin-glazed earthenware barber-surgeon bowls
England, 19 C
Left: Stoke-on-Trent, Maker: W. Adams & Sons, July 26, 1845
Habana pattern. Portraits of Spanish royalty around rim. English export for Spanish market.
Diam: 25.4 cm

Right: Staffordshire, early 19 C

Tin-glazed earthenware barber-surgeon bowls
Continental Europe, 18 C
Left: Possibly Switzerland
Late 18 C – early 19 C
L: 16.7 cm

Right: France, possibly Moustiers, 18 C

Not fulfilling the barber's use, smaller bowls were commonly used for bleeding. These are often difficult to distinguish from porringers, but if lines are present for marking measurements, it is generally accepted that the bowl is for bleeding. Some were pottery or porcelain, many were pewter or silver.

Syringes belonging to apothecaries or physicians — ear, vaginal, urethral, or enema — were commonly pewter. One of particular interest, is an intra-uterine (intra-vaginal) syringe designed to be used by a priest or midwife to christen an unborn child, whose life was uncertain.

Breathing a Vein
Coloured etching by James Gillray
London, Jan. 28, 1804
26.9 × 19.6 cm

Metal bleeding bowls
Left: Pewter, England, ca. 1650
Capacity: 440 cc

Right: Pewter, France, 18 C – 19 C
Handle stamped with 7 rosettes, and 66^{D} HS^{T}A
Graduations 100–500 g.
Capacity: 570 cc

Centre: Silver, London, 1652
Maker: R.F. From the Cromwellian period, a rare survivor
Capacity: 340 cc

Tin-glazed earthenware bleeding bowls
England
Left: Possibly Lambeth, 2nd half 17 C
Capacity: 540 cc

Right: Probably Bristol, ca. 1720
Capacity: 700 cc

Specialized items used by priest, or rabbi
Pewter intra-uterine syringe, England, 18 C
Designed to spray in form of a cross for christening the unborn
L: 30.4 cm extended

Silver box marked: Hollandia, 1738
West Frisia
Part of a circumcision set
Diam: 2.0 cm

Stone cosmetic pot
Egypt, 2000 BC
Diam: 7.6 cm
Probably a mortar used to grind galina, stibium, etc. for eye shadow

People treasured articles relating to personal hygiene used in caring for the eyes, the teeth, the mouth, the ears, and the hair. Care of the eyes has been significant since ancient times. Just as football players today put a dark, greasy absorbent substance below their eyes to protect them from the sun, so the early Egyptians put kohl around their eyes to guard against the strong tropical rays. The kohl or stibium (powdered black antimony) was kept in kohl pots made of wood, pottery, anhydrous gypsum, alabaster, or glass, and applied with metal or stone rods. This was the ancient forerunner of eye shadow. As Egyptian women used more cosmetics their equipment became more sophisticated. Below are shown a cosmetic pot, a mirror, a comb, and the decorative side of a black slate cosmetic slab, the reverse or practical side of which has four diagonal grooves used for grinding kohl into a powder.

Ophthalmic ointments have been widespread for centuries, but ophthalmic solutions are more recent. Eye cups which fitted snuggly around the eye were made of silver, glass, pottery, or porcelain. Their use was recommended for eye washing until well into this century, when it was realized that eye infections were being transmitted by the cups.

Poor or failing sight was first alleviated with eye glasses in mediaeval times. One pair pictured is identical to those worn by the doctor in the caricature on page 226. Samuel Johnson had such bad eyesight as a child, at the beginning of the eighteenth century, that it contributed to his frequent stumbles. Yet with spectacles such as these, which he wore all his life, he was an avid reader and a copious writer and managed to compile his large dictionary.

Ancient cosmetic aids
Left: Mirror in pottery frame
Roman Palestine, ca. AD 100
6.3 cm square

Centre: Wooden comb, Egypt, AD 300–400

Right: Slate cosmetic slab, Egypt (grooved on back)

Eye cups and glasses
Glass, Bristol blue, England, 19 C
Silver ? France, 19 C
Ht: 5.7 cm
Soft paste porcelain, blue transfer printed
England, Worcester, 18 C

Silver rimmed lorgnettes, with a tortoise shell handle/case
Tortoise shell rims and temples
Silver rims and adjustable temples

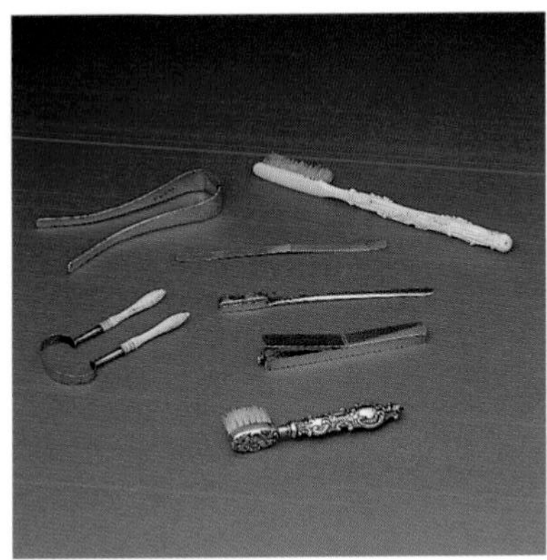

Toothbrushes and tongue scrapers
Centre set of three, silver, London, 1799–1800. Maker: W.P. (William Parks).
Tongue scraper
Toothbrush, replaceable bristles, l: 12.3 cm
Tooth powder container

Upper left: Silver tongue scraper
London, 1781–1782
Lower left: Tongue scraper
Two ivory handles
England, 19 C

Upper right: Carved ivory toothbrush 19 C

Lower: Silver repoussé child's toothbrush, Birmingham, 1901–1902
One of a pair

Brouzet (1754) is credited with the first mention of care of the teeth. This was about the time that toothbrushes were introduced. They were a luxury, initially obtainable only by the wealthy, or, shocking as it may seem today, shared by many. Nineteenth-century novels about the Mississippi river-boats occasionally refer to the elegant toothbrush chained beside the communal wash basin.

The appearance of the tongue was a subject of concern for centuries. Paulus Aegineta (625–690) advised that in cases of roughness of the tongue it should be kept moist and clean. He prescribed washing with a decoction of linseed, then rinsing with water, followed by rose oil and honey, or various other potions.[21]

Tongue scrapers became plentiful and were widely used. Handwritten notes inside the cover of Buchan's 1769 edition of *Domestic Medicine* include "When the Taste is diminished by filth, mucus etc. the Tongue ought to be scraped and frequently washed with a mixtue of water, vinegar and honey, or some detergent... " About the same time Armstrong listed a furred tongue among the symptoms accompanying a high fever during teething.[22] Well into this century, when examining a child, the doctor first looked at the tongue. Today physicians seldom pay attention to the coating of the tongue.

The popularity of toothpicks has an interesting history. H. Sachs traced their use from ancient times through the days of Caesar when both Greeks and Romans used natural straw and quills, to the finely crafted toilet sets of the seventeenth century. By the fourteenth century, minstrels' songs made mention of toothpicks and the word for toothpick first appeared in the Latin-German dictionary of Martin Myluis in 1579. Bronze, silver, and hand-carved bone picks had been in production for more than a century when they were introduced into France in 1590. They became so fashionable as to be carried everywhere.[23]

By the seventeenth century, decorated and sometimes jewelled cases were popular to hold delicately crafted toothpicks and earspuds, often with a mirror in the lid and other specialties such as a hunting whistle. Ladies carried them in their hands or suspended from the neck or the waist; men kept them in their pockets. Retractile toothpicks were later developed, frequently heavily jewelled and beautifully worked in silver and gold.

Toothpick cases
England, 18 C – 19 C
Centre: Ivory, inlaid with gold and silver, 18 C, l: 7.3 cm
Clockwise from upper left:
1. Ivory with braided hair in lid, 19 C
2. Shagreen covered, silver cartouche, 19 C
3. Ivory, watch incorporated in lid, open to show ivory toothpick and earspud, mirror inside lid, 18 C
4. Silver, 1823
5. Mother-of-pearl, edged in silver, 19 C
6. Ebony with silver framed cameo on lid
7. Tortoise shell with silver piqué* inlay on lid, 19 C

Lower right: Silver toothpicks and earspud, 19 C

* Delicate gold or silver inlay, usually in tortoise shell or ivory, first developed in 17 C

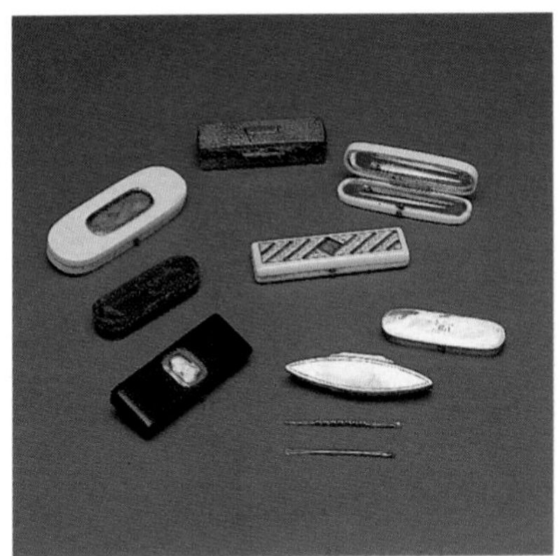

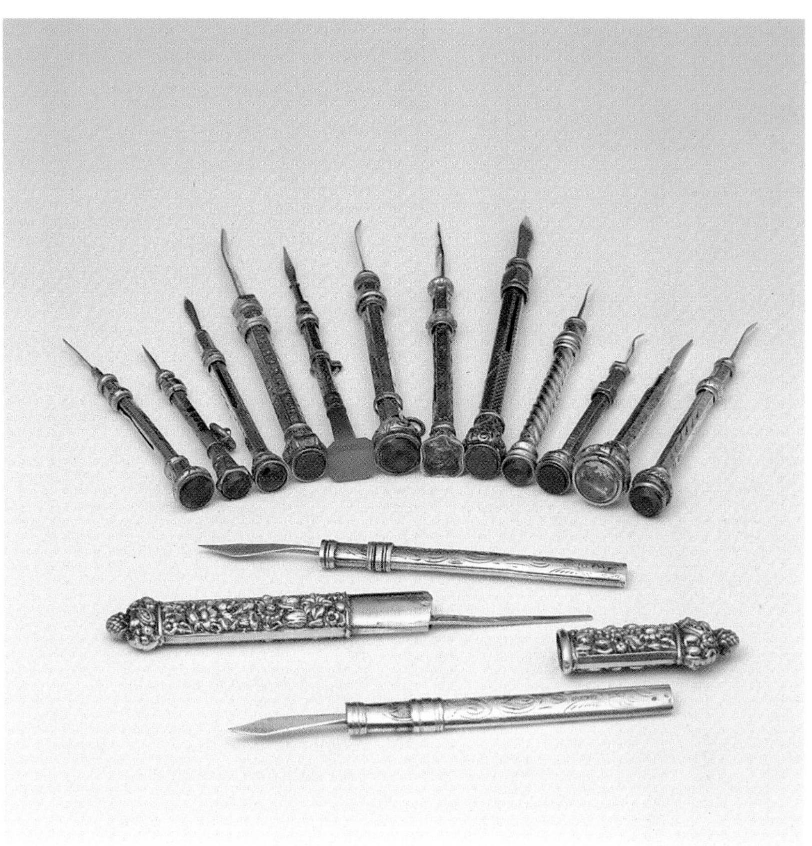

Retractile toothpicks
England, 19 C
Upper 12: Delicately worked gold and silver retractile toothpicks, with jewelled finials, some marked Birmingham

Horizontal pieces: Silver gilt case, France, 1884
Heavily embossed in floral pattern, containing a gold bodkin, toothpick, and earspud, also embossed

Two silver retractile toothpicks
Birmingham, 1894–1895
Chased in scroll design
Maker: F&W , l: 7.6 cm

Following the introduction of the toothbrush in the mid-eighteenth century, toothpicks not only lost popularity but fell into disrepute; their use in public was spurned as ill-mannered.

A number of the toothpicks shown are coupled with earspuds. These were used for cleaning the ears of children, including infants, and adults, just as the Q-tips (cotton-tipped sticks) were commonly used earlier in this century. Damage to the ears, possibly even deafness, was a risk in the process; probing in the ears is no longer recommended.

Until recent times nothing could be done for deafness, and diagnosis of hearing problems in the very young was difficult. It is doubtful that small children used the cumbersome ear trumpets of earlier days, but the benefit derived by the hard-of-hearing justified the inconvenience. The establishment of a home for the deaf and dumb children in England in 1792 certainly indicates that by then the special needs of such children were receiving attention. A booklet entitled "The Asylum for the Deaf and Dumb Children of the Poor," London, 1792, is in the Collection.

Silver chatelaine
Asia, 18 C
Enamel mount suspending tweezers, earspud, three flat instruments and a small leaf-shaped enamelled container
L: 38.7 cm

Consultation de Médicins
[Doctors' Consultation]
Lithograph by Delpech after L. Boilly (1761–1845)

Note use of ear trumpet.

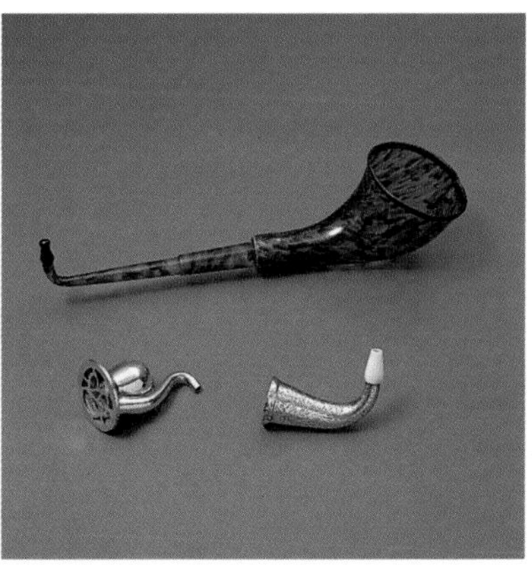

Ear trumpets
Above: Tortoise shell design. Early 20 C
L: 38 cm

Left: Nickel-plated brass with grille, ca. 1905

Right: Silver plate with ivory tip. Marked: F.C. Rein and Son, patentees, inventors, 108 Strand, London, 1867–1917.

Compare with ear trumpets in Elisabeth Bennion's ***Antique Medical Instruments,*** University of California Press, Sotheby, Parke, Bernet, 1979, pp. 228–230.

With the demise of the wig in the late eighteenth century in England and elsewhere, care of the hair took on a new character. Bear grease and macassar oil were thought to keep the hair healthy and to achieve the approved appearance. A treatise in the Collection extols the virtues of macassar oil:

Pottery bear grease pots
England, Staffordshire, 19 C
Right, marked: ROSS AND SONS' GENUINE BEARS' GREASE PERFUMED 119 and 120 Bishop's gate street, London
Diam: 7.6 cm

Note underglaze cartoons on lids

> Applied to the roots to prevent dryness, it keeps the hair healthy: prevents baldness, promotes growth, restores hair, retains colour and a strong curl. It produces an elegant gloss and is equally good on artificial hair. The oil is of vegetable origin from the Island of Macassar
>
> *A Treatise on Inestimable Virtues of the Genuine Macassar Oil,*
> in English, French and Italian, including Directions for Use.
> Entered at Stationers' Hall, J. and C. Evans, Long Lane, London, n.d.

The jars or pots in which the perfumed bear grease was sold had lids which became another vehicle for the political cartoonists of the day. These were the earliest forms of potters' work to be adorned with such pictures. The pioneers of this form of pictorial pottery were Felix Edwards Pratt and Jesse Austin of the firm of Messrs. F. & R. Pratt & Co., of Fenton, Staffordshire.[24] Many lids and some pots survive.

Certain accoutrements in the sick room facilitated patient care. Invalid feeding cups, caudle cups, or larger pap boats with thumb holds made it easier to give nourishment. Similar food, caudle or posset, was served as refreshment to family and visitors.

Invalid feeders
England, early 19 C
Left: Porcelain, probably Derby
Capacity: 300 cc

Right: Creamware, Staffordshire
Shorthose inscribed on bottom (J. Shorthose, potter, 1785–1823)

Tin-glazed earthenware serving vessels
For caudle or posset, 17 C – 18 C
Left: England, late 17 C – 1730
Capacity: 650 cc

Right: Netherlands, late 17 C – early 18 C
Capacity: 4300 cc

Some toilet aids, now only for the sick room, were in daily use. Chamber pots were in every household, bedpans and urinals in few. The last items were common in hospitals and available in apothecary shops. Usually tin, some were more elegant.

The patient with congestion of the respiratory tract found relief in the use of Dr. Mudge's[25] inhaler. Lying completely under the bed clothes and clutching the hot-water-filled vessel in the arm-pit, the patient breathes through the ivory mouth-piece. On inspiration air enters through holes in the hollow handle, is drawn down into the water and bubbles up as moist vapour to be drawn into the lungs. On expiration the air collects on the surface of the water, the pressure increases and lifts a valve in the top of the chamber to escape as moist air under the bed clothes.

Ceramic chamber pot and urinals, 19 C

Left: Earthenware female urinal (bourdaloue),* England, l: 19.7 cm

Centre: Earthenware chamber pot, England
This pot it is a present sent
Some mirth to make is only meant
We hope the same you'll not refuse
But keep it safe and oft it use.
And when you in it want to pis
Remember them that sent you this.
(A verse in similar vein on other side)

Right: Porcelain bourdaloue, France, Sèvres
A large eye painted inside, bottom

* The bourdaloue was perhaps so named after the Jesuit preacher Père Louis Bourdaloue, whose lengthy sermons at the court of Louis XIV necessitated its use.

Metal necessities of the sick room, 18 C – 19 C
Centre: Pewter bedpan, England, 18 C
Touchmarks: Newcastle 1760–1795.
William Hogg, Cross and Crown
Diam: 29.2 cm
Few of these survived because easy removal of the handle produced an attractive rose bowl.

Clockwise from upper left:
Pewter male urinal, England, 18 C

Child's pewter chamber pot, England, 19 C

Child's pewter bedpan, ca. 1800.
SJN on bowl and handle

Copper female urinal, England, 19 C

Tin female urinal, England, 19 C

Mudge's pewter inhaler
Touchmark ca. 1787 (Henry and Richard Joseph)
Capacity: 2 pints

Shown in his book open at p. 134

Apothecary and Related Tokens

In the seventeenth century an apothecary shop was, relatively speaking, a big business. As grocers earlier had carried apothecary items in their spicery sections, so, like the druggist today, apothecaries stocked miscellaneous items for the convenience of the neighbourhood. They received messages, notes, letters — to be picked up by later passers-by. They kept money and valuables for safe-keeping and lent money to those they trusted. This "banking" service was often necessitated by travellers' difficulties with getting their own money from distant towns.

In 1644, when parliament suppressed the use of farthings, the coinage of which had been delegated to patentees, and then failed to strike any coins to replace them, the apothecaries decided to produce their own small coins. Other traders such as the grocers' company, did the same.[26] Birmingham had one of the best factories and some of the finest craftsmen of the country, and so struck Warwickshire coins and those of other counties.[27]

The Drake Collection contains tokens of several trades such as grocers. Those of the seventeenth century relating to medicine include tokens of apothecaries (103, of whom four were women), barber-surgeons (6), and hospitals (3). Made of copper, brass, or bronze, occasionally lead, most of the tokens were worth a farthing or a half penny, very few, a penny. Initially the tokens were honoured only by the traders who had issued the coins, but before long shops accepted tokens of other trades and the coins became neighbourhood currency. A mother buying a nostrum for her feverish baby might give the clerk a shilling and get her change in apothecary tokens. Received in Birmingham, they would be honoured there, but not likely in Nottingham, Bristol, London, or elsewhere. In 1692 under Charles II the use of tokens was forbidden by Royal proclamation.[28]

A few examples from the numbers above are significant. Most tokens were round, but a few were square, oblong, octagonal, or diamond- or heart-shaped. These are relatively rare.

Tokens of grocers' trade
OBV:
BLADUD, FOUNDER OF BATH, SUCCESS TO THE BATH WATERS, around bust left
E:
PAYABLE AT ANGLESEY, LONDON OR LIVERPOOL, 29.0 mm

REV. of similar token:
SPICES, TEAS, SUGARS, COFFEES around M. LAMBE & SON, GROCERS BATH
E:
PAYABLE AT ADAM SIMPSON'S*

* It is significant to note that of the two otherwise identical grocers' tokens shown (obverse of one and reverse of the other) the edge inscription indicates a different shop for the redemption of each token.

Apothecary tokens, 17 C,
OBV: Upper row:
Left: WILLIAM CULLY 1660 around apothecary arms

Centre: HENRY BIGG OF around mortar and pestle

Right: APOTHECARIE around TP (Thomas Pigeon)

Second row:
Left: MARIE CRESSENER IN around mortar and pestle

Centre: JANE SMALL around shield with apothecary arms (Louth, Lincolnshire, 1668), 18 mm

Right: MARGRET EAT[on] around apothecary arms (Plymouth, Devonshire, 1665)

Third row:
Left: WILLIAM HERENDEN around shell

Right: IN KINGS STREETE around mortar and 2 pestles (2 unusual)

Lower row:
Left: JOHN BERRIDGE IN around shield bearing apothecary arms

Right: HENRY BOLLARDT around pot of lilies

Note tokens representing three 17 C female apothecaries, probably widows of apothecaries (Margret Eaton's husband Christopher, apothecary, was mentioned in the siege of Plymouth, 1642–1646)

Apothecary tokens, 17 C
REV: Upper row:
Left: IN WANTAGE in floral wreath around $\overset{C}{\text{WI}}$ (Berkshire)

Centre: FELSTEAD, 1669 around HIS HALF PENY

Right: IN COVENTRY around apothecary arms

Second row:
Left: ST. EDMONDS BURLY, around MC (Suffolk)

Centre: LOWTH, 1668 around HER HALF PENY 18 mm

Right: IN PLIMOUTH, 1665 around M.E.

Third row:
Left: APOTHYCARYE 1651 around $\overset{H}{\text{W.A.}}$ (no town recorded)

Right: WESTMINSTER 1651 around $\overset{M}{\varepsilon\text{.A}}$ (Probably a member of the Malthus family, next door to the home of physician Thomas Sydenham)

Lower row:
Left: NOTTINGHAM APOTHECARY around ·I B·

Right: APOYTCARY IN DUBLIN around $\text{H}\overset{B}{\underset{I}{\text{O}}}\text{E.}$ 1654

Heart-shaped 17 C token
OBV:
Left: SAMUEL DOUER APOTHECARY

REV. of duplicate:
Right: IN IPSWICH HIS HALFE PENNY
Maximum width: 20.0 mm

Barber-surgeons' tokens, 17 C
OBV:
Upper left: THOMAS UNDERWOOD around ⚓
17.0 mm

Upper right: ROBERT TIPPETS IN around
Barber-Surgeons Arms

Lower left: THOMAS BULL 1659 around
Barber-Surgeons Arms

Lower right: EDWARD GOLDINGE around
HIS HALFE PENY $\overset{G}{E.A}$
[Berkshire] 1668

REV:
Upper left: IN READING 1666 around $\overset{V}{T.M}$

Upper right: PORTSMOUTH 1666 around $\overset{T}{R.E}$

Lower left: OF. MANUDINE around
HIS HALF PENY

Lower right: OF. FARINGDON, 1668 around
Barber-Surgeons Arms

Hospital tokens, 18 C

OBV:	REV: (duplicate coins)
Warwickshire	
FORD'S HOSPITAL FOUNDED 1529 around hospital	THE ARMS OF COVENTRY, 1797 around elephant arms 29.0 mm
BABLAKE HOSPITAL FOUNDED 1506 around hospital	THE ARMS OF COVENTRY 1797 around elephant arms
Middlesex, London	
IRONMONGERS ALMSHOUSE ERECTED MDCCXII [1712] around hospital	LONDON PENNY TOKEN around arms of London

Hospital token and token for the poor, 17 C
OBV:
Left: THIS HALF PENY BELONGS TO YE around shield 20.0 mm

Right: HELP:O:ANDEVER 1666 around lion under tree

REV:
Left: HOSPITALL OF BRIDEWELL LONDON around shield

Right: FOR YE POORES BENEFIT around figure on crutches

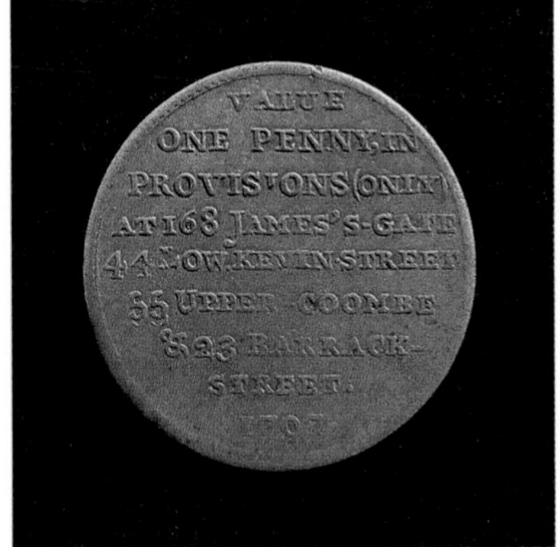

Irish token for the poor
OBV:
VALUE ONE PENNY IN PROVISIONS (ONLY) AT
168 JAMES'S-GATE
44 LOW KEVIN STREET
55 UPPER-COOMBE &
23 BARRACK STREET. 1797

REV:
(not shown) TO PREVENT THE ABUSE OF CHARITY IN THE CONSUMPTION OF WHISKEY, THIS IS GIVEN TO THE POOR IN DUBLIN. F.

A similar dearth of small currency toward the end of the eighteenth century stimulated another series of tokens, which again was discontinued in 1817 by an Act of Parliament. After this, the only tokens that continued to be issued were penny tokens for the poor, and trade tickets in the form of tokens with no monetary value, for the purpose of advertising. Into this last category fall the tokens of Basil Burchell mentioned previously. As well as advertising the famous anodyne necklace, they recommend his "sugar-plumbs for worms." These tokens were plentiful by the end of the eighteenth century.

Burchell's tokens

OBV:

BASIL BURCHELL CUTTING TEETH around SOLE PROPRIETOR OF THE ANODYNE NECKLACE FOR CHILDREN

Left: brass, 29.0 mm
Right: white metal
Lower: copper

REV:

BASIL BURCHELL LONG ACRE around SOLE PROPRIETOR OF THE FAMOUS SUGAR-PLUMBS FOR WORMS

Left: No 79
Right: No 79
Lower: No 78*

* There are 96 of Burchell's tokens in the Collection, including one of his first issues with the address incorrect: 78 instead of 79 Long Acre, London. The mistake makes this particular token very rare and valuable.

Many other eighteenth- and nineteenth-century tokens and plaques are in the Drake Collection: hospitals (93), schools (77), alms houses (22), bath and spa (38). School tokens are discussed with education. Though in England apothecary tokens had ceased to be struck, it is apparent that some were produced in Canada in the nineteenth century.

Canadian pharmacy token 19 C
OBV:
PHARMACIE des TROIS-RIVIÈRES, QUE.
around building, 31.0 mm
REV. of duplicate:
•R.W. WILLIAMS•
TROIS-RIVIÈRES around PHARMACIEN
CHIMISTE around mortar and pestle

Notes

1. Cushing 1940:342.
2. Kremers and Urdang 1963.
3. Parey 1635:647.
4. Plinius Secundus 1635:398.
5. Phaer 1550:[48].
6. Paulus (Transl. 1844); Vol I, Bk I: 625–690.
7. Sainte-Marthe 1797.
8. Letter from Dr. J. M. Campbell, Glasgow, Nov. 24, 1951, quoting information from a privately printed book "by Waters on tokens."
9. Drake T.G.H. Antiques of Paediatric Interest. *Journal of Paediatrics,* 1932; 1(2): 244.
10. Brouzet was the first physician to write about the care of the teeth. He felt that the period of dentition in children should be supervised by a dentist. Surprisingly, he observed that childhood diseases affected the buds of the teeth, scarring their development. Today it is recognized that high fevers mar incoming teeth.
11. Harris 1694:71–72.
12. The Chair in the History of Medicine at Memorial University, Newfoundland, is named for John Clinch.
13. Brouzet (1755) emphasized the importance of utilizing the mother's colostrum as a purge.
14. Underwood's treatise, first published in 1784 went into many editions, several of which are in the collection, French, Italian, and American among them.
15. Buchan 1804:147.
16. Roberton 1827:277.
17. Arrêt du Conseil D'Etat du Roi, du 25 April, 1777, 960.1.1031.
18. Plinius Secundus 1635; Bk 13: 383.
19. [n.a.] *The Queen's Closet Opened* 1683:38.
20. Plinius Secundus 1635: Bk 7, Ch 59.
21. Paulus (Transl 1844); Vol 1, Bk II, Sect LIV.
22. Armstrong 1771:69.
23. Sachs 1913.
24. Clarke 1955.
25. Mudge 1782.
26. Trease G.E. Apothecaries and their Tokens, 1648–1679. *The Pharmaceutical Journal,* September 25, 1965.
27. Davis 1895.
28. Watson G.M., Lewis G.F. Apothecary Tokens. *The Pharmaceutical Journal,* 1958; 181:381.

The Society betwixt Parents and Children
Line engraving, early 18 C
5.0 × 7.0 cm

Married Persons (by the blessing of God) have issue and become Parents. The Father begetteth, and the Mother beareth Sons and Daughters (sometimes Twins). The Infant is wrapped in Swadling-cloathes, is laid in a Cradle, is Suckled by the Mother with her Breasts, and fed with Pap. Afterwards it learneth to go by a Standing-stool, playeth with Rattles, and beginneth to speak. As it beginneth to grow older, it is accustomed to Piety and Labour, and is chastised if it be not dutiful. Children owe to Parents Reverence and Service. The Father maintaineth his Children by taking pains. . .

DAILY NURTURING

> But were none to engage in a State of Wedlock in order to Become Parents, till their Abilities to train up their little Offspring were try'd and approv'd, I am of Opinion the Number of Marriage Licences would be greatly abridg'd.
>
> James Nelson. *An Essay on the Government of Children.*
> 1753, Introduction p. 1

Nourishment is the most frequently and fully discussed topic in the Collection's books on child rearing. Other aspects of nurturing are also debated: bathing, dressing, sleeping, fresh air and exercise.

Bathing

> There is an odd Notion enough entertained about Change, and the keeping of Children clean. Some imagine that clean Linnen and fresh Cloaths draw, and rob them of their nourishing Juices. I cannot see that they do any thing more than imbibe a little of that Moisture which their Bodies exhale. Were it as is supposed, it would be of service to them; since they are always too abundantly supplied, and therefore I think they cannot be changed too often, and would have them clean every Day; as it would free them from Stinks and Sournesses, which are not only offensive, but very prejudicial to the tender State of Infancy.
>
> By a physician [William Cadogan].
> *An Essay upon Nursing and the Management of Children.*
> 1748, p. 12

In ancient times the bath of the newborn was unique: Greeks and Romans, after cleansing the infant with oils, wines, spices, and other fragrances, salted the entire body, including the head, before swaddling. To Jews and Christians alike, in biblical times, this was a religious ritual, considered to be good for the health and strengthening to the skin. The custom persisted: Metlinger advocated salting of the newborn in 1473. According to G.F. Still the healthful advantages were debunked and the habit had generally died out by the sixteenth century,[1] but in 1565 de Vallambert recommended cleansing with salt at birth; Sainte-Marthe, about 1600 advised anointing the skin and all around the joints with the finest salt; Raulin in 1769 claimed that cleansing with salt was still advocated in some parts of France.

A number of sixteenth- and seventeenth-century writers made no mention of using salt with the first bath. About 1500 E. Roesslin, whose textbook of obstetrics was the first to be published in English and remained in vogue for a century, recommended the newborn be cleansed with oil then bathed in warm water.[2] This approach was generally adopted. Underwood's suggestion in 1784 to put salt in a warm bath at birth was undoubtedly a carryover from the early practice of salting.

European peasants in centuries past had little experience with bathing. It was reserved for special occasions: at birth, before marriage, and at death. Where practised, routine cleansing was different. In early times when swaddling was so prevalent and the bands were left for a day or a week undisturbed, the importance of cleanliness was not understood, and one wonders how often some infants were washed. Metlinger specified warm baths in winter, lukewarm in summer—always warmer for a girl than for a boy!—daily for six months and less often thereafter.[3] Phaer advised washing two or three times a week with warm water, putting herbs in the bath water;[4] Parey simply wanted the baby kept neat, clean, and cheery.[5] Sainte-Marthe added spices and wine, as well as herbs, to the warm water of the daily bath.[6]

Sainte-Marthe took strong exception to the habit in Germany of plunging infants into the freezing water of the Rhine. Many felt this was invigorating and strengthening, especially to a weak child. That all Germans did not support this practice is evidenced by the earlier warning of F. Wuertz to avoid baths being too hot.[7] The idea of cold baths spread to England, no doubt encouraged by the writings of John Locke and later of J.J. Rousseau, both of whom put forward a toughening attitude to young children. The principle was widely accepted. The method was to bathe with increasingly cool water until the ultimate goal of cold baths was a reality.

> Cold bathing, or washing, is of the utmost service to children, particularly those who are puny and weakly, and which nothing can exceed or equal as a bracer and strengthener: it ought not to be omitted with those who are healthy, strong, and thriving.
>
> William Moss. *An Essay on the Management and Nursing of Children.* 1781, p. 131

This "English passion," as it became known, reached its zenith at the end of the eighteenth century as expressed by S.H. Jackson. Beginning with a gentle, warm bath at birth, he moved to washing with cold water, then cold baths, the colder, the better. By observing the infant's breathing, the nurse could plunge the child into cold water after a deep breath. This, he claimed, could be repeated at bed time![8]

Not all physicians in England adopted this treatment. Cadogan, in his instructions for the Foundling Hospital, gave no specific directions for bathing, but he made clear his feelings about cleanliness in the quotation on page 259. He inferred that babies were not changed, and consequently not washed, often enough. This opinion was strongly supported half a century later by Struve, a German doctor who showed considerable interest in English practices.[9] Believing cleanliness vital, he refuted the bracing and strengthening effects of cold baths and emphasized the cleansing

La Nourrice ou Le Bain Forcé
[The Wet Nurse or the Routine Bath]
Stiple engraving by Vangeliati after Linguatei
Paris, early 19 C
40.4 × 31.7 cm

ability of tepid water with resultant increased tone and vigour of all functions. Other English authorities, including Buchan[10] and Herdman,[11] began to think the German habit was cruel and advocated caution against the English passion; by the early nineteenth century these cautions were heeded. Roberton deplored the frequency of skin disorders, which were the result of filthiness from lack of bathing, and recommended cold baths be postponed until the child was older, healthier and stronger.[12] In criticizing the Scottish practice of cold baths at two weeks of age, he pointed out that though the Greeks were inured to the habit, the natural low temperature of the water in Scotland made it absurd.

In France the attitude toward bathing differed. Mauriceau in 1668 and Brouzet almost a century later[13] urged the nurse to open swaddling bands several times a day, even at night to keep the baby clean. In 1769, Raulin stated that methods varied with the locale, but in general warm baths with or without herbs were common. The French were aware and critical of the English passion, and did not adopt the habit.

At the beginning of this century Emmett Holt in New York advocated a quick, warm, full tub bath after ten days, followed by drying with soft flannel. The present habit, generally speaking, is to sponge the baby with warm water until the navel is healed. Routine is less emphasized and mothers are advised to bathe the baby at their convenience, missing the odd day if more practical. Most children after the first few weeks, enjoy their baths and have a certain play time in the tub.

Dressing

Nor then forget that wrappers be at hand,
Soft flannels, linen, and the swaddling band,
T'enwrap the babe, by many a circling fold,
In equal lines, and thus defend from cold.

Sainte-Marthe: Paedotrophia.
1797, p. 67, first written about 1600.

In *Il Bambino nell' arte* [The Child in Art],[14] examples of swaddling in ancient Roman art and mediaeval religious works are numerous. It was the first dress used until the age of three months, sometimes much longer. Some peoples, among them the Egyptians, never took up the habit, but where adopted it lasted for many centuries. The practice began as a means of ensuring that the body would develop a good shape, as the limbs at birth are so soft and pliable. Often wrappings were unbelievably tight, giving the impression that one could grasp the feet and hold the infant erect like an ice cream cone.

Early writers ordered swaddling immediately following the bath at birth: Metlinger[15] and Bagellardo,[16] keeping the arms straight at the sides; Phaer, cautioning against "bynding to strayhte;"[17] Roesslin, insisting on great care, straight, with several changes a day;[18] and Parey, trying to keep the neck and the backbone straight and in line.[19] By the sixteenth century swaddling was abused by some, for Toletus emphasized the need to avoid swaddling too tight lest the infant suffocate.[20] De Vallambert a little later approved swaddling with the arms straight to the knees, but thought no binding should be done with the aim of shaping, and that after three or four months the arms and legs should be left free for rubbing.[21]

Sainte-Marthe in his typical gentle way, advised swaddling with care to avoid the bands being too tight and advocated leaving the arms and legs free.[22] At about the same time Gallego de la Serna recommended swaddling with the arms at the side and the hands on the chest, the position resembling that of a corpse.[23]

Writing in 1668, Mauriceau gave details of the "French Fashion" of swathing.

> . . . beginning first to cover the Head with a small linnen Biggen, putting a woolen Cap upon it, having first put upon the Mould of the Head a fine linnen Rag, three or four double, and four fingers broad; which (that it may not stir) pin to the Biggen with a small Pin on the outside, that it may not prick the Child: this double Rag serves to defend the Child's Brain (which is not as yet covered over in this place with a Bone) as well from cold, as other injuries: Let her put small Rags behind the Ears, to dry up the filth which usually is there ingendred: this done, let her put other Rags, as well upon the Breast, as in the folds of the Arm-pits and Groyns, and so swathe it, having wrapped it up in Beds and warm Blankets. It is not necessary to give a particular direction how this ought to be done, because it is so common, there is scarce a Woman but knows it; but we'l only say in general, that a Child must not be swathed too strait in his Blankets, especially about the Breast and Stomach, that so he may breath the freelier, and not be forced to vomit up the Milk he sucks, because the Stomach cannot be sufficiently extended to contain it; and such a practice may possibly in time, converting this vomiting into an habit, prove a very great prejudice to the Child; Wherefore to avoid it, let his Arms and Legs be wrapped in his Bed, and stretched strait out, and swathed to keep them so, viz. his Arms along his Sides, and his Legs equally both together, with a little of the Bed between them, that so they may not be galled by rubbing one another; after all this, the Head must be kept steady & streight, with a Stay fastned on each side the Blanket, and then wrap the Child up in Mantles or Blankets to keep it warm. He must be thus swadled, to give his little Body a streight Figure, which is most decent and convenient for a Man, and to accustom him to keep upon the Feet, for else he would go upon all four, as most other Animals do.

Francis Mauriceau. *The Diseases of Women with Child and in Child-bed.* 1683, pp. 363–364.

Woodcut showing swaddled child
Metlinger. 1550 edition, p. III
5.2 × 6.2 cm

In the mid-eighteenth century, Astruc maintained that swaddling, not too tight, was best for children.[24] Brouzet detailed the procedure practised in France, revealing it to be unchanged since Mauriceau's description a century earlier. Brouzet remarked that the biggens [bonnets], and in some areas the stay bands as well, bend the ears to the head. He suggested this caused the ears to lose their mobility; without this humans might be able to direct their ears to catch sounds, as other animals do!

A couple with swaddled child
Etching resembling work of Jacques Callot (1592–1625)
? France, ? 17 C
14.3 × 9.5 cm

Brouzet then set about assessing swaddling. The only advantage he could see was the ease of carrying the child around. Disadvantages were many: cries of the infant; redness of the skin; suffocation and violent coughing, too often fatal, resulting from compression of the chest; dislocated hips and crooked feet caused by unfavourable positioning of the legs. For ease of carrying, the child could be put in a portable cradle or box. So Brouzet cast aside the use of swaddling altogether. Customs of other nations strengthened his decision. Among many who laid their children naked in hammocks or cradles, he listed Icelanders, modern Greeks, negroes, and the "savages" of Canada—yet they walked early and were not deformed.[25]

In France, the popularity of swathing gradually decreased but it was slow to disappear. Huxham in 1752 and Raulin in 1769 labelled swaddling as harmful and recommended loose clothing that was easy to change. Rousseau agreed.[26] Lefebvre in 1782 devised a long, loose sac covering the feet, later shortened with holes to liberate the legs.[27] Icart in 1784 condemned swaddling except in cases of deformity and A.-B. Richerand in 1812 advocated swathing the weak and deformed. Protat in 1803 advised easy clothing for boys and girls. Yet Léger in 1825 still felt an infant for two or three months should wear a shirt and *une couche* [swaddling from the shoulders down].

In Germany, as early as the sixteenth century Wuertz was in favour of a garment with a cap and sleeves and no strong bandages. Yet Struve in 1802 still advised loose swaddling without the arms and legs included.

Rosen von Rosenstein in Sweden in 1776 was against hard swaddling but outlined the procedure with mention of the necessary precautions. He described an instance when an infant cried incessantly and was treated with drugs to no avail. Finally a young visitor requested the removal of the swaddling bands. The baby's right arm was blue, having been caught to the back between the bands. The crying ceased. Rosen von Rosenstein decided it was best never to swaddle.

In England swaddling was given up more quickly. Thomas Tryon wrote scathingly about swaddling at the end of the seventeenth century. Observing the prevalence of deformities in England, especially among young girls in London, he attributed them to hard swathing in infancy, to the tyranny of foolish, pernicious fashions over straight lacings and stiff stays, and to the habit of putting six- to seven-year-old girls to sewing seven or eight hours a day.

Il Bambino by della Robbia
Italy, 372 A207
June 28, 1937

Cadogan, in his instructions to the Foundling Hospital in the mid-eighteenth century, was highly critical of swaddling.

> . . . But besides the Mischief arising from the Weight and Heat of these Swaddling-cloaths, they are put on so tight, and the Child is so cramp'd by them, that its Bowels have not room, nor the Limbs any Liberty, to act and exert themselves in the free easy manner they ought. This is a very hurtful Circumstance, for Limbs that are not used, will never be strong, and such tender Bodies cannot bear much Pressure:
>
> By a physician [William Cadogan]. *An Essay upon Nursing,* 1748, p. 10

In keeping with the natural approach of the prominent spokesman, John Locke, Cadogan urged

> . . . laying aside all those Swathes, Bandages, Stays and Contrivances, that are most ridiculously used to close and keep the Head in its Place, and support the Body. As if Nature, exact Nature, had produced her chief Work a human Creature, so carelessly unfinish'd, as to want those idle Aids to make it perfect.
>
> Cadogan, p. 11

Balia/Nourice
[The Wet Nurse]
Hand-coloured engraving and etching
? France, 1780–1815
12.6 × 8.8 cm

Instead he described a simple outfit which he considered desirable.

> A little Flannel Waistcoat without Sleeves, made to fit the Body, and tie loosely behind; to which there should be a Petticoat sew'd, and over this a kind of Gown of the same Material, or any other, that is light, thin and flimsy. The Petticoat should not be quite so long as the Child, the Gown a few Inches longer; with one Cap only on the Head, which may be made double, if it be thought not warm enough.
>
> Cadogan, p.11

In 1771 Armstrong followed suit by supporting the idea of nothing tight with as few pins as possible. Buchan, Moss, Underwood, and Jackson also supported Cadogan's principles. Buchan and Underwood attributed to Cadogan the most influence in ridding Britain of swaddling, though later authorities gave this credit to Buchan, himself administrator of the foundling hospital at Ackworth in Yorkshire.

Herdman, so outspoken against cold baths, denounced swaddling as a work of cruelty. This was in 1807, and by 1813 James Hamilton was able to announce that tight swaddling had been discarded in favour of light, simple clothing which is easy to change.[28] John Roberton's general statement summed up the thinking of the early nineteenth century: clothing should provide the necessary warmth and protection from the elements, with no part of the baby compressed and no movement or growth impeded.[29]

Beyond the age of the infant no special clothing styles were developed for children before the Renaissance period. When they outgrew swaddling they graduated to long, loose clothing and then short coats. Being regarded as little adults they were dressed accordingly. Until the sixteenth century clothes were fairly comfortable for all, but high fashion in the time of Elizabeth I put an end to comfort for the upper class. This was coincident with the abuse of swaddling, and as tight swaddling faded in the eighteenth century, older children too, were given more consideration and were dressed in clothes compatible with physical activity. One of the strongest influences was the availability of cheap, washable cottons, making the care and dress of both infants and children easier, and more hygienic.

Early this century, remnants of the swaddling habit were recommended by Holt in New York: a broad flannel over the abdomen to four months; a knitted band to one year.[30] A binder around the navel for a week or two after birth was in vogue until the middle of this century.

The Foundling Dress, as it became known, conceived by Cadogan and developed at the London Foundling Hospital, had far-reaching influence. Nightgowns used almost exclusively for most of this century, opened down the back and fastened with ties. They still enjoy some popularity.

The short sac suggested by Lefebvre must surely have been the forerunner of the romper, popular for so many years. No longer termed a romper, and somewhat modified by newly available materials and fasteners, the romper-type garment is still a standard style of dress.

Sleeping, Fresh Air and Exercise

> Hard Lodging strengthens the Parts; whereas being buried every Night in Feathers melts and dissolves the Body, is often the Cause of Weakness, and the fore-runner of an early Grave.
>
> John Locke. *Some Thoughts Concerning Education.* 1693, p. 23.

For centuries infants slept in cradles or with mothers or nurses. At least as long ago as the first century cradles were in use, for recently a beautifully preserved example was excavated at Herculaneum, destroyed with Pompeii in AD 79. About the fifteenth century authorities began considering the sleeping infant as to comfort, fresh air and exercise. By the seventeenth century the use of cradles was under close scrutiny.

When babies were swathed, often for lengthy periods of time, their exercise was largely limited to crying and rocking in the cradle. In the fifteenth century Bagellardo and Metlinger recommended singing to the child while rocking; in the sixteenth and seventeenth centuries Phaer, Roesslin, Parey, and de Vallambert advocated gentle rocking. Following the bath, before swaddling, Metlinger urged exercising the legs, and de Vallambert advised rubbing all over the body for good exercise, and over the bladder to encourage urination before wrapping. It is interesting to note that de Vallambert advised sleeping with the window open, in a room not too hot, and where the air was fresh; he was against babies being near tanneries, breweries, or any other source of unpleasant odours.

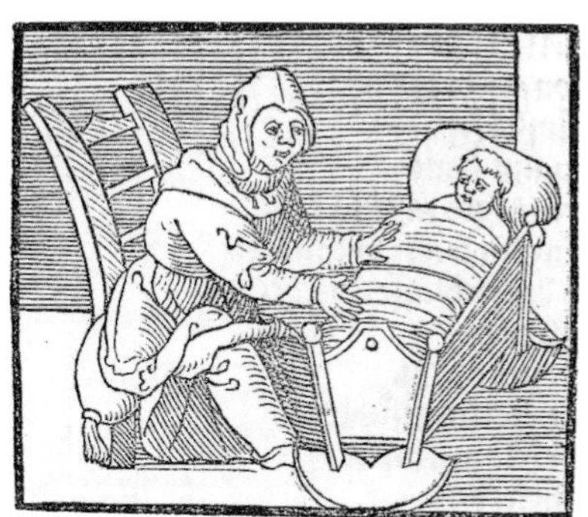

Woodcut showing mother rocking child
Metlinger, 1550 edition, p. VIII
6.2 × 5.1 cm

Metlinger and Parey felt the head should be raised above the body in the cradle, to enable excremental humours to flow from the brain. Wuertz would put the child on its side. Parey opposed placing the infant on its side for fear of causing a crooked back. He also advised a vault of wickers over the baby's head to diffuse the light, thereby preventing the eyes from wandering. One sixteenth-century writer, Huarte y Navarro, spoke against cradles and recommended a hard bed,[31] such as was later confirmed by John Locke in the quote given. Others expressed no concern, or valued the exercise of rocking.

Sainte-Marthe at the beginning of the seventeenth century described his wishes: a soft cradle; not too cold and not too hot; rocking gently with singing, and good fresh air. He felt the child was best preserved from harm by exercise and after the morning bath should be danced in the nurse's arms, then taken outside in the forenoon. He also regarded crying, as did Parey before him, as good exercise.

In the mid-seventeenth century, Primrose and Mauriceau favoured the baby on its back, head raised on a pillow, in a cradle near the nurse's bed where she could occasionally, but should not habitually, rock the cradle. They also specified a mantle over the head to protect the face from dust and to keep out excess light. Mauriceau's conviction that the child sleep in its cradle and not in bed with the mother or nurse, was prompted by his experience of knowing a wet nurse who rolled over on and killed an infant.

La Devotions Maternele
[Maternal Devotions]
Engraving by Amadeo Gabrieli (d. 1817)
After Miss Julia Conyers
27.5 × 20.5 cm
Note wicker cradle with hood

Mother exercises her baby in the fresh air
Etching by Henri Leforth after R. Collin
France, 1840–1880
16.9 × 11.8 cm

Lullaby by Stanislav Sucharda
Czechoslovakia, B147
1937

Chasing the Butterfly
An early cradle pictured in Jacques Stella's book *Les Jeux et Plaisirs de L'Enfance*, p. 1
Paris, 1657
9.8 x 13.8

Note also rattle in infant's hand and walker for his brother

The oak cradle in the Collection is typical of the sturdy specimens surviving from the seventeenth century. It lacks the slits of earlier cradles for strapping to hold the child in place, but it has the depth to accommodate all the blankets and pillows felt necessary for warmth and protection from drafts.

Tryon, supportive of the ideas of his contemporary, John Locke, as expressed in the quote beginning this section, preferred a hard straw mattress on a bed, explaining that feather beds are too warm and hold unclean vapours that spread disease. He emphasized exercise of the arms and the need for exercise for good health at all ages.

Both in England and in France, probably following the sentiments of Locke and Rousseau, authorities in the late eighteenth century and the nineteenth century placed more importance on fresh air and exercise and less on sleeping in a cradle. One anonymous writer in England in 1761, enthusiastically in favour of fresh air and exercise, advised rubbing the infant all over, rolling on the bed, tossing about by the hips, sitting up at one month, beginning to walk at three months, and plenty of fresh air outside.[32] No doubt this type of activity prompted Struve to say that exercise in the cradle was preferable to a rough nurse. The trend was to use the cradle for daytime activity but not for sleeping. Underwood, however, in 1784, still favoured the cradle for sleeping, as did Raulin in France, but was in tune with other contemporaries in insisting upon a cool, well-ventilated nursery. He believed that "a warm nursery fills a cold churchyard."[33] Common advice for children who were wakeful at night, was to keep them awake more in the day and give them more exercise in the nurse's arms, often outside. More time outside became increasingly popular.

A few authorities in the late eighteenth and early nineteenth centuries abandoned the cradle completely: Rosen von Rosenstein in Sweden, Protat in France, and Herdman and Jackson in England. James Hamilton in Edinburgh, believing that nature never intended a baby to have exercise during sleep, prescribed that cradles be attached to the sides of adult beds. Rosen von Rosenstein and several nineteenth-century advisers felt that a cradle suspended by cords, or a swing cot, was good. Roberton thought a swing cot was still good exercise while a cradle was more easily abused.

In the spirit of Moss's statement that cradles were for exercise and convenience, they remained popular for many years. Their prevalence led to their becoming a symbol for babies. The small pottery cradles in the Collection are thought to have been given as engagement gifts wishing fecundity to the couple, or as christening presents.

Pottery Cradles
England
Left to right:
Prattware
Staffordshire, 18 C – early 19 C
L: 20.3 cm

Agate ware
Third quarter, 18 C

Astbury ware
Staffordshire, 18 C

3rd quarter, 18 C

Oak cradle
England, 17 C
L: 91.5 cm

Dr. Drake kept this cradle by his Tudor bed to hold his bed-time reading. The hood appears to have been added later.

Woodcut shows three-wheeled device for exercise
Metlinger, 1550 edition, p. IX
5.1 × 6.2 cm

Having outgrown a cradle or a swing cot, a child graduated generally to a full-sized bed or, where space was a limiting factor, to a trundle bed. Where cost and space were not of significant concern, a child might have a cot such as the oak one in the Collection. Such cots are not common, as a bed of one's own was a luxury enjoyed by few.

As the child matured other forms of exercise were appropriate. Cadogan, the adviser to the Foundling Hospital, was adamant on this subject and placed great emphasis on walking, claiming that by the age of three children could be taught to walk two miles without tiring themselves.[34]

In his work of 1577, Ferrarius advocated the use of a wooden walker similar to those in the prints shown.[35] This was both a learning and an exercising device; in some situations it prevented the child from touching a hot stove or fireplace. Ferrarius illustrated a metal form to be worn on the child's head while using the walker, for protection in the event of a fall. The woodcut from Metlinger shows a three-wheeled wooden contraption of a structure similar to the walker which would have given plenty of exercise to a competent child. Brouzet in the mid-eighteenth century advocated exercise in a wicker walker supporting the child under the arms. Such a walker is shown in Mazzini's *Il Bambino nell' arte,* and a variation, designated as a baby cage, is in the picture shown from Stella's book depicting the sixteenth-century cradle (p. 268). A tapestry also shows a child exercising with yet another primitive walking aid.

Walker
Lithograph by G.W. Thomley after F. Boucher
Paris, 1850–1880
21.5 × 16.0 cm

Visite chez Nourrice
[Visit to the Wet Nurse]
Lithograph by Lemercier (fl. 1854)
After V. Adam, France
20.7 × 27.5 cm

Walker
Tapestry
ca. 1700
45.7 × 50.8 cm

Walkers, however, did not gain great popularity. In the sixteenth century Wuertz stated that the value of walkers was questionable and that learning to walk should be left to nature.[36] Later, Primrose warned not to allow a child to walk before one year: his feet are not strong enough.[37] Though Brouzet approved walking devices in 1754, Lefebvre strongly opposed their use 30 years later. Raulin during the same period advised no walking until the fontanelles are closed and no exercise for the purpose of learning to walk; he did not recommend lead strings on a harness, another training device, and thought they were especially dangerous if attached in front. Buchan agreed with the use of no aids to walking, other than the hand of the nurse.

Child's oak bed
England, ca. 1700
L: 156 cm

Nutrice [Wet Nurse]
Coloured lithograph by Gae Dura
Italy, 1850
17.5 × 12.0 cm

One of several prints of wet nurses in native costume

Cadogan and Huxham encouraged children to learn to walk as soon as possible. Cadogan felt it very important that they take this step to freedom from the nurse. Later Struve, also deploring the use of walkers and lead strings, stipulated that children should first crawl, then stand, and then walk.

Walking devices have been modified again and again to improve their safety. They do provide good exercise, and they are an excellent way of keeping an active child off a cold floor when circumstances warrant. Lead strings today are used by some to keep a child safely nearby, not to teach to walk.

After children become competent walkers, many possibilities for exercise become available. At the end of the eighteenth century, Buchan felt boys and girls should be encouraged to run and play, and Struve advocated increasing the activities of children two to three by enticing them with playthings to contribute to their physical powers.

Roberton's opinions of the early nineteenth century remain standard even to the present day. He believed fresh air essential; the nursery should be cool and well-ventilated. At an early age infants exercise themselves with laughing, crying, and instinctively stretching and tossing their limbs. When carried about they should be comfortable and moved gently. When a child begins to walk he should be left to his own efforts, not taught. Exercise should cease short of exhaustion. Roberton went on to discuss choosing a school at some distance from home.[38] With the prevalent use of cars and school buses today, the purpose of his last recommendation has been lost.

Bronze medal
By Rene Boudichon
OBV: Mother teaching child to walk
REV: (not shown) Parent bird over nest of young
6.3 × 4.3 cm
Note lead strings attached in front and baby far from walking capability

La Nourrice Ligurienne
[The Ligurian Wet Nurse]
Aquatint by Lamaire after Courtaille
32.7 × 24.6 cm

Notes

1. Still 1912.
2. Roesslin 1604. First published 1545.
3. Metlinger 1473.
4. Phaer 1550.
5. Parey 1649.
6. Sainte-Marthe 1797. First published in Latin ca. 1600.
7. Wuertz 1656.
8. Jackson 1798.
9. Struve 1802.
10. Buchan 1804.
11. Herdman 1807.
12. Roberton 1827.
13. Brouzet 1755.
14. Mazzini 1933.
15. Metlinger 1473.
16. Bagellardo 1487.
17. Phaer 1550.
18. Roesslin 1604.
19. Parey 1649.
20. Toletus 1538.
21. de Vallambert 1565.
22. Sainte-Marthe 1797. First published in Latin ca. 1600.
23. Gallego de la Serna 1634.
24. Astruc 1746.
25. Brouzet 1755.
26. Rousseau 1762.
27. Lefebvre 1782.
28. Hamilton 1813.
29. Roberton 1827.
30. Holt 1917.
31. Huarte Y Navarro J 1698. First published in Spanish ca. 1600.
32. Author unknown. *Observations upon the Proper Nursing of Children from a Long Series of Experience,* 1761.
33. Raulin 1769.
34. Cadogan 1748.
35. Ferrarius 1577.
36. Wuertz 1656.
37. Primrose 1659.
38. Roberton 1827.

"At Home" in the Nursery, or "The Masters and Misses Twoshoes Christmas Party"
Coloured etching by George Cruikshank (1792–1878)
27.5 × 21.5 cm

PLAY AND EDUCATION

We suppose the necessity of play for children to be acknowledged, and indeed this necessity is evident.

N. Brouzet. *An Essay on the Medicinal Education of Children.* 1755, p. 158.

Besides, Children are more Inquisitive by many degrees, and more violently desirous of Knowledge the five first Years of their Age... For this reason it is, That whatever a child is taught to imitate at Three or Four Years of Age... takes double the root, and makes deeper Impressions upon them than what they are taught at Five; and that at Five, double to what they are taught at Ten; and so on proportionably till Fifty or Sixty Years of Age.

Thomas Tryon. *A New Method of Educating Children.* 1695, pp. 34–35.

The inseparability of play and education has been recognized for centuries. Toys to encourage role modelling, toys to teach skills, and games to develop coordination and physical prowess have been universal. The Greeks sought harmony and grace; the Romans aimed for vigour of mind and body. Both wrote with a stylus on a wooden tablet filmed with wax. The Collection does not portray the history of education, but books and artifacts reflect the theories and practices of various periods.

All cultures developed appropriate toys, but children played with whatever was at hand: sticks, stones, mud, or parents' possessions left within their grasp.

Objects appearing to be toys have been found in ancient graves and considerable doubt has been expressed as to their original purpose. Were they intended to be used by the deceased in the next world, or were they solely of an amuletic nature? Early pottery figures of animals in miniature, some containing pebbles or seeds to rattle, and small doll-like figures are commonly open to question. Items mentioned in this chapter may not have been created expressly as toys, but whenever accessible to children they would have been welcome playthings.

Pets were important in the family life of the Greeks and were frequently portrayed as images or miniature models. Many examples survive: goats, horses, birds, pigs and more.

Other peoples bordering on the eastern Mediterranean during the same period and for several centuries later, also treasured little pottery animals.

Wooden slate with stylus
Roman London, ca. AD 100
Surface was coated with wax. Point of stylus was then used for writing and the dull end for erasing.
L. of stylus: 10.1 cm

Greek pottery animals, Cyprus
Horse and rider, 600 BC

Goat, 800 BC, l: 12 cm

Birds, 650–600 BC

Greek animals
Pottery rattle, Greece
Boy on pig, ca. 350 BC
L: 7.5 cm

Pottery rattle, Cyprus
Pig, ca. 300 BC

Lead lamb, Greece, 200 BC

Pottery animals, Eastern Mediterranean
Stag
Phoenician from Cyprus, ca. 500 BC

Lion
Palestine, AD 300

Horse
Palestine, ca. AD 300
Ht: 10.3 cm

Whether intended as fetishes or toys, ancient dolls must have been popular with the children. Some of the simple bone dolls would make excellent teething sticks for babies.

An Egyptian and a Greek pottery doll are very early forms. Later Greek dolls have articulated limbs. One shown has lost its movable arms; the other has all its jointed limbs and wears a short dress with a hood coming up over the head, identical to that pictured in *Les Poupées Anciennes*.[1] Typical of Greek pottery dolls, the faces and limbs are delicately formed while the bodies are crude, intended to be dressed. Making doll clothes was a traditional method of educating girls for motherhood, continuing to the time of their betrothal.

The oldest Egyptian dolls are of wood, a rare commodity in that country. One from 1000 BC is seen with several later bone dolls.

Two Roman dolls are not at all alike. One of bone found in Egypt is pierced where arms would be attached. The other, a pottery head only, found in England, has holes for hair covering the scalp area.

Egyptian and Greek pottery dolls
Left: Egypt, 800 BC
Ht: 13.4 cm

Sitting: Cyprus, ca. 250 BC

Jointed: Greece, 6 C BC

Right: Terra cotta, Cyprus, 900 BC

Pottery toys
Head of a doll
England, Roman period, AD 200–300
Ht: 6.5 cm

Boat
Roman Egypt, AD 300

Roman bone doll
Hawara, Egypt, ca. AD 300
L: 13.0 cm

Egyptian dolls, probably fetishes
Left; Wood, 1000 BC
L: 12.7 cm

Others: Bone, Coptic, AD 500

Dice
Long bone: Italo-Greek, 200 BC
L: 7.5 cm

Cubical bone: Pompeii, Italy
Before AD 79

Polygonal pottery: Greece, ca. 300 BC
20 sides, each bearing a Greek letter, alpha to omega with four letters omitted

Other playthings were plentiful among the Ancients. Pull toys were common to Greek children and boats a popular toy. The pottery example with a hole for a pull string on page 278 was found in Egypt but could have come from the seafaring Greeks. Controversy surrounds this artifact, as some believe it to be a lamp meant for hanging. Nevertheless it strongly resembles the Greek pull toy, and may be just that.

Balls and marbles have enjoyed great popularity through the centuries. Balls from Egypt show the same pattern continued for over a millenium. The largest and most recent is well worn; the others appear to have had little or no use. A print in the Collection shows a ball of similar pattern on the floor of a sixteenth-century nursery (see p. 57).

The marbles from Egypt are mostly mosaic glass, moulded by hand into imperfect spheres. They are strikingly similar to the spherical glass, porcelain, and pottery specimens of early nineteenth-century England.

Gambling by throwing dice was a common pastime. Preceding the familiar cubic dice of today, were cowrie shells, and, as depicted in Brueghel's sixteenth-century paintings, astralaguses or knucklebones. A knucklebone from Egypt is pictured with glass facsimiles which are Roman, found in Palestine; beside them are a few samples from a large number of counters for tossing and scoring, found in Gibraltar. Resembling dice of today are four bone cubes found at Pompeii, Italy; like the long dice still used in Eastern countries are the two bone pieces from Greece. The unusual polygonal die resembles that described by G. Hilton Price,[2] used in some game or for incantations. A similar die bearing Roman numerals appears in *The Way to Play*.[3] Such a plastic die is used in the modern game *Future*.

Balls and Marbles
Top group of five:
Balls, Egypt, glazed composition
Largest 100 BC
Diam: 6.3 cm
Others: 1360 BC

Left group of five:
Sampling of marbles, Egypt
Mostly mosaic glass, ca. AD 100

Right group of five:
Sampling of marbles, England
Glass, porcelain and pottery, early 19 C

Game pieces
Astralaguses (Knucklebones)
Used as dice

Left: Knucklebone, Egypt, ca. 300 BC
2.5 × 1.3 × 1.3 cm

Right: Two glass knucklebones, Roman found at Mount Carmel, Palestine, ca. AD 100

Glass and polished stone counters
Roman found at Gibraltar
Diam: 0.6–1.9 cm

Board games such as chess and backgammon were popular in ancient times for both adults and children. The pottery game pieces from Egypt and the later coralline pieces from Roman London were probably for chess, and the bone discs of the Roman period for backgammon or children's games, from which emerged the modern "parchesi" or "snakes and ladders." Rectangular pieces of wood or bone incised with pips are just like today's dominoes.

Dishes were among the playthings popular with Egyptian children, especially girls. As with dolls, such play prepared them for their adult role.

Game pieces
Roman London

Domino, bone, l: 3.2 cm
Large disc, wood
Other discs, bone

Ancient game pieces
Upper right: Faience, Egypt, probably for chess, 600–300 BC

Ht: Extreme right, 4.4 cm

Lower left: Four coralline, two faience (right)
Roman London, AD 100

Miniature pottery dishes
Faience, Egypt

Upper row, left to right:
Vases 1, 3, 4: 1000 BC
Papyrus flower dish 2, ca. 300 BC
Diam: 2.0 cm

Lower row, left: 100 BC, right: 300 BC

One of the few times in ancient Greece when the child was accorded special attention was during the Spring Festival of Dionysius. The second day was designated Children's Day, and was part of the religious festival to ensure and then to celebrate the renewal of life. Greek children from a very young age walked to the sanctuary of Dionysius wearing wreaths of flowers in their hair. As presents, they received small jugs, replicas of those used by their elders for tasting the wine. These miniatures were often decorated with childhood scenes and, if a child should die, were buried with him along with other small treasures. Consequently many have survived.

Miniature pottery juglets of the type given on prize day at Spring Festival

Left to right:
Italo-Greek, ca. 100 BC
Greece, Athens, ca. 400 BC, ht: 6.3 cm
Feeder, southern Italy, Italo-Greek, ca. 200 BC
Cyprus, Greco-Phoenician, ca. 500 BC
Greece (not Athens), 900–700 BC

Miniature pottery bowls
Upper left (4): Roman Egypt, ca. 100 BC

Lower left: Italo-Greek, 100 BC

Centre and below (2): Greece, 300 BC

Upper right:
Large: Cyprus, 1000–850 BC
Diam: 8.4 cm
Small: Corinth, 500–450 BC

Lower right:
With handles: Greek found at Syracuse
200 BC
Black glaze: Athens, ca. AD 300

Most of the information about Greek children—their games, pets, toys, and activities—is gleaned from the decoration on vases. Exercise ranked high in importance to build the strong, healthy bodies the Greeks held in such esteem. From the child's early age, toys were chosen to encourage physical activity, dexterity, and harmony: hoops, balls, peg-tops, swings, see-saws, kites, hobby horses, go-carts, and pitch and toss. For the infant, rattles could be added to the list.

Curious rattles from Roman London survive in part. These were more likely shaken by older children much as we would use a clapper or a noise-maker today. A rattle of metal, too heavy to be managed by an infant, seemed puzzling until its duplicate was seen hanging from the waist of a young girl painted by Titian. Probably this rattle was worn for amuletic effect, in the belief that the sound would ward off evil spirits. Shaken by an adult, it would, of course, amuse a baby. The bone rattle, containing a metal bell, is also unusual.

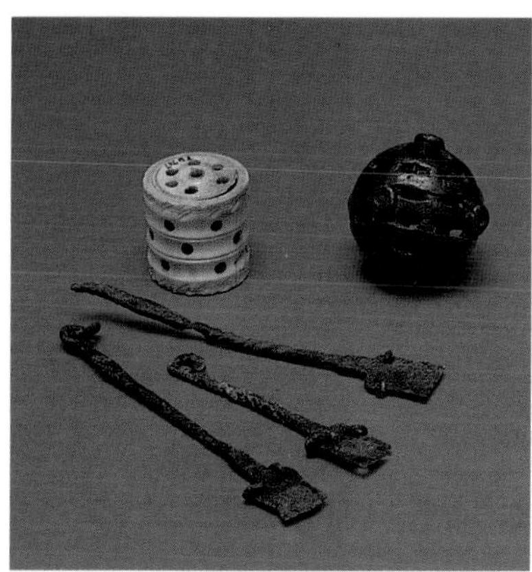

Rattles from AD 100 to 1700
Left: Bone rattle, London, 17 C

Right: Metal rattle, London, 15 C
Diam; 5.0 cm

Lower: Iron rattles, wooden parts missing
Roman London, ca. AD 100

Most appealing for their beauty are the rattles of the eighteenth and nineteenth centuries, of which there are 50 in the Collection. Some are simple rattles; others incorporate a teething stick, bells, and perhaps a whistle. Silver or gold is combined with coral, mother-of-pearl, ivory, or bone. Not only was coral soothing to a child's sore gums, but was felt to dispel evil spirits. Coral and bells, commonly in use since the Middle Ages, are seen held by children or by an adult to amuse an infant, in a number of prints in the Collection.

Une fille des Strozzi
[A daughter of the Strozzis]
Titian (1477–1546)
Chas. Moreau-Vautier. *Les Portraits de l'enfance.* p. 68

Rattles
Left to Right:
England, Birmingham, 1876–1877
Bells, coral teething stick, whistle
France, ca. 1838
Bells, mother-of-pearl teething stick, whistle
England, Birmingham, 1921. l: 12.0 cm
Belgium, 1831–1869 (cf. p. 219)

Jacques Stella's seventeenth-century book depicting the games and pleasures of children in France portrays cherubic young boys playing marbles, hop scotch, cards, and dice; tossing counters, rolling and jumping hoops, spinning tops, shooting firecrackers, and juggling with cup and ball sets—all in the out-of-doors.[4] These activities are certainly reminiscent of games recommended by the Greeks. Artifacts from England photographed with the prints, verify that similar play was popular there. In both countries much of this play has continued.

The Peg Top
Stella p. 22
9.7 × 14.0 cm

Peg top, England, ca. 1800

Peg top, London, 17 C
L: 8.0 cm

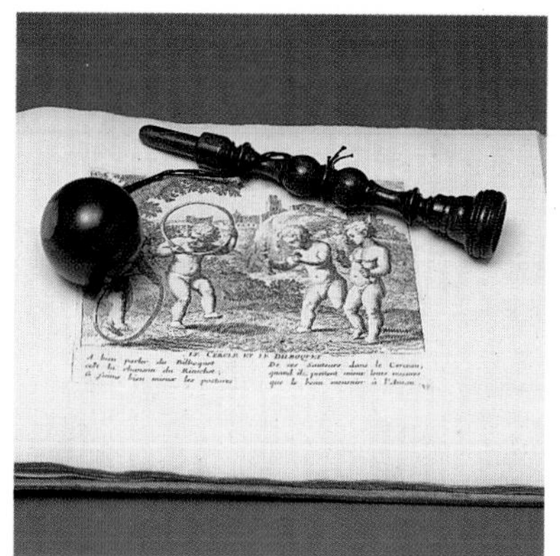

Hoop and Cup and Ball
Stella p. 39
9.8 × 14.3 cm

Wooden cup and ball, England, 19 C
Ht: 16.0 cm

Small guns
Stella p. 25
9.5 × 14.0 cm

Metal key for activating firecrackers
Found in the "Paris Gardens", a pleasure resort just south of London in 17 C
England, 1600–1680
L: 4.4 cm

Toys, England

Three cup and ball sets, 19 C
Outer two, wood
Centre, bone, ht: 19.0 cm

Peg top, left: African rosewood, 17 C
Spin top, centre: wood, 19 C
Whistle, wood, 17 C
Hunting horn, bronze, 18 C
Two brass petronels, 17 C
Brass cannon, 17 C

Commonly used by children and adults as a pastime in England from the medieval period, the cup and ball was popular among the Indians in Canada, and a counterpart was carved of bone by the Inuit. Cup and ball sets are still found for sale in America and Europe.

Of the toys just described, most were enjoyed by boys; girls were more limited to dolls, dishes, and stitchery. Dolls after the sixteenth century were made of: wax; wax heads and limbs on a body of leather or cloth stuffed with rags or sawdust; pottery or porcelain heads and limbs on a stuffed body. Later some were made of rubber and other composite materials. Many were elaborately dressed.

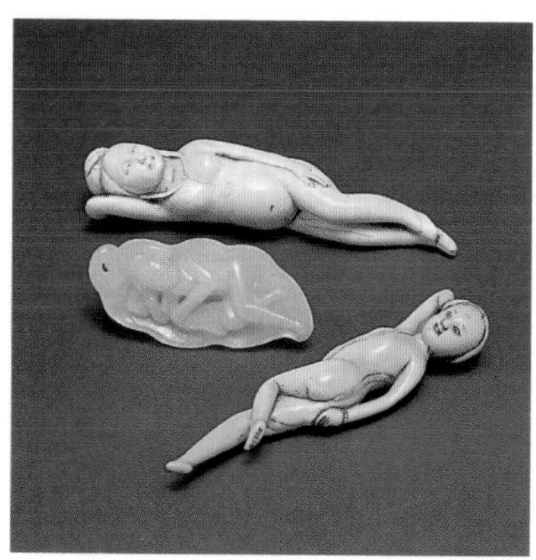

Male dolls
Japan
Ivory heads and hands, dressed in fine silk, depicting Samurai
Ht: 16.0 cm

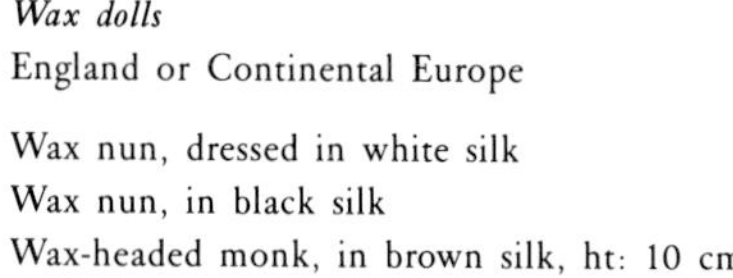

Wax dolls
England or Continental Europe

Wax nun, dressed in white silk
Wax nun, in black silk
Wax-headed monk, in brown silk, ht: 10 cm

Little girls continue to dress and care for their dolls; the dolls, their clothing, and their accoutrements have become extremely varied and elaborate. Particular dolls have become fads, and entire doll families have been devised.

Some dolls in the Collection do not fall into the category of playthings. They are the carefully and beautifully carved Chinese medicine dolls of wood, ivory, or semi-precious stones. Those pictured here are ivory and jade. A lady in China did not reveal herself to her doctor, but kept her medicine doll with her and pointed out on the doll where any ache, pain, or other disorder was located.

Medicine dolls
Ivory (2), China, l: 12.7 cm

Jade, China, K'ien Lung Dynasty (1736–1795)

Dolls, 19 C
Stuffed doll depicting peasant, British Isles ca. 1830
Ht: 14.0 cm

Rag doll with pottery head, England, 1830–1840
Ht: 23.5 cm
Note when apron is lifted a white pocket is revealed tied around the waist. Women and men wore such pockets under skirts or coats to carry treasures such as keys or important documents. Being separate entities, they could be lost and advertisements for lost pockets were seen in newspapers. So, the nursery rhyme: "Lucy Locket Lost her Pocket. . ." was understandable to a child of the 19 C.

Miniature metal carriage containing two porcelain babies, England, 19 C

The toy pipe shown here would appeal to little boys. Utensils and dishes, found in abundance, enabled the girls to mimic their mothers in housekeeping tasks.

The earliest tea set in the Collection is Chinese-export, though English factories are well represented. Caughley and Leeds are shown.

Metal toys and clay pipe, 16 C – 18 C
Latten dish, Tudor rose in centre.
London, 1560
Diam: 8.0 cm
Found in River Walbrook, very rare

Clay pipe, miniature. England, 1620–1650[5]
Stem bore: 3.12 mm

Strainer, Europe, 17 C

Spoon, London, mid-18 C

Cream skimmer, England, 18 C

Toy dishes
Centre and below: Porcelain saucer and tea bowl
Chinese-export, 18 C

Across top: Pottery bowl and saucer, tureen and egg cup.
England, Leeds, late 18 C
Ht: egg cup, 5.0 cm

Lower left and right: Porcelain tea set
England, Caughley, late 18 C

With the rise of the middle class and new interest in domestic surroundings, doll houses became popular in Europe, particularly in the Netherlands and England. Trade in fine miniatures thrived as women indulged their desire to accumulate elegant household furnishings. The miniature walker and chair would add grace to any doll house, as the caudle cups and pap boat would enhance the small table for a tea party. The tiny rattle would suit a doll but was possibly worn as jewellery.

French fashion prints of the early nineteenth century depict some of the play activities of children, and stamps from around the world, some regular issue and others with surcharges for specified causes, record their pastimes into the twentieth century.

Parisian fashion
1813
15.3 × 9.2 cm

Parisian fashion
1830
Fashions specified for 3- to 6- and 6- to 9-year-olds

Miniature silver and gold pieces
Clockwise from upper left:
Caudle cup, silver, Edinburgh, 1814–1815
Capacity: 28cc

Chair, Netherlands, 83.3–93.4% silver
After 1883, ht: 3.2 cm

Walker, Amsterdam, 83.3–93.4% silver,
Maker: J.L. (Johannes Lutma), 18C

Caudle cup, silver gilt, London, 1718
Rattle, gold and coral, with bells and whistle
London after 1854

Pap boat: Great Britain, ca. 1730

One might suppose that play and playthings simply developed, and to some extent they did. But just as the Greeks encouraged physically demanding play, so later writers offered guidance with different goals, often educational, in mind.

In France in the mid-eighteenth century, Brouzet, quoted at the beginning of this section, divided play into two classes: the first to exercise the body, such as racing, leaping, wrestling, or imitating hunting, war, and the laborious arts; the second, to exercise the mind while sitting in the house — story-telling, chess, draughts, tick-tack, and sedentary arts.

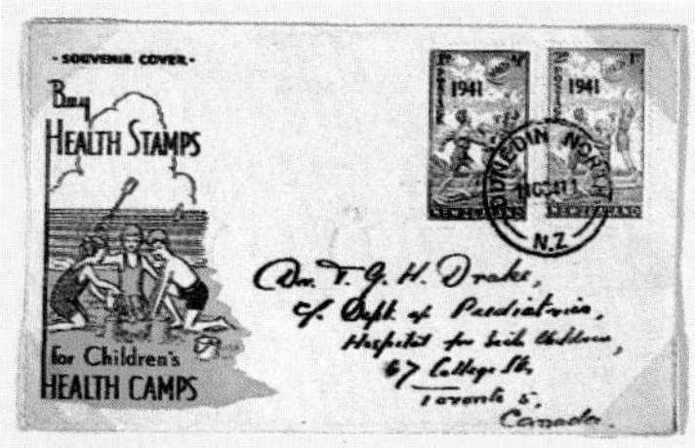

Souvenir cover
Children at play
New Zealand, B18 and B19
Oct., 1941

Rolling hoops
Netherlands Antilles (Curaçao), B14
1951

Children at seashore
Yugoslavia, B85
May 1, 1939

Children on swing
New Zealand, B20
Oct. 1, 1942

London Bridge
Netherlands Antilles (Curaçao), B13
1951

Children playing hane-tsuki
(similar to badminton)
Japan, 424
Dec. 13, 1948

Children under five, Brouzet said, not yet being instructed, should avoid the first class of competitive play and be concerned only with their little amusements and activities of the second class which are easily within their grasp. Older children already under instruction must interrupt their study to relax their minds, by periods of play of the first class. By this time their bodies need to develop strength, but exercise should be regulated to be compatible with their future station in life. He made no distinction between the sexes before puberty.[6]

Early in the nineteenth century in Germany, Struve proposed much the same approach as Brouzet had earlier, emphasizing the need to break up long tasks with recess times for play. He suggested nursery activities such as unravelling silk, counting and arranging grains, scrawling on paper or slates, and he specified somewhat different activities for girls such as knitting, sewing, and spinning. Whenever possible he favoured playing in the fresh air; he objected to having children sit for hours in nursery chairs. Struve offered advice on choosing toys, with consideration for safety: avoiding poisonous materials, cutting edges, and sharp points.[7]

Roberton, Struve's contemporary in England, supported his views. He preferred toys and games that ensured exercise and amusement, but imparted knowledge as well. In the nursery his favourite toy was building blocks: simple, durable, versatile and safe. Horrified by the practice of restricting girls to dolls, trinkets, and sewing, and believing boys and girls to be alike in their early years, he recommended activities such as skipping, riding, and gardening for both. For older boys, he condemned harmful playthings—gunpowder, bow and arrows, sharp tools—and favoured many sports like bowling, football, and cricket, always under supervision.[8]

It is interesting to note that Struve in Germany and Roberton in England were both concerned about planning open areas in cities for exercise and other pleasurable activities.

Falling into Brouzet's second category of games — sedentary ones exercising the mind — are spillikins, which also requires physical dexterity, and two games by Edward Wallis. In the first, after a random toss, one spillikin at a time must be picked up without disturbing any others. Each stick is different and has its own count. A modern version is called *Jackstraws* and in Canada, *Pick up Sticks*. Chinese play the game with many more and elaborate ivory pieces.

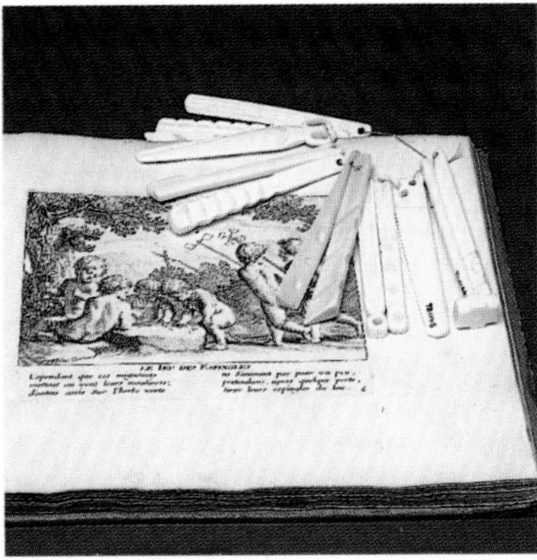

Spillikins
Stella p. 6
9.5 × 14.0 cm

Ivory game pieces
England, 19 C
Scissors, l: 9.5 cm

The *New Game of Genius* was a game to encourage knowledge of "the Arts, Science and Manufactures... for the Amusement and Instruction of Youth of both Sexes." It was designed to enable a player to move from square to square on the basis of mental skill, and possibly to move back with the lack of it. Another game produced by Wallis was played on similar principles: ***Picturesque Round Game of the Produce and Manufactures of the Counties of England and Wales.*** How like the ***Trivial Pursuit*** of today!

Material for learning may be presented to children in a number of ways: by casual exposure to facts and ideas, through experience, and in a formal routine of education. In nineteenth-century England moral and political messages were conveyed through pictures, cartoons, and printing, often in verses and songs. The social effects of drunkenness, graphically illustrated by William Hogarth in his ***Gin Lane*** series, were still much in evidence in the nineteenth century; music hall singers entreated, "Don't give no more drink to my father..." In Leeds, Yorkshire, a group of juvenile abstainers who took the pledge of temperance, formed what they called a ***Band of Hope.*** More groups formed and children's plates appeared bearing messages and illustrations. One reads: "Train up a child in the way he should go. Remember now thy creator in the days of thy youth." Another shows ***The Sabbath Breakers.*** The plate from Swansea, Wales, with embossed daisy border, is another example of efforts to influence. It reads: "Hush my dear lie still and slumber: Holy angels guard thy bed: Heavenly blessings without number Gently falling on thy head."

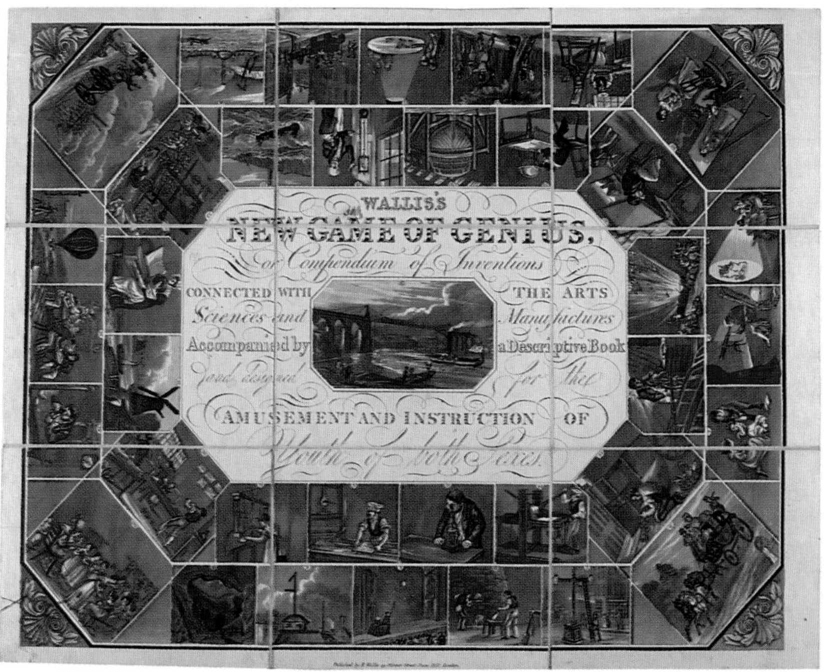

Mat board for Wallis's *New Game of Genius*
England, 19 C
Composition: 36.2 × 45.6 cm

Children's pottery plates
Left and right: BAND OF HOPE
England, 19 C
Diam: 13.3 cm

Centre: Swansea, Wales, 1810–1820

Morals occupied a prominent place in the advice given concerning education. This is reflected in the rare books of the Collection, mostly from Europe, especially England. For example, Sainte-Marthe about 1600 stated the aims of education thus: to teach morals, to discourage vice, and to encourage emanation of the divine.[9] The acquisition of skills and knowledge and the development of thought varied in importance with different advisors, and the methods of learning, even as today, were diversified.

Among the earliest guides for teaching young children is Metlinger's Regimen of 1473, in German, in which he discouraged harsh treatment and engendered kindness. For school age children, in line with later authorities, he favoured breaking up long and strenuous tasks with recesses.[10]

In England, Sir Thomas Elyot in the early sixteenth century described, in great detail, how to raise a son to be a gentleman who might hold public office. Extraordinary precautions to enable the child to learn manners by example included hiring a nurse of no servile condition, and a second nurse to shield the child from bad influence in the nursery. Only physicians should enter there. Later, carefully chosen friends should be his companions. A nobleman could teach his son, alluring him sweetly with praises and pretty gifts. At seven, a boy should be taken from the company of women and assigned to an exemplary tutor who would treat him with gravity. If the tutor is also learned, the more commendable: he will teach what the child wants and is best suited to learn.[11]

Elyot concentrated on teaching boys. His near-contemporary, Huarte Y Navarro in Spain, dismissed girls from his consideration in the belief that only boys have wits. As did Elyot, he emphasized the importance of assessing a boy's aptitude before beginning his training. If *Triers of Wit* appointed by the state, were to observe children at play and during visits to tradesmen's shops, they could choose suitable education. "By these means, there would be fewer Dunces in the Universities, as well as fewer Bunglers in the Shops,"[12] and many in the schools of higher learning would be sent to study the Trades and Manual Arts. Huarte Y Navarro must have agreed with the general concepts of his time, that a girl was educated if she could curtsy and sew a sampler.

Most of us expect samplers to convey moralistic messages like those mentioned earlier on children's plates, but the original intent of samplers was to record examples *(exemplaires)* of embroidery stitches. A girl visiting a friend or relative would take along her sample cloth, a very long, narrow rectangle, on which to copy any appealing stitch or pattern to be used later on her household linens. The earliest record of samplers is in Elizabeth of York's accounts of 1502.[13] Though samplers were kept, willed, and collected into reference libraries by royalty, few of the early random-patterned pieces of the sixteenth century survived. Pattern books first printed in Germany in 1523 and in England in 1587 were slow to gain popular usage: samplers functioned as originally intended to the end of the sixteenth century, many for a long time thereafter.

Samplers and pattern books of the seventeeth century are numerous. ***The Embroidery and Alphabet Sampler Book*** in the Collection, removed from its embroidered case, unfolds in accordian fashion to reveal the letters in different styles and a variety of stitches and patterns.

The neat rows in most surviving seventeenth-century samplers suggest a school exercise. One in the Collection has the W first worked upside down, then repeated right side up, corrected, perhaps by a mistress; in some cases it is possible to identify the school in the work. A print depicts such instruction.

Teaching embroidery
Engraving, dated 1573
31.7 × 24.3 cm

Donald King. *Victoria and Albert Museum Samplers.*

Earliest samplers were simply as defined: examples of rows of stitches and/or patterns, usually without colour. Those in the Collection demonstrate well the development of these works from this base. One sees, for instance, the introduction of the letter U into the alphabet in the late seventeenth century.

After 1650 religious and moral inscriptions became more common. Half of the eighteenth-century samplers have such messages; numbers, dates, initials or names, sometimes the child's age, and even the name of the teacher, appeared more frequently. Similarities of stitches and patterns are evident in contemporary pieces. Eighteenth- and nineteenth-century examples reflect the trend to more elaborate patterns, especially in the borders: the exercise in embroidery creates a picture.

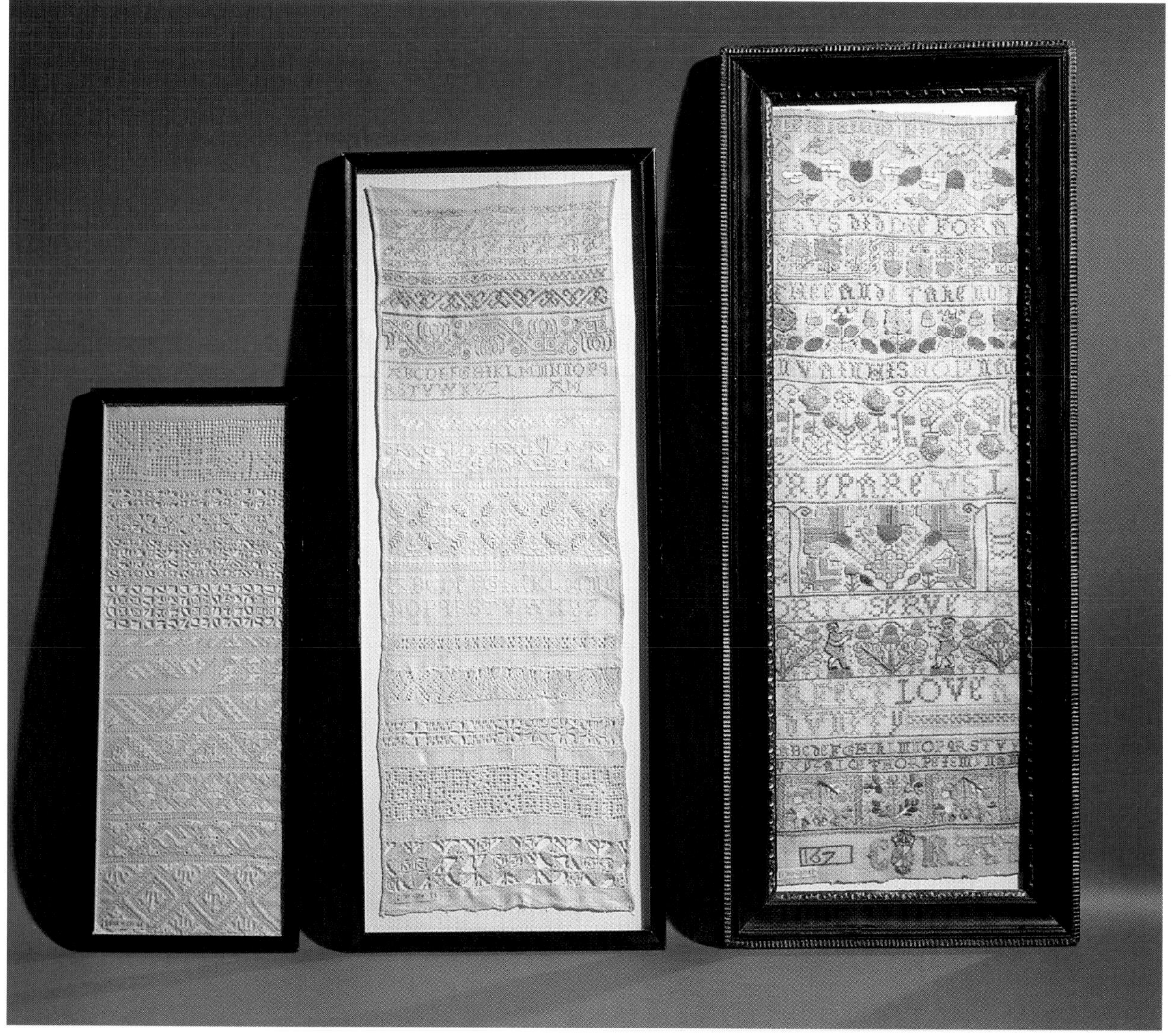

Samplers, England 17 C
Left to right:
Earliest style, no letters or numbers, no colour
42.0 × 15.5 cm

Some colour, letters, no J or U in alphabet, no numbers
59.7 × 23.5 cm

Latest style, colour, alphabet including U, moral message, crest of King Charles, between C and R, incomplete date 167–, worked by Alice Thorpe, and initialled AT
61.6 × 19.7 cm

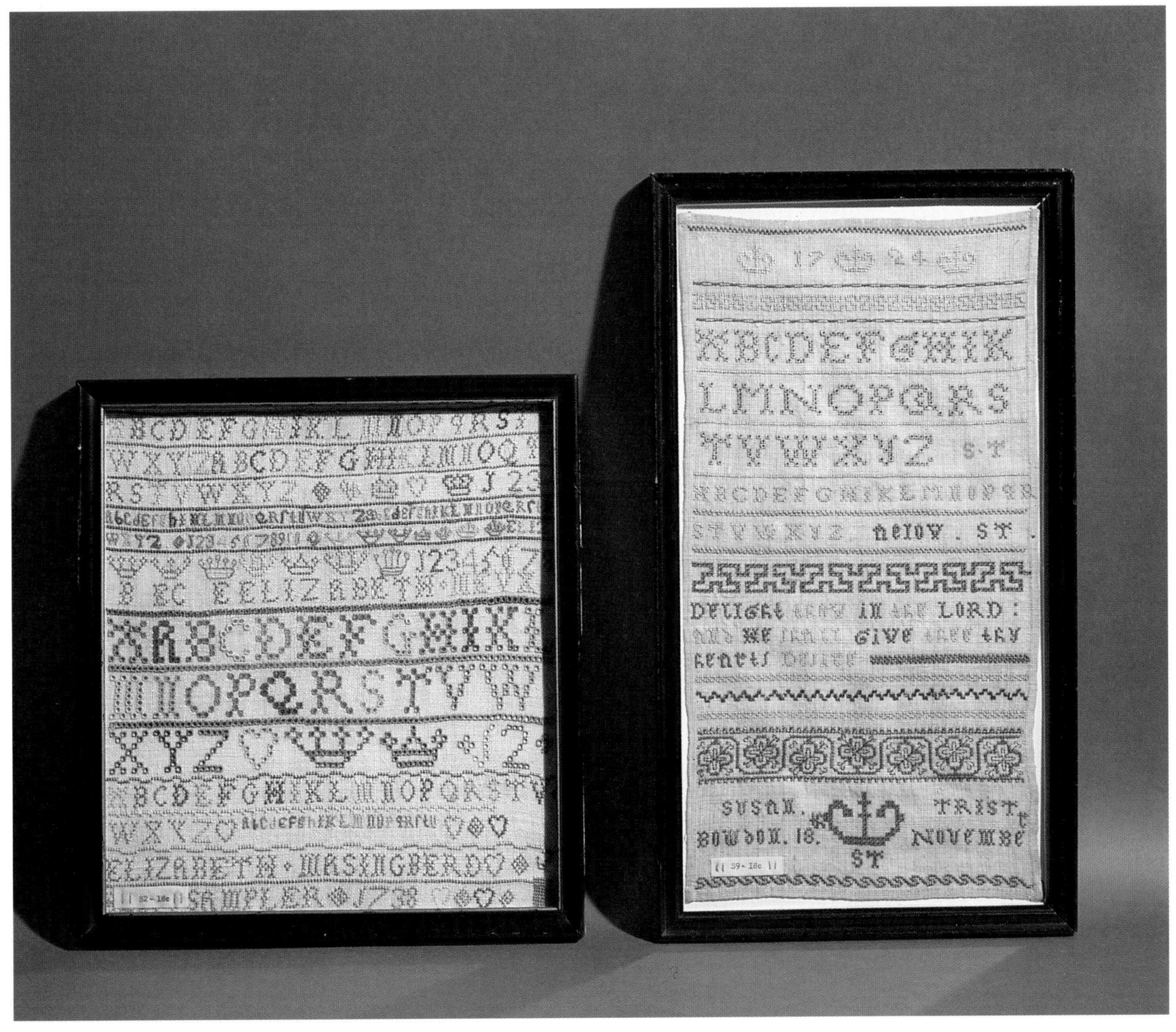

Samplers, England 18
No J, no U in alphabets

Elizabeth Wasingberd, age 12, 1738
Alphabet, numbers, no message, signed and dated
23.5 × 21.6 cm

Susan Trist, 1724
Alphabet, no numbers, message, signed and dated
32.8 × 17.5 cm

Samplers, England 18–19 C
Verses of prayer and praise
No alphabet, no numbers
Highly decorative

Elizabeth Shayler, 1746
Signed and dated*
34.3 × 31.1 cm

* In a note Leonard Shuffrey, great-great-grandson of Elizabeth Shayler Shuffrey, who married in 1751, is acknowledged to have restored the frame in 1905.

Hannah Cummine, age 10–11, Dec. 9, 1819
Signed and dated
43.5 × 31.7 cm

Samplers, England 19 C
Alphabet, numbers
Highly decorative

Jane Dyson, age 13
Message, signed and dated, Dec., 1878
33.0 × 25.0 cm

Ann Williams Hills, age 7
No message, signed, not dated
51.1 × 40.6 cm

The teaching guide of the early eighteenth century has the complete alphabet as used today, yet none of the samplers before the nineteenth century in the Collection show both I and J, and only one, that of the 1670s, U and V. After 1800, all letters are commonly, but not always, included. It took time for the new letters to come into general use.

Though the print showing group instruction in a classroom appears to be a contented scene, it was not always so. Indeed school mistresses stood over girls as they stitched ready to bring a rod down on the knuckles of idle fingers. According to Thomas Tryon, a century after the death of Huarte, girls were kept at stitchery up to eight hours a day, beginning at age six or seven. Samplers in the Collection so marked, show the ages of the sewers to range from seven to 13. It seems a miraculous accomplishment. The patience and co-ordination needed would demand an attention span far beyond normal limits. Strain on the eyes would be one of several hazards. Tryon was horrified by these practices, as he believed girls needed the same relief as boys during lengthy tasks. He deplored physical deformities brought on by long periods of sitting in crooked positions and the dull, sleepy attitude resulting from habitual boredom. What of the child who lacked the necessary skill?

Pewter teaching guide
England, 1727. Engraved "St. Paul's" on back. Worn like a horn book, hanging from waist or around neck by children learning alphabet.
12.7 × 6.3 cm

Both Huarte and Tryon were convinced that from birth children learned effortlessly by example and imitation. Therefore it was important that their companions speak and behave well. But in contrast to Huarte, Tryon observed, "It is a great Truth though very little believed That the Females are naturally as fit for, and capable of all excellent Learning, as Men, even the Mathematics itself: and if there be any difference the Advantage is on the Women's side."[14] He stipulated that the education of women was particularly important because a mother sows the first seed in a child's mind. No tutor can effectively substitute for her.

Tryon's portrayal of a mother as a versatile linguist of impeccable manners and morals and a fountain of knowledge with an imperturbable disposition is quite overwhelming. Believing that an individual's learning capacity decreases rapidly with time (see quote introducing this section), he advised mothers to start teaching the infant in the cradle and to progress according to the child's ability.

It was a long time before stitchery was removed from its pinnacle of importance in the education of young girls, in spite of the views of Tryon and other writers in the field. As is apparent in viewing samplers through the seventeenth, eighteenth and nineteenth centuries, they ceased to fulfill their original purpose as a collection of useful embroidery stitches and became pictures created with artistry and skill. The emphasis on stitchery as a talent and a measure of education in young women persisted. In 1821 a mother giving advice to her daughter away at school concentrated on conduct, mostly of a moral nature. When authorities were condemning or belittling the emphasis on stitchery for girls, this mother expressed her concern: ". . . but I should be extremely sorry if that excellent little instrument, the needle, was entirely excluded, for its use is a woman's province, and one of the ornaments of her sex."[15]

Of the apprentices sent to London to train with mercers, drapers, and silk men in the seventeenth century, Tryon claimed only one in 20 served full time and attributed this poor success rate to lack of variety in their learning. Huarte might have explained it on the basis of the child's innate ineptitude, though today we would certainly give consideration to the conditions of work and the treatment received in the shops. In many instances apprentices may have left because of poor health.

Assuming good health to be a prerequisite to learning, educators included advice for good sleep, good exercise, fresh air, and good nourishment in their treatises. These aspects have been dealt with previously.

Having the same underlying philosophy as his predecessors, John Locke believed that education must produce "Habits woven into the very Principles of his [the pupil's] Nature,"[16] and to achieve this he introduced a firmness based on reward and punishment, emphasizing the former. While Tryon avoided instilling fear in children, Locke was convinced that removing hope and fear brought an end to all discipline: "Good and Evil, Reward and Punishment are the only Motives to a rational Creature."[17]

Not much later, Robert South, in sermons published in 1724, expressed grave concern with the laxity in education. To this he attributed all the problems of the nation. He determined that virtues must be taught early and the natural propensity to vice countered by those responsible: parents, teachers, and clergy. Bodily chastisement, he warned, may be used so as not to injure, and so that the child understands that punishment stems from love, for his own good. Boys must become men, their spirit bent, not broken. His approach included more emphasis on punishment than Locke had intended.[18]

In the mid-eighteenth century, James Nelson began from the premise that "Health is a nice Affair, and Life precious to every Individual."[19] Naming love as the most important ingredient in child-rearing, he was against severe and frequent whipping. Curiosity, he wrote, should be cherished as "The Gate of Knowledge."[20] One should avoid creating fears in children — of water, of the dark, of various superstitions. Nelson's prime aim in education was to create good manners in the broadest sense, for he believed they make for a just society.

Nelson proposed that early education should be light, easy, and pleasant, but school should be serious. A genius should be encouraged early, but for most, age seven is soon enough for formal training. Education should fit children for employment useful to society and suited to their condition in life. It is possible, but not probable, to raise one's children's station. Of a baker educating his son, Nelson felt it a pity that a good baker should be spoiled.

The different educational streams Nelson described were for: (1) noblemen, (2) gentry, (3) men of trade and commerce, (4) men of inferior trades, and (5) peasantry and dwellers of city slums. In the belief that women should be educated, he gave specific advice for males and females.

For a nobleman, in order of importance, he listed: firstly, Latin, Greek, French, Italian, Spanish, Portugese; secondly, philosophy, mathematics, laws and manners, history; thirdly, literature, poetry, painting, music, and lastly, dancing, fencing, riding, and architecture. For the lady, he advised: reading—to be able to read aloud well, writing—to acquire an easy elegance, and needle work: then French, Italian, and music; then arithmetic, geography and drawing, and lastly moral and experimental philosophy. Parents should advise girls about books to read and encourage virtuous sentiments, noble deportment, and actions to contribute to the happiness of others as well as to their own.

Sons of men of other classes should be educated as he detailed, but at less expense and with modifications practical for their class, keeping in mind the motto "Manners make the Man."[21] Girls must know, in addition, the whole "Oeconomy of Family."[22] The fifth class should be taught reading, writing, and arithmetic.

Nelson observed that uneducated parents wanted their children to be scholars, whereas parents of rank were often indifferent. This statement in particular reflects the security of the upper classes in those times when birth and wealth guaranteed their lifestyle.

The unknown writer of 1761, quoted on page 268, was in full agreement with Nelson regarding the necessity for developing varying types of education for different social classes. She was confident that children could be improved much earlier than imagined by the examples and teaching of mothers. A mother who has raised and instructed a child to the age of five or six and sees her child graceful, healthy, and possessing good virtues will find more satisfaction than in all other diversions and fashionable amusements. She wished some means could be found "to train up Girls, to the proper Management of Young Children; which I think might be done in *Workhouses, Free Schools, etc. also in Noblemens and other great Families."[23] Her footnote is reproduced here, for her suggestion was often quoted by authorities in the next hundred years—in fact, it made its way into the *Encyclopedia Britannica* before the end of the century.

> * If a premium was given to Free-schools, Workhouses, etc. to those that brought up the finest Child to one Year old, either in Workhouses or by Parish Nurses, it would [be] a means of Encouragement to them, as well as to all other useful Improvements: and I may venture to say, of as general Utility. But I only give Hints, which I hope to live to see improved and enlarged upon.
>
> Author unknown. *Observations upon the Proper Nursing of Children from a Long Series of Experience.* 1761, p. 17.

In France trends in education were similar to those in England. In the late seventeenth century there appeared a small book written by an unknown author, about children who studied and became famous. It included biographies of Pliny the Younger, Augustus, Tiberius, Caligula, Pascal, and Henry VII and Henry VIII of England. It is presumed these examples were intended not only to inform youngsters of these notable men who had been precocious children, but to provide them with inspiring role models.

Echoing Huarte's sixteenth-century concern for aptitude, a writer in Paris in 1707 expressed similar sensitivity. He emphasized that material taught must be within the child's understanding and within his field of interest; it is important to teach a child first what he wants to know.

By the mid-eighteenth century, in France, J.J. Rousseau was expounding his theories on education. Though Rousseau's back-to-nature philosophy simulated that of John Locke earlier in England, his ideas on education were somewhat different. Wishing to delay formal education until age 12, Rousseau urged fathers to educate their boys in a practical, natural way. For example, when out for a walk, discuss: how can we build a bridge over this stream?, or how can we measure the height of that steeple? The aim should be to teach the child to think for himself. He believed girls were less capable of reasoning and their training should be geared to motherhood and caring for a husband.

Regulations for schools in France in Rousseau's time reflect the beliefs of other writers of the period. Emphasis was placed on teaching through example, leading to obedience and compliance with regulation. Reading was censored; religion and catechism were stressed. Discipline was to be achieved without anger, temper, or violence; slaps and cuffs were forbidden; the rod was to be used only when all else failed: the ultimate punishment was expulsion.

In the late eighteenth century, when English samplers and children's plates were carrying ethical messages, children's books were frequently of a moral nature. A *Hieroglyphick Bible* (author unknown) of 1788 is directed to parents, guardians, and governesses of Great Britain and Ireland. It is elaborately illustrated and has pictures frequently substituted for words. J. Harrison's picture book for the nursery has 70 engravings with such titles as: A covetous man is never contented; A house on fire! What a dreadful sight!; Lord Modish and Lady Squander; You must not touch Sister's dolls, Fred; Lady Bountiful visiting the Sick. Humour and amusement are absent.[24] *The Mother's Fables* (author unknown), written in verse in 1814 by a mother as told to her children, was intended to amuse and to teach virtue and benevolence.

In France two card games served as aids to learning. One, designed to teach children of four or five to read in three or four months, contains charts of sounds for repetition and suggests flash cards, each with an object pictured: legs, chair, broom, man. The other is a deck of 48 cards, each bearing a biography of a British monarch. It is implied that this is one of a series of games, brought to the attention of fathers and instructors to create a desire to learn in both boys and girls. The success claimed in both England and France indicated that students grasped more in a few months in all branches of learning than in several years by ordinary paths!

Considering the position of women in society, Hannah More stressed the value of their education. Mothers are responsible for the early education of all children and almost exclusively for the continuing training of girls. She believed, as others stated, that fashionable arts such as dancing and painting do not fulfill the goal of education, and that when a man of sense comes to marry, he wants a companion, not an artist. This echoes the sentiment of Nelson half a century earlier, who wrote: "A rational man should chuse a rational companion."[25]

Struve's thoughts approximated the ideas of Tryon and Brouzet in the previous century. He was convinced that children learned more in their early years during play than under a teacher's instruction and that they should not be sent to school before the age of five. Whereas Nelson suggested school at seven, and the encouragement of a genius early, Struve advised that the school hours of a genius should be shortened: a boy should be put part-time to labour manually, a girl to sew or knit, a practice based on the concept used today: enrichment for the bright child.

In nineteenth-century England Roberton's main thrust in his views on education was to intersperse exercise with learning, particularly for girls, and especially in boarding schools. He believed that boys tended naturally to exercise and that girls did not.

Belief in the importance of example as a teaching technique remained prevalent. In France, in the nineteenth century, Léger placed major emphasis on choosing carefully the child's companions at school and play.[26]

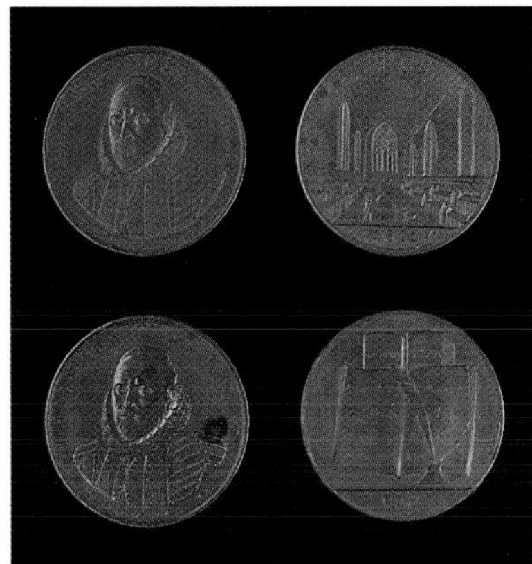

Philemon Holland medals
OBV: PHILEMON HOLLAND. M.D. DIED 1636 AGED 85
REV: FREE SCHOOL COVENTRY
E: Penny Token Payable By E.W. Percy Coventry. Very rare
36 mm

OBV: PHILEMON HOLLAND. M.D. DIED 1636 AGED 85
REV: An open book resting against two others, lettered *Britannia Cykopaedia.* The first page of the open book is inscribed WITH ONE SOLE PEN I WROTE THIS BOOK MADE OF A GRAY GOOSE QUILL; and on the other, A PEN IT WAS WHEN I TOOK IT A PEN I LEAVE IT STILL. By the book is an inkstand with a quill in it. 1801 I.G.H.
E: Penny Token Payable by E.W. Percy Coventry X. Extra rare. The dies were destroyed (Davis, W.J.)[27]

A medal was struck in France to celebrate the laws guaranteeing free education at the primary level in the late nineteenth century.

Many medals were struck for free schools in England. The purpose is uncertain but several suggestions may be made: they were sold as a means of raising funds; they were used as rewards to boys for behaviour and for accomplishment; they substituted for coinage for the boys to obtain credit from local tradespeople. The last suggestion is supported by the edge inscription on some, indicating where they could be redeemed.

It was Philemon Holland who translated Pliny's *Historie of the World.* In 1608, he was appointed usher of the Free School (Coventry), in 1612 presented with the Freedom of the city, and in 1628 was made master. He translated *Romanes Histories* which he claimed to have written throughout with one pen. This he solemnly kept and it was ultimately enclosed in silver by a lady of his acquaintance.[27]

Free education medal
OBV: INSTRUCTION POPULAIRE [Public Education]
70 mm

REV: LOIS D'ENSEIGNEMENT PRIMAIRE GRATUIT OBLIGATYOIRE LAIQUE [Laws making primary secular education free and obligatory]
16 JANUARY 1881
28 MARCH 1882
30 OCTOBER 1886

Free school medals
OBV: JOHN HALES FOUNDED
REV: THE FREE SCHOOL COVENTRY, ANNO 1545
28 mm

OBV: FREE SCHOOL OLD FRONT
TAKEN DOWN 1794
REV: THE ARMS OF COVENTRY 1707
P. KEMPSON FECIT

OBV: BLUE SCHOOL, ERECTED 1724
REV: P. KEMPSON, MAKER OF BUTTONS,
MEDALS, ETC., BIRMINGHAM

OBV: BLUE COAT CHARITY SCHOOL,
ENLARGED 1794
REV: P. KEMPSON, MAKER OF BUTTONS,
MEDALS, ETC., BIRMINGHAM

On many estates in England, classes were held in the home. A tutor was hired, and cousins or close friends were invited to join the nobleman's children for their education. In some cases promising children living on an English manor would be asked to take advantage of the education. Such group teaching also occurred in less wealthy family situations. Classes were held in rooms designed expressly for the purpose or in nurseries large enough to double as classrooms. Some of the 27 pieces of children's furniture collected by Dr. Drake would have been found in such settings.

It is appropriate to close with mention of an early parchment document pertaining to youth, rather than children. This is a copy of a portion of Alexandre de Villedieu's thirteenth-century Latin grammar, *Doctrinale puerorum,* written in verse in Paris in 1209. The book of 12 chapters was used by students in France as a basic text for long and comprehensive study until the end of the fifteenth century. This portion was printed in Parme in 1478; it is directed to 12- to 16-year-old boys preparing to enter university. At that time theology was the focus of study at the university, the discipline followed to prepare clergy, royal administrators, and academic teachers.[28]

Evolution from stool to stool chair, to chair
England
Foreground: oak joined stool or stool table ca. 1600

Left: Elizabethan oak stool chair, ca. 1600
Ht: 89 cm.

Right: oak chair with padded seat, dated 1618, the earliest dated English child's chair on record (cf. chair in "Teaching Embroidery", p. 299)

Childrens' low chairs
England, 17 C
Walnut chair, ca. 1675
Infant-sized, ht: 71.2 cm
Initials of probable carver "R.W." on lower back rail
(cf. high chair, p. 106)

Oak chair, ca. 1650
Infant-sized, ht: 71.2 cm
(cf. high chair, p. 107)

Nursery or classroom furniture
Child's Yew Windsor chair, England, 18 C
Ht: 82 cm

Infants' oak bench, England, ca. 1700
L: 69 cm

Oak press, England, 17 C.
Could have held children's treasures, but lock suggests it stored teaching aids for parent, nurse, or tutor.
L: 55 cm

Oak layette basket
England, 1765 (dated)
Intricately carved, originally used for christening gifts, but undoubtedly handy in the nursery for diapers, laundry or swaddling bands
L: 67 cm

Notes

1. Sézan 1930, plate IV.
2. Hilton Price 1897:40.
3. The Diagram Group. *The Way to Play* Toronto/New York/London: Corgi Books, 1975: 40.
4. Stella 1657.
5. Clay pipe dated according to James Deetz's table of stem bores and dates, Deetz 1967:41. Date also conforms with the description in *Country Life*, May 3, 1964.
6. Brouzet 1755:56.
7. Struve 1802.
8. Roberton 1827.
9. Sainte-Marthe 1797.
10. Metlinger 1473.
11. Elyot 1534.
12. Huarte Y Navarro 1698. First published in Spanish ca. 1600.
13. King 1960:2.
14. Tryon 1695:14.
15. Sargent 1821:100.
16. Locke 1693:44.
17. Locke 1693:53.
18. South 1724.
19. Nelson 1753:150.
20. Nelson 1753:163.
21. Nelson 1753:356.
22. Nelson 1753:368.
23. Author unknown. *Observations upon the Proper Nursing of Children. . . Experience.* 1761:17.
24. Harrison [n.d.] Published after *Robinson Crusoe* by Daniel Defoe (1660–1731).
25. Nelson 1753:332.
26. Léger 1825.
27. Davis 1895:94.
28. Document 960.1.727.

MUSEUM CATALOGUE NUMBERS

Historical Background

p. 4 TDPA 170

Maternal Nursing

p. 10 TDPA 724
p. 14 TDPA 177
p. 15 TDPA 15
p. 16 TDPA 360
p. 17 TDPA 182
p. 18 TDPA 616 TDPA 58
p. 19 TDPA 634 TDPA 280
p. 20 TDPA 428
p. 22 AD161 AD163 AD166 DD24 DD246 DD245 DD243, TDPA 565
p. 23 TDPA 109
p. 24 CD385 CD404
p. 25 DD281 CD397 DD278, CD395 CD394
p. 26 TD137, TD148
p. 27 TD123
p. 28 TD1236, CD411, CD410
p. 30 891, TDPA 292
p. 31 844
p. 32 884, 873

Wet Nursing

p. 34 TDPA 152
p. 36 960.1.1272, TDPA, 261, CD406
p. 37 886, TDPA 515, TDPA 196
p. 39 846, 845
p. 40 TDPA 4
p. 41 960.1.1193, TDPA 358
p. 42 960.1.1217
p. 43 TDPA 163
p. 47 960.1.1142, 960.1.1143
p. 48 TDPA 12
p. 49 TDPA 167
p. 50 TDPA 257, TDPA 126
p. 51 TDPA 132, TDPA 142
p. 52 TDPA 349, TDPA 185, TDPA 7
p. 53 TDPA 141
p. 54 TDPA 809
p. 55 TDPA 107, TDPA 229, TDPA 307
p. 56 TDPA 289, TDPA 144
p. 57 960.2.13, 960.2.19, TDPA 164
p. 58 897
p. 59 906.1.1375
p. 60 TDPA 191, TDPA 267
p. 62 TDPA 351
p. 64 820
p. 65 CD400

Dry Nursing

p. 68 887
p. 70 TDPA 564
p. 71 841, 11, 34, 54
p. 72 CD407
p. 73 TDPA 277
p. 76 CD45 AD18, CD726 CD21 CD644 CD2
p. 77 DD583
p. 81 TDPA 244.1, TDPA 244.12
p. 82 DD174
p. 83 TD223 TD18 TD14 TD233 TD34 TD238
p. 84 TD165 TD160 TD17 TD161 TD252
p. 85 TD28 TD15 TD181 TD274
p. 86 TD13, TD228, CD36 CD328
p. 88 CD312 CD326 CD327, CD273 CD288 CD306, CD234 CD37
p. 89 CD126 CD125, DD574 DD586 DD568
p. 90 DD106 DD589 DD105 DD101
p. 91 AD31 AD26
p. 92 DD107 AD24 DD173
p. 93 CD236 CD138 CD600 CD96, CD137 CD101 CD583, CD62 CD582
p. 95 CD121 AD114
p. 96 CD454 CD161 CD430 CD421, CD81 CD61 CD616
p. 97 DD91 AD68 DD88, AD58 AD49 AD46 AD70 AD34

p. 98 AD66 AD36 AD61 AD62
p. 99 TDPA 720 TDPA 153
p. 100 CD11 CD49
p. 101 CD51 CD53 CD50
p. 102 CD22, CD8 CD345
p. 103 CD19 CD16 CD35, CD41 CD284
p. 104 CD346 CD281, DD177 DD180
p. 105 CD134 CD584 CD578 CD133, AD6 AD2 AD9
p. 106 960.2.25
p. 107 960.2.3 960.2.23 960.2.24
p. 108 960.2.22 960.2.24 960.2.5

Foundlings

p. 110 TDPA 353
p. 113 TDPA 453
p. 114 TDPA 115
p. 115 TDPA 458
p. 116 TDPA 455
p. 117 TDPA 133
p. 118 TDPA 8 TDPA 445
p. 119 TDPA 2
p. 120 TDPA 36 960.1.1197
p. 121 960.1.1196
p. 122 CD396, 831
p. 123 TDPA 447
p. 124 960.1.0027 960.1.0029, TDPA 155
p. 125 TDPA 352
p. 127 960.1.1204
p. 129 TDPA 786
p. 130 227 & 228
p. 131 TDPA 57
p. 132 TDPA 259
p. 134 710 & 712
p. 135 TDPA 417
p. 136 857
p. 137 859 860 247 858
p. 138 960.1.1299 863

Amulets and Magic Medicine

p. 140 AD1000
p. 143 TD138 TD286 TD134
p. 144 TD583 581 582
p. 145 TD198 TD201 TD557
p. 146 TD704 TD985 TD990 TD586 TD189, TD721, TD345 TD980, TD967
p. 147 TD952 TD905 TD268 TD906 TD902 TD942–5 TD1105–13
p. 148 TD889 TD872 TD168
p. 149 TD407 TD401 TD430 TD578 TD548 TD551 TD562
p. 150 TD94, TD972 TD971
p. 151 TD132
p. 152 TD730 TD728 TD729 TD390 TD92, TD757 TD786, TD104 TD1057
p. 153 TD56 TD58 TD51 TD7 TD1
p. 154 TD634 TD632 TD135, TD725 TD758, TD616 TD607
p. 155 TD663 TD666 TD664, TD106 TD105 TD178 TD969
p. 156 TD47
p. 157 TD145 TD231 TD196 TD647
p. 158 TD449 TD455 TD458 TD171 TD172 TD174 TD764
p. 159 TD162 TD163 TD180 TD765 TD856
p. 160 TD439 TD438, TD470 TD244, TD463–6 TD468
p. 161 TD446 & 7 TD461 & 2 TD442 & 3
p. 162 TD996 & 7 & 8 TD991–3 TD999–1001 TD1003–6 TD1013–6 TD1098–11 TD1102 & 3, TD293 TD692
p. 163 TD434 TD437 TD248
p. 164 TD46 TD45 TD44 TD960 TD42 TD624, TD1104 TD 194
p. 165 TD211
p. 166 CD651
p. 167 AD202 AD443 AD441
p. 168 802 803 801 810 809, 807 808 811 806 804
p. 169 813 814 815 816
p. 170 TD226 TD225
p. 171 TD213 TD544 TD212 TD222 TD217, TD18 TD303 TD1032 TD869

Touching for the King's Evil

p. 181 767 772 774
p. 183 776 777 778
p. 184 780 781 785 794 793
p. 185 800 795 792 798
p. 187 782 783 792 786 791

Against the Yll Ayres

p. 190 TDPA 374
p. 192 TDPA 33 TDPA 46
p. 193 AD119 AD361, AD358 AD359
p. 194 AD345, AD352
p. 195 AD104, AD301 AD294 AD346
p. 196 AD130 AD128, AD258 AD266 AD261 AD370 AD147 AD305
p. 197 AD245 AD277 AD290 AD281 AD124
p. 198 AD246 AD129 AD242 & 3, AD324
p. 199 TD1185 AD397 AD357
p. 200 TD82 TD1071 TD297 TD1076 TD1063 TD84
p. 201 TD259 TD258 TD257 TD89 TD10 TD72 TD1073 TD1078
p. 202 AD394 AD420, AD144 AD421
p. 203 DD39 AD460, AD385 AD423, AD406 AD400 AD413 AD379 AD43
p. 204 AD290 AD285
p. 205 AD381 AD424 AD410 AD391
p. 206 AD329

'Pothecaries, Potions, Purges, and Palliative Care

p. 210 CD566
p. 216 AD4329 AD430 CD881 AD445, AD437 AD179 AD171 AD435 AD185
p. 217 TDPA 222 TDPA 220
p. 219 TDPA 265
p. 220 CD649 DD590 AD997 AD538
p. 221 AD712 AD787 AD46 AD519 AD542 AD726 AD773 AD960 AD788 AD774
p. 222 AD527 CD739, DD31a–f
p. 223 TD489 TD113 TD513 TD497 TD542 TD280 TD281 TD515 TD514 TD283
p. 224 DD124 CD559 TD1221, TDPA 73 TDPA 39
p. 225 TDPA 747 TDPA 105 TDPA 746 TDPA 24
p. 226 TDPA 54
p. 227 TDPA 272, AD91 AD89 CD239 CD246 DD216
p. 228 TD77 TD65 TD78 TD85 TD76
p. 229 CD646 CD720 CD669 CD641, CD670
p. 230 TD479 TD35 TD61 & 2, TD241, TD859 TD242 TD193 TD482 TD240
p. 231 TD108
p. 232 CD721 CD256 & 8 CD708 CD710 CD661, CD706 CD606 CD707 CD660 CD684 CD662 CD697
p. 233 CD637 CD648, CD719 CD665 CD561 CD666
p. 234 DD311 AD326, AD454 AD456 AD449
p. 235 TD1308 TD1319 TD1306, TD1300 TD1298 TD1316 TD1321 TD1312 TD1302
p. 236 DD158 CD277 DD154 DD115, CD723
p. 237 DD435 TD1293
p. 238 CD337 CD663 CD23, CD280 CD17 CD15
p. 239 CD30 CD14, CD29 CD279
p. 240 TDPA 60, DD175 DD178 AD22
p. 241 CD135 CD722, DD130 AD348
p. 242 TD342, TD270 TD269 TD329
p. 243 DD257 AD118 DD267 TD1148–50
p. 244 AD236–8, AD230 AD237 AD207 AD212, AD474 AD944 AD806 AD792 AD794 AD833 AD465 AD928 AD832
p. 245 AD912 AD911 AD917 AD897 AD888 AD919 AD800 AD896 AD887 AD890 AD895 CD861 & 2 CD856 & 7 AD900 & 1
p. 246 CD874, TDPA 91, TD1202 AD98 AD39
p. 247 CD200 CD197 CD196, CD136 CD625, CD724 CD717
p. 248 CD217 CD139 CD189, DD120 DD153 DD122 DD121 DD1242 DD1243
p. 249 DD151

Apothecary and Related Tokens

p. 250 412 416
p. 251 104 123 189 202 200 199 196 144 192 152 105 124 188 201 200 199 196 144 152 192
p. 252 177 178, 204, 208, 206, 205 204, 208, 206, 205
p. 253 401, 397, 382, 400, 298, 383
p. 254 209, 211, 758
p. 255 474 282 456
p. 256 761 & 2

Daily Nurturing

p. 258 788.1
p. 261 TDPA 18
p. 264 TDPA 425
p. 265 TDPA 210
p. 267 TDPA 158 TDPA 227
p. 268 CD731 CD111 CD372 CD735
p. 269 960.2.21
p. 270 TDPA 148 TDPA 195
p. 271 S22, 960.1.20
p. 272 TDPA 523 881
p. 273 TDPA 187

Play and Education

p. 274 TDPA 527
p. 276 TD96 & 7
p. 277 TD365 TD157 TD380 TD41, TD149 TD396 TD658, TD644 TD158 TD156
p. 278 TD392 TD159 TD358 CD394, TD357 TD101
p. 279 TD671, TD1124 TD388 TD389 TD676 TD674 TD675
p. 280 TD300 TD299 TD706–9 TD292, TD364 TD382–5 TD695 TD698 TD691 TD688 TD690, TD367 TD369 TD373 TD376 TD375, TD218 TD327 TD325 TD778 TD770–6 TD766 TD769 TD780
p. 281 TD1095 TD739 TD753 & 4 TD749 TD751, TD175 TD359 TD699 TD356 TD731 TD360 TD678–81 TD84 & 5, TD276 TD1049 TD278 TD262 TD301 TD379
p. 282 TD341 TD247 TD302 TD24 TD330
p. 283 TD1039–42 TD338 TD312 TD308 TD232 TD868 TD1035 TD350

p. 284 TD747 TD1083 TD1084–6
p. 285 AD196 AD193 AD198 AD192
p. 286 TD466 TD1092, TD1096, TD1159
p. 287 TD477 TD1151 TD1153 TD1188 TD1193 TD1094 TD1121 TD1127 TD1120
p. 288 TD1194 TD1193, TD1191 TD1192 TD1190
p. 289 DD288 DD274 DD275 TD1196 TD1195 TD1181
p. 290 TD863 TD1180 TD1114–6
p. 291 CD552 & 3 CD222 & 3 CD228 CD219 CD548–50 CD557
p. 292 TDPA 475 TDPA 472
p. 293 AD19 AD150 AD103 AD20 AD133 AD442
p. 295 TD1133–45
p. 296 TDPA 318
p. 297 CD567 CD575 CD573
p. 300 S1 S7 S10
p. 301 S2 S9
p. 302 S17 S14
p. 303 S18 S13
p. 304 DD116
p. 308 573 572 570 & 1
p. 309 378 & 9 368 & 9 356 277 359 360, 856
p. 310 960.2.14 & 14a 960.2.18 960.2.17, 960.2.7 960.2.6
p. 311 960.2.15 960.2.10 960.2.13, 960.2.2

BIBLIOGRAPHY

Armstrong, George
1771 *An Essay on the Diseases Most Fatal to Infants.* London: T. Cadell.

Armstrong, George
1777 *A General Account of the Dispensary for the Infant Poor.* Included in the 1777 edition of *An Essay on the Diseases Most Incident to Children. London: T. Cadell* (see Armstrong, 1771).

ASCSA Series
Thompson, D B
1959 *Miniature Sculptures from the Athenian Agora.* Princeton, N J: American School of Classical Studies at Athens.

1963 *Lamps from the Athenian Agora.* Princeton, N J: American School of Classical Studies at Athens.

1974 *Pots and Pans of Classical Athens.* Princeton, N J: American School of Classical Studies at Athens.

1977 *Cure and Cult in Ancient Corinth.* Princeton, N J: American School of Classical Studies at Athens.

Astruc, John
1746 A General and Compleat Treatise on All the Diseases Incident to Children. London: John Nourse.

Aucoc, L
[after 1811] Mémoire sur la Nécessité du Rétablissement des Tours. (n.p.).

(Author unknown)
(ca 1500) *La Vie de Madame Saincte Marguerite.* (n.p.).

(Author unknown)
1649 *A Miracle of Miracles, Wrought by the Blood of King Charles the First.* London.

(Author unknown)
1683 *The Queen's Closet Opened.* London: Printed for Obadiah Blagrave at the sign of the Black Bear in St. Paul's Church Yard.

(Author unknown)
1688 *Des Enfants deVenus célèbres par leurs études ou par leurs écrits.* Paris: Degalier.

(Author unknown)
1707 Lettre à Mr. De XXXX Sur Une Méthode particulière pour instruire les petits Enfans. Paris: J. Estienne.

(Author unknown)
1759 *Foundling Hospital, An Account of the Hospital for the Maintenance and Education of Exposed and Deserted Young Children* (n.p.).

(Author unknown)
1761 *Observations upon the Proper Nursing of Children from a Long Series of Experience.* London: R. and J. Dodsley.

(Author unknown)
1788 *Hieroglyphick Bible.* London: T. Hodgson.

(Author unknown)
1814 *The Mother's Fables.* London: Darton.

Bagellardo, Paolo
1487 *De Infantium Aegitudinibus et Remediis.* Padua: Matthaeus Cerdonis.

Baldini, F
1786 *Manière d'Allaiter les Enfans à la Main au Défaut de Nourrices.* Translated from Italian. Paris: Buisson.

Ballexserd, J
1762 *Dissertation sur l'Education Physique des Enfants.* Paris: Vallat-la-Chapelle.

Beckett, William
1722 *A Free and Impartial Enquiry into the Antiquity and Efficacy of Touching for the Cure of the King's Evil.* London: J. Peele.

Bergonier
1842 *Le Guide Maternel.* Paris: De Truchy.

Bierce, Ambrose
1911 The Devil's Dictionary. New York: Thomas Y Crowell, and Toronto: Fitzhenry and Whiteside. (Reprinted 1979).

Boehn, Max von
1932 *Dolls and Puppets.* Translated by Josephine Nicoll. London: George G Harrap.

Boerhaave, Hermann
1759 *Traité des Maladies des Enfans.* Avignon: Saillant et Nyon.

Bonner, Campbell
1950 *Studies in Magical Amulets.* Ann Arbor: University of Michigan Press.

Braybrooke, ed.
1825 *Pepys Memoirs and Diary (1659–1669).* London: Frederick Warne and Co.

Brouzet, N
1755 *An Essay on the Medicinal Education of Children and The Treatment of Their Diseases.* Translated from the original 1754 French edition. London: Thomas Field.

Browne, John
1684 *Adenochoiradelogia.* Bk 3. London: Tho Newcomb for Sam Lownde.

Brownlow, John
1847 *The Foundling Hospital.* London: S. Low.

Buchan, William
1769 *Domestic Medicine.* Edinburgh: Balfour, Auld, and Smellie.

1793 *Domestic Medicine* Boston: J. White
1804 *Advice to Mothers on the Subject of Their Own Health; and on the Means of Promoting the Health, Strength, and Beauty of their Offspring.* Philadelphia: John Bioren.

Budge E A T W
1930 *Amulets and Superstitions.* London: Oxford University Press.

Burns, John
1811 *The Diseases of Women and Children.* London: Longman.

[Cadogan, William]
1748 *An Essay Upon Nursing and the Management of Children, by a Physician.* London: J Roberts.

Clarke, Harold George
1955 *Under-glaze Colour Picture Prints on Staffordshire Pottery.* London: Courier Press, Nelson House.

Claubry, C D G de
1783 *Nouvel Avis aux Mères qui Veulent Nourrir.* Paris: Lottin.

Clay, Rotha Mary
1909 *The Mediaeval Hospitals of England.* London: Methuen & Co.

Clifford, James L
1955 *Young Sam Johnson.* New York: McGraw-Hill.

[Clinton, Elizabeth]
1662 *The Countesse of Lincolnes Nurserie.* Oxford: J Lichfield and J Short.

Coysh, A W
1970 *Blue and White Transfer Ware 1780–1840.* Great Britain: David and Charles Ltd.

Culpeper, Nicholas (1616–1654)
1737 *A Directory for Midwives* or *A Guide for Women.* London: Printed for A. Bettesworth, and C. Hitch, at the Red-Lyon; J. Bettley, and J. Wood, at the Dore, in Pater-noster-Row; S. Ballard, at the Blue Bull, in Little Britain; S. Birt, at the Bible in Amen-Corner; and J. Hodges, at the Looking-Glas on London Bridge.

Cushing, Harvey
1940 Life of Sir William Osler. London, New York, Toronto: Oxford University Press.

Davis, W J
1895 *The Token Coinage of Warwickshire.* Birmingham: Hudson.

Deetz, James
1967 *Invitation to Archeology.* Garden City, New York: Natural History Press.

Dendy, Walter C.
1833 *The Book of Nursery.* London: Whittaker, Treacher, & Co.

Dick, Wm B
1975 *Dick's Encyclopedia of Practical Receipts and Processes or How They Did it in the 1870's.* New York: Funk and Wagnalls.

Elworthy, Frederick
1895 *The Evil Eye.* London: John Murray (Reprinted 1970, New York and London: Collier and Collier-MacMillan).

Elyot, Sir Thomas
1534 *The Boke named the Governour.* London: the House of Thomas Bertholet.

Farquhar, Helen
1916-1920 Royal Charities, Pts I–IV *British Numismatic Journal*
1916, Vol *XII,* pt *I*

1917, Vol *XIII*, pt *II*
1918, Vol *XIV*, pt *III*
1919-20, Vol *XV*, pt *IV*

Ferrarius, D
1577 *De Arte Medica Infantum.* Brixiae [Brescia] Italy: F Apud and P Mariam.

Flaubert, Gustave
1950 *Madame Bovary.* Great Britain: Penguin Books.

Fraser, Antonia
1966 *A History of Toys.* London: Weidenfeld and Nicholson.

Gallego de la Serna, Joannes
1634 Opera Physica Medica Ethica Quinque Tractalibus Comprehensa. Lugduni [Lyons]: I and P Prost, fr.

Gardien, C M
1807 *Traité d'Accouchements de Maladies des Femmes.* Vol 3. Paris: Crochard.

Garrison, Fielding Hudson
1923 *History of Pediatrics. In System of Pediatrics.* I Abt (ed.) Philadelphia: W B Saunders.

[Glasse, Hannah]
1755 *The Art of Cookery by a Lady.* 5th ed. London: Printed and sold at Mrs. Ashburn's China-Shop, the corner of Fleet-Ditch.

Graunt, John
1676 *Natural and political Observations... Made Upon the Bills of Mortality.* London: J Martyn.

Hamilton, Alexander
1792 *A Treatise on the Management of Female Complaints, and of Children in Early Infancy.* Edinburgh: P Hill.

Hamilton, James
1813 *Hints for the Treatment of the Principal Diseases of Infancy and Childhood.* Edinburgh: Peter Hill.

Handley, J
1721 *Mechanical Essays on the Animal Oeconomy.* London: A Bettesworth.

Hanway, Jonas
1767 *Letters to the Guardians of the Infant Poor; and to the Governors and Overseers of the Parish Poor.* London: A Miller.

Harmand de Montgarny, J P
1806 *Félébriologie ou Dessertation Physique, Morale, Politique Medicale.* Châlons-sur-Marne: Martin.

Harris, Walter
1694 *An Exact Inquiry into and Cure of the Acute Diseases of Infants.* Translated from Latin by William Cockburn. London: printed for S.C. and sold by John Wyat at the Rose in St. Paul's Church-yard. Six other editions between 1689 and 1742 in the Collection: 3 Latin, 2 French, one other English. Harris was physician to King William and Queen Mary.

Harrison, J
(n.d.) *Harrison's New Nursery Picture Book.* London: Devizes [published after *Robinson Crusoe* by Daniel Defoe, 1670–1731].

Harrison, Sarah
1757 *The House-keeper's Pocket Book, and Compleate Family Cook.* London: Printed for R. Ware at the Bible and Sun, on Ludgate Hill.

Hartley, Dorothy
1954 *Food in England.* London: Macdonald and Co.

Hayens, H
[n.d., after death of Jenny Lind, 1887] *Children of Other Times.* Bk III. London and Glasgow: Collins.

Hayes, J W
1983 *Greek, Roman and Related Metalware in the Royal Ontario Museum.* Toronto: Royal Ontario Museum.

Herdman, John
1807 *Discourses on the Management of Infants, and the Treatment of their Diseases.* London: Jordan and Maxwell.

Herring, Francis
1636 *Certaine Rules, Directions or Advertisements for this Time of Pestilentiall Contagion.* London: T. Paine. Reprinted from original, 1603.

Hilton Price, F G
1897 *Egyptian Antiquities.* London: B Quaritch.

1908 *Egyptian Antiquities,* Vol. II. London: B. Quaritch.

Holt, L Emmett
1917 *The Care and Feeding of Children.* New York: D. Appleton.

Huarte Y Navarro, J [1530–1592]
1698 *Tryal of Wits.* Translated from original Spanish by Mr. Belamy, London: Richard Sare.

Hughes, G Bernard
1949 Pomanders and Vinaigrettes. *Country Life.* December 30, 1949.

Hunter, John
1778 *A Practical Treatise on the Diseases of the Teeth.* London: J. Johnson.

Hurlock, Joseph
1742 A Practical Treatise Upon Dentition. London: C Rivington.

Huxham, Jean
1775 *An Essay on Fevers.* London: J Hinton.

1776 *Essais sur les Differentes Espèces des Fièvres.* Paris: D'Houry.

Icart
1784 *Leçons Practiques sur l'art des Accouchements.* Castres: PG de Robert.

Jackson, Sir Charles James, F.S.A.
1921 *English Goldsmiths and their Marks.* Los Angeles and Toronto: Borden Publishing.

Jackson, Seguin Henry
1798 *Cautions to Women Respecting the State of Pregnancy Including Directions to Midwives and Nurses.* London: GG and J Robinson and J Robson.

King, Donald
1960 *Victoria and Albert Museum Samplers.* London: Her Majesty's Stationery Office.

Kitchiner, William
1838 *The Cook's Oracle.* Edinburgh: Robert Cadell. London: Whittaker and Co. Dublin: John Cumming.

Klein, Anita
1932 *Child Life in Greek Art.* New York: Columbia University Press.

Kremers and Urdang
1963 *History of Pharmacy.* Revised by Glenn Sonnedecker. Philadelphia: J B Lippincott.

Landais
1781 *Dissertation sur les Avantages de l'allaitment des Enfants par leurs Mères.* Genève: Méquignon.

Lefebvre, G R
1782 *Le Manuel des Femmes Enceintes.* Paris: Servière.

Léger, Théodore
1825 *Manuel des Jeunes Mères.* Paris: Chaboüille.

Lenoir, J
1780 *Detail sur Quelques Etablissemens de la Ville de Paris.* Paris.

Ley, Hugh
1836 *An Essay on the Laryngismas Stridius or Croup-like Inspiration of Infants.* London: J Churchill.

Locke, John
1693 *Some Thoughts Concerning Education.* London: H. and F. Churchill.

MacIver (Mrs)
1774 *Cookery and Pastry.* Edinburgh: Printed for the Author; and sold by her at her house, Stephen Laws Close, Back of the City Guard and by W. Drummond, W. Gray, C. Elliot, and other booksellers.

Madelaine, Stéphen de la
1847 *Une Partie de Campagne.* Paris: Belin-Leprieur et Morizot, Editeurs, Imprimerie de Gustave Gratiot.

Mauriceau, Francis
1683 *The Diseases of Women with Child and in Child-bed.* Translated by Hugh Chamberlen. London: J. Darby. First written in 1668.

May, Robert
1671 *The Accomplisht Cook or the Art and Mystery of Cooking.* London: Printed for N. Brooke and to be sold by Tho. Archer at his shop under the Dyal of St. Dunstan's Church in Fleet Street.

Mazzini, Giuseppe
1933 *Il Bambino nell'arte visto da un medico.* Milano: Ulrico Hoepli.

Metlinger, Bartholomaeus
1473 *Ein Regiment der gesuntheit fur die jungen Kinder.* Augsburg: No title page.

1550 *Ein Regiment der gesuntheit fur die jungen Kinder.* Franckfurdt am Mayn: Herman Gülfferichen. With woodcuts.

More, Hannah
1799 *Strictures on the Modern System of Female Education.* London: T. Cadell.

Moreau-Vautier, Chas
(n.d.) *Les Portraits d'Enfance.* [Paris:] Hachette.

Moss, William
1781 *An Essay on the Management and Nursing of Children.* London: J. Johnson.

Mudge, John
1782 *A Radical and Expenditious Cure for a Recent Catarrhous Cough.* London: J.G. Koven.

Muffett, Thomas
1655 *Healths Improvement.* Corrected and enlarged by Christopher Bennet, Fellow of the College of Physicians. London: Printed by Tho. Newcomb for Samuel Thomson, at the sign of the White Horse in Paul's Churchyard.

Nelson, James
1753 *An Essay on the Government of Children, Under Three General Heads: Viz. Health, Manners and Education.* London: P and J Dodsley.

Newman, Harold
1967 *Veilleuses 1750–1860.* South Brunswick and New York: A.S. Barnes and Company; London: Thomas Yoseloff Ltd.

Nichols R H, Wray F A
1935 The *History of the Foundling Hospital.* London: Oxford University Press.

Ovid (43 BC – AD 18)
1955 *Metamorphoses.* Translated by Rolfe Humphries. Bloomington, Indiana. Indiana University Press, Bk 4.

Parey, Ambrose
1649 *The Workes of that Famous Chirurgeon Ambrose Parey.* Translated by Tho. Johnson. London: R. Cotes and W. Dugard.

Paulus Aegineta
1844 *The Seven Books of Paulus Aegineta.* Original book written prior to AD 690. Translated from Greek by Francis Adams, London.

Pentreath, Guy
1964 *Hellenic Traveller.* London, Faber and Faber.

Petrie, W M Flinders
1914 *Amulets.* London: Constable.

Pettigrew, Thomas Joseph
1844 *On Superstitions Connected with the History and Practice of Medicine and Surgery.* London: J Churchill.

Phaer, Thomas
1550 *The Boke of Chyldren.* Addendum to: *Regiment of Lyfe* (a goodly bryefe treatise of the pestilence, the boke of chyldren). London: Whitchurch.

Plinius Secundus [Pliny] (AD 23–79)
1635 The Historie of the World. Translated by P Holland. London: Adam Islip.

Primrose, James
1659 *Partes Duae De Morbes Puerorum.* Roterdam: A Leers.

Protat, Ed
1803 *Elémens d'Education Physique des Enfans et de Médicine Domestique Infantile* Paris: Graham.

Quennell, Marjorie and C H B
1931 *A History of Everyday Things in England 1066–1799.* London: B.T. Batsford Ltd.

Raffald, Elizabeth
1780 *The Experienced English Housekeeper.* London: Printed for the author, and sold by R. Baldwin, No 47, in Pater-noster-Row.

Rambaud, Pierre
1915 *Les Nourrices d'Autrefois en Poitou.* Poitiers: G. Roy.

Raulin, J
1769 *De la Conservation des Enfans.* Paris: Merlin.

Reid, William George
1871 *A Descriptive Catalogue of the Works of George Cruikshank.* London: Bell and Daldy.

Richerand, Anthelme-Balthesar, Baron
1812 *Des Erreurs Populaires Relatives à la Médicine.* Paris: Caille et Povier.

Roberton, John
1827 *Observations on the Mortality and Physical Management of Children.* London: Longman, Rees, Orme, Brown and Green.

Roesslin, E
1604 *Book of Women.* Translated by Thomas Raynald. London: T. Adams. First published in Latin in 1545. First book on obstetrics to be published in English.

Rogers, James E Thorald, M.P.
1894 *Six Centuries of Work and Wages.* London: Swan, Sonneschein and Co.

Rosen von Rosenstein, Nicholas
1776 *The Diseases of Children and their Remedies.* Translated by Andrew Sparrman. London: T. Cadell.

Rousseau, Jean Jacques
1762 *Emile: On Education.* Paris.

1763 *Emelius and Sophia.* Vol I. Translated from 1762 French edition. London: T Becket and P A de Hondt.

Rowlandson, Thomas
1815 *The English Dance of Death.* Vol II. London: R Ackermann.

[Rundle, Mrs]
1811 *The New Family Receipts Book.* London: Squire and Warwick.

Sachs, Hans
1913 *Kullurgeschichte der Zahnheilkunde in Einzeldar Stellungen. I. Der Zahnstocher und Seine Geschichte.* Berlin: H. Meusser. Translated by M. Bardeleben, 1979.

Sainte-Marthe, Scavole de
1797 *Paedotrophia or The Art of Nursing and Rearing Children.* Translation from original Latin, ca. 1600, by H W Tytler. London: J Nichols.

Sargent, J A
1821 *Letters from a Mother to her Daughter.* London.

Several Hands, among them Mary Kittelby
1734 *A Collection of above Three Hundred Receipts in Cookery, Physick, and Surgery for the use of all Good Wives, Tender Mothers, and Careful Nurses.* Fifth edition to which

is added a second Part. London: Printed for the Executrix of Mary Kittelby; and sold by W. Parker, at the King's Head in St. Paul's Church-yard.

Sézan, Claude
1930 *Les Poupées Anciennes.* Paris: Les Editions Pittoresques.

Shorter, A W
1937 *The Egyptian Gods.* London: K. Paul, Trench, Trubner.

Smith, Hugh
1767 *Letters to Married Women.* London: G. Kearsley.

Smith, Mary
1772 *The complete House-keeper and Professed Cook.* Newcastle: T. Slack.

South, Robert
1724 *Twelve Sermons and Discourses.* London: J. Bowyer.

Squire, Peter
1916 *Companion to the British Pharmacopoea.* 19th ed. London: J. and A. Churchill.

Stahl, P J
(n.d., 19C) *Mon Petit Frère, Première Visite à la Nourrice.* Paris: Bibliothèque d'Education et de Récréation, J. Hertzel et Cis.

Steegmuller, Francis
1949 *Maupassant: A Lion in the Path.* New York: Random House.

Stella, Jacques
1657 *Les Jeux et Plaisirs de l'Enfance.* Paris: Aux Galleries du Louvre chez la ditte Stella. 50 plates engraved by his niece, Claudine Bouzounet.

Still, George Frederic
1912 *Common Disorders and Diseases of Childhood.* London: H Frowde, Oxford Medical Publications.

Struve, C A
1802 *A Familiar View of the Domestic Education of Children.* London: Murray and Highley.

Stuart, D M
(n.d.) *The Boy Through the Ages.* New York: Doubleday Doran.

Symonds, R W
1949 Furniture in the Nursery. *The Antique Collector:* May-June, p. 98.

Theobald, J
1764 *The Young Wife's Guide in the Management of her Children.* London: W Griffin.

Thompson, C J S
1946 *Magic and Healing.* London: Rider and Company.

Tooker, William
1597 *Charisma Sive Donum Sanationes.* London: J Windet.

Toletus, P
1538 Opusculum Recens Natum de Morbis Puerorum. Lugduni [Lyons]: Apud G Rose.

Torrent, A J C
1819 *Considérations sur les Avantages de l'Allaitement Maternel.* Paris: D Jeune.

Trease, G E
1965 *The Evaluation of Pharmacy in Britain.* Poynter FNL, ed. Springfield, Ill: CC Thomas.

Tryon, Thomas
1695 *A New Method of Educating Children.* London: Sainsbury.

Underwood, Michael
1784 *A Treatise on the Diseases of Children.* London: J Mathews. Also in the Collection are 13 later editions, the last in 1846. Of these 3 are in French and one in Italian.

Vallambert, Simon de
1565 *Cinq Livres, De la Manière de Nourrier et Gouverner les Enfans de Leur Naissance.* Poictiers: Marnefz and Bouchetz, fr.

Vogel, Alfred
1885 *A Practical Treatise on the Diseases of Children.* (Third American edition from eighth German edition). New York: D. Appleton.

Wiseman, Richard
1676 *Several Chirurgical Treatises.* London: R Royston.

Walsh, J H
1858 *A Manual of Domestic Medicine and Surgery.* London: G Routledge.

Witkowski, G J
1898 *Anecdotes Historiques et Religieuses sur les Seins et L'Allaitement.* Paris: à Maloine.

Woolf, Noel
1979 The Sovereign Remedy: Touch-pieces and the King's Evil. *British Numismatic Journal,* Vol. XLIX:99

Wuertz, F
1656 *An Experimental Treatise in Surgery in Four Parts.* London: G. Dawson. Wuertz (1518-1574) wrote the first work dealing with infant surgery, published in 1616 and translated into English by A. L. Fox.

INDEX